This book is a gift to:

Joshua

From:

Chrissie

Date:

December 2006

Message:

A Backpack full of stunning stories

for Jesus' kids

Anne McFarlane

CHRISTIAN ART
PUBLISHERS

Published by CHRISTIAN ART PUBLISHERS
PO Box 1599, Vereeniging, 1930

© 2004

First edition 2004

Cover designed by Christian Art Publishers

Scripture taken from the *Holy Bible*, New International Version®. NIV®.
Copyright © 1973, 1978, 1984 by International Bible Society.
Used by permission of Zondervan Publishing House. All rights reserved.

Scripture quotations from THE MESSAGE. Copyright © by Eugene H. Peterson
1993, 1994, 1995. Used by permission of NavPress Publishing Group.

Set in 11.5 on 13.2 pt Palatino BT by Christian Art Publishers

Printed in China

ISBN 1-86920-284-8

04 05 06 07 08 09 10 11 12 13 – 10 9 8 7 6 5 4 3 2 1

DEDICATION

Thanks to my friends Jancis, Liana, Marie-Louise and Venterien, who helped, encouraged and inspired me while I was collecting and writing these stories.

PREFACE

FOR PARENTS

This book focuses on issues that are important for eight-to twelve-year-olds. But because this is the time when preadolescents begin preparing for the teenage years, some of the stories address issues that they will probably not face until they start high school. Dr. James Dobson illustrates the point so well when he says that no one begins to learn football rules in the first match that they play. You learn the rules beforehand and spend many hours practicing and perfecting your game so that you know what to expect on the match day. All that the coach can do during the game is to encourage and motivate from the sidelines. Then his chance to turn his players into excellent sportsmen is over. In the same way young children need to be made aware of the challenges and temptations that they will encounter as teenagers. When they reach puberty, parents and teachers can only remind them of the things that they have already been taught. Basic moral values need to be established before they reach high school. It is true that morality and humanity need to be established when children are still young or they will grow up morally illiterate.

My desire is that kids will enjoy to read the stories in this book. That is why I have written a story for each day. I want them to see how relevant the Bible is for their daily lives, which is why each story is based on a Scripture verse. I trust that they will think about the issues and apply them to their own lives, therefore each story has an activity for them to do or a question for them to ponder on.

I hope that teachers, Sunday school teachers, and youth leaders will also find this book helpful. At the end of the book is a topical index that will help them find stories that are relevant to various themes and truths that they are covering in class or at youth meetings. Children expect grownups to lead them in the right direction and to equip them for life, and it is the responsibility of all of us who educate children to do so as diligently and in as interesting a way as possible.

Parents who want their children to be happy and live with integrity will find this book a great help – children can read it on their own, or the stories can be used as part of family devotions and discussions.

FOR KIDS

Our Heavenly Father loves you dearly, and this book was especially written to remind you of that truth. I hope that knowing this will encourage you to read it regularly. It was with this in mind that I sat down to write these stories for you to enjoy. God laid it on my heart to write a story for each day of the year that will help you to think about God's love for you and His plan for your life.

He wants you to get to know Him better day by day and to learn to love the Bible and read it often, because life is a great adventure that is not always easy. We all need advice and help to make the best of it.

I pray that this book will help make the year ahead a very special one for you.

Anne

January

PLANS FOR THE NEW YEAR

Tom couldn't wait for the midnight service to end. His parents had insisted that he go to church with them first. "We want to start the New Year with the Lord," they said. But the other neighborhood kids were all at the Jefferson's and Tom certainly didn't want to miss out on all the fun. When he arrived, the party was already in full swing. Some kids were playing pool and others were setting off fireworks in the garden. The radio was loudly playing the latest top twenty hits.

Just as he was going through to the kitchen to get himself a soda, his friends rushed toward him and sprayed fizzy lemonade all over him. "Hey, dude," they shouted, "you should wash off the sins of the old year!"

The party lasted until the early hours of the morning. Dawn was breaking when Tom finally got into bed, and for the first time he thought about the church service he had attended with his parents the previous evening. The minister had emphasized how important it is for God's children to set time aside every day to talk to Him and listen to what He says. He then read Mark 1:35. He pointed out that even Jesus found it necessary to spend some time alone with God.

"We all find it easy to keep our appointments with our friends," the minister said. "But how many days just go by without us talking to our best Friend?"

At the end of the service, just before the church bells started to ring in the New Year, the minister gave everyone the opportunity to talk quietly to the Lord. It was then that Tom had made his new year's resolution: He would have a quiet time every day. "Help me, Lord, to keep my appointments with You," he prayed before he fell asleep.

Will you make a similar resolution? You could use this book during your quiet times. Remember to look up the passages from the Bible.

JANUARY 2

DON'T BE AFRAID!

In January in the Western Cape, beautiful new Disas flower in the mountains of the Boland. Some families from the nearby town of Paarl often go camping together in the mountains during the holidays. On the first day of the New Year, they climb up to Dwars River, where a stunning waterfall cascades down between the ferns. At the foot of the waterfall is a deep, dark pool.

Each New Year's day they swim in the rock pool, and don't return until they've picked a Disa. Unfortunately, these unusual crimson flowers sometimes grow on steep and dangerous cliffs. Often one of the more experienced climbers has to climb up the slippery, moss-covered rocks to reach a Disa.

One year, the flowers were again beautiful to look at, but difficult to reach. "We will have to let someone down the cliff on a rope to try and reach the flowers that grow lower down," the group leader said. Sean came forward. "I will go down!" he announced boldly. "But my dad has to hold the rope."

Sean was only twelve years old and the leader's son. With the rope around his waist, he climbed down the cliff until he reached a beautiful big Disa. He carefully picked the flower. Then the group leader and some of the other men pulled him up again.

Everybody cheered when he arrived with the flower held tightly in his fist. They marveled at the beautiful petals. His dad gave him a hug. "Well done, my boy!" he said proudly.

Our Heavenly Father also holds the rope for us when we go into dangerous places. He says in Hebrews: *"I'll never let you down, never walk off and leave you"* (Heb. 13:5 THE MESSAGE).

Learn Hebrews 13 verse 6 by heart. Think of these words when you have to do something difficult.

The Best

The station was in uproar! Charlene was very excited. Their softball team was going to play in a tournament in Cape Town and they were traveling in a train that had been specially chartered for all the teams from Port Elizabeth.

All the players were waiting on the platform with their sports bags. Miss Cohen, the coach of Charlene's team, was getting ready to let the girls know which train coach they would be in. Some of the carriages were quite smart and fancy, while others were more run down. Charlene hoped that she would be allowed to travel in the comfortable green first class coach.

Miss Cohen started reading out the names and the number of the coach the girls had to get into. Children yelled and shouted when they heard their names and rushed toward the train as though it was already pulling out of the station. Above the noise, Charlene heard her name. "Charlene Rankin, Carriage 6, compartment C." She groaned. She was going to have to travel all the way to Cape Town in the scruffy blue coach right in front of her. She grumbled as she picked up her things and scarcely greeted her mother who put a box of cookies into her hands.

She was, however, pleased to see that her best friend Stephanie was in the same compartment. Stephanie, who was also the team captain, beamed with joy. "Nice that Amandla School got the green carriage, don't you think!" she said as she put her bag under the seat. "It's great that they get the chance to experience a little luxury!" For the first time Charlene thought of the rundown apartments where many of these kids lived and the comfortable homes she and her teammates lived in. She didn't reply immediately, but when Stephanie started singing loudly, "We are the champions and we're gonna win!" she sang along heartily.

**Who do you think needed to read
Philippians 2:4: Miss Cohen, Stephanie, or Charlene?**

Look not only to your own interests, but also to the interests of others.   Phil. 2:4

WORKING BEHIND THE SCENES

Grandpa and Stewart were walking home after the school's annual prize giving. They did not talk much. Each was busy with his own thoughts about what had happened that night. Many kids had received book prizes, certificates, diplomas, trophies, or medals. But Stewart didn't get anything. His class captain did receive a banner because their class had raised the most funds at the school fete, though. And the captain of their soccer team did receive a trophy because they had played so well during the season. But Stewart felt a little cheated.

His best friend received a scholarship to attend the State Science Fair for a project he had done. But Grandpa and Stewart both knew that he had also worked very hard on that project. He had gone to Gavin's house almost every single day after school and together they had climbed the hills looking for the seeds of special plants for Gavin's project.

"Have you ever heard of Joseph Lister?" Grandpa asked. Stewart thought for a while and then asked, "Isn't that the man that invented stuff like Dettol?" "Yes," Grandpa answered, proud that his grandson was so smart. "And Philip Semmelweiss?" "No!" Stewart replied. "Who was he?"

"He was the man who, long before Lister, said that some diseases are transmitted by germs and that there would be fewer illnesses if doctors washed their hands with a disinfectant before they examined a patient. But nobody wanted to believe him. Years after his death, Joseph Lister said that he would never have achieved his successes if it hadn't been for Semmelweiss."

Stewart kicked away a stone on the sidewalk. "And today no one knows about Semmelweiss," he said. He knew why Grandpa had told him this story now. "But God knows about him," Grandpa replied as he squeezed Stewart's arm encouragingly.

That evening Stewart's grandpa read him Matthew 6:4. Do you know why?

A DREAM COME TRUE

Look at a map of the world and see if you can find the South Pole. Yes, it is the middle point of that huge ice continent right at the bottom of the world. There was a time when nobody had ever set foot there. But in England there was a young man with a dream: his name was Robin Falcon Scott and he wanted to be the first person to reach the South Pole.

Unfortunately, his first expedition failed. One of his teammates became ill and the dogs that pulled the sleighs became so weak that he had no choice but to turn back. But he didn't give up! For his next expedition, he took motorized sleighs, 34 dogs, and a few tough ponies. In 1907, he left England on an old whaleboat, with a crew of 59 men.

Scott was a Christian and every morning he read a passage from the Bible to the crewmembers. Then he led the crew in a few hymns and a prayer. Dr. Wilson, the team's scientist and also a Christian, would tell the men that many things in nature were hidden so that people could discover them and praise God for His greatness.

Three years after they had left England, they began their journey across 500 miles of ice. The motorized sleighs soon broke down and the ponies couldn't stand the cold. Many of his crewmembers, as well as the dogs, had to turn back. The remaining twelve men had to pull the sleighs, heavy-laden with their food supplies, themselves.

Only four men tackled the last stretch. On 16 January 1912, they reached their goal. But what a disappointment! Another group from Norway had reached the South Pole before them. But they planted the British flag and then started their long journey home. Captain Scott is an example of somebody who "fought the good fight" to make his dream come true. He had indeed earned the right to copy the words of 2 Timothy 4:7 in his diary.

Look up this text in your Bible.

JANUARY 6

IT'S A LIE!

Josephine's mom was very upset. She was looking through one of Josephine's schoolbooks and reading some of the notes that she had taken at school. "I am going to see your teacher about this!" Mrs. Davis exclaimed. "Christians do not believe these things and it isn't right that you're taught this at school." "What things are wrong?" Josephine asked.

"Well, it says here that we don't have to look far for the truth, because it's hidden within ourselves. But the Bible teaches us that there is nothing good within us and that Jesus is the way, the truth and the life." "My teacher did say that Jesus was a great Teacher," Josephine replied. "He is much more than that!" her mother said. "He is the Son of God."

She continued reading. "I don't agree with this statement either." Her mom read out loud: "All forms of religion are attempts of the human race to reach God. One religion isn't better than another. There are many different roads to the top of the mountain."

Her mother looked very serious. "These are teachings of the New Age movement," she said. "If there were many ways in which people could be saved, it wouldn't have been necessary for Jesus to die on the cross."

"My teacher said that heaven and hell aren't real," Josephine announced. "He said that after we die we come back and live on earth in another life form."

"That is not what the Bible teaches us," Mrs. Davis replied. "I will give you a few verses from the Bible to look up." "Yes, please!" Josephine said. "Then I can show them to my friends as well."

Look up the verses that Josephine found:
John 14:6; 2 Thessalonians 1:8-9; Hebrews 9:27.

LASTING MESSAGE

How Bill Brady managed to make it onto the basketball team, no one could say. Maybe the coach gave him a place on the team because he never missed a practice. Lots of guys were stronger and faster than he was, but they often skipped practice. Bill attended every practice, come rain or snow, even if something more interesting was happening in town that day.

He was a hero on the team even though he sometimes made mistakes on the court. The crowd never chanted his name at games or cheered him for scoring the winning points. Other players, like the captain, often heard "Ro-wan! Ro-wan! Ro-wan!" as the crowd on the bleachers egged him on.

That was why it was such a special thing that happened on the last day of school. Rowan wanted to sign Bill's T-shirt!

Traditionally, team members wrote messages for each other on their shirts at the end of the season. Rowan signed his name with a black felt pen on the back of Bill's shirt and wrote next to it: THANKS FOR WHAT YOU MEANT TO ME.

Bill displayed that shirt on the wall in his bedroom and, years later, when Rowan was playing for the NBA, Bill proudly showed that shirt to his friends.

Do you always thank people who have helped you? Do you know what a word of encouragement can mean to people? The Bible says: *"Encourage one another and build each other up."* (1 Thes. 5:11)

Think of someone who needs encouragement. Write a letter in which you say something nice about that person. Then quietly slip it into his pocket or mailbox.

January 8

Stranger

Marc felt like an alien visiting earth. But he was only a stranger in the new town his family had recently moved to. His dad had been transferred and the whole family had to move, lock, stock and barrel, to a new town. And the first day at his new school lay ahead! Marc had had to change schools before and he knew only too well what was waiting for him: most of the kids would simply pretend that he didn't exist. Others would stare at him and make rude comments behind his back. Nobody would take the trouble to make him feel at home. He knew he would have to find his way around the new school on his own. He felt really lonely.

Marc's parents were very understanding. His mother brought him an article about friendship from a Christian magazine. It talked about how to make new friends and keep them. The author wrote: "Give your smile, your attention and your help away freely. Throw all the what-ifs in a bag and put them out with the trash. *What if I say something stupid? What if they don't like me? What if they think I'm pushy?* Thoughts like these will not help friendships grow. Rather follow the advice of the heavenly Gardener who says, *"Honor one another above yourself,"* (Rom. 12:10) and *"Serve one another"* (Gal. 5:13). Then watch how those friendship plants thrive."

Marc suddenly remembered how he and Paul had become friends. He had helped Paul in computer class and later they became best friends. And it was Paul who had given him a letter when they left their old town. He glanced at it again: **"Marc, my friend: Remember that God's children are everywhere. They just have different faces. I'll pray for you!"** Suddenly he felt much better.

**Think of what you can do to make the
new kids at your school feel welcome.**

January 9

Arbor Day

Chloe got the first prize at school for her essay about Arbor Day. She did a lot of research for it on the Internet and spent a lot of time in the library reading up about it. Do you want to know what she wrote? Her title was: WE HAVE TO LEARN FROM OTHERS' MISTAKES. And this is what she said:

> Long, long ago the island of La Gonave was one of the most beautiful islands on earth. The island was covered with green trees in which the birds nested and under which lush ferns grew. But then people started to cut the trees down. They made furniture from the wood and even used it for firewood. They also sold it to people who passed by on ships.
>
> They never planted new trees and as time went by, there were fewer and fewer trees. Today the mountains and hills on that island are totally stripped of their trees. When it rains, there is nothing to stabilize the ground. That is why there are often big floods that wash away houses, churches, and farmlands. The people of La Gonave now suffer heavily from the mistakes they made. Please let's not do the same in our country! Let's not chop down trees unnecessarily and let's often plant beautiful new trees.

Don't you think we can also learn something from the mistakes the people on that island made?

The Lord asked Adam and Eve to look after and protect the garden where they lived (see Gen. 2:15). The people of La Gonave did not do what God had commanded and have had to pay the price ever since.

**What things can we do today to
obey God's command about conservation?**

January 10

Letter at Midnight

Charlize had talked to her youth leader and he suggested that she write a letter to her parents. It's now eleven-thirty at night and she is sitting at her desk. She writes:

Dear Mom and Dad,

I've been very unhappy the last few weeks. I hate it when you fight. They say all married couples do that, but to me it feels as though you're mad at each other all the time. Don't you want to go and talk to our pastor? Anne says her parents went to a counselor and now things are going much better. I know that Dad has a lot of stress at work and that Mom has a hard time making ends meet. And I sometimes make life difficult for you as well. I don't do as well at school as you would want me to. Mr. Roberts called me in today and I promised him that I would try to work harder. I think I could manage that if the situation at home was better.

I love you both and I really appreciate everything you do for me. Mom, I'll try to keep my room tidy. And Dad, if you want, I'll wash the car on Saturday. Then you and Mom can go and play a game of tennis for a change.

I pray a lot for us as a family and I believe the Lord will help us to live together happily.

Love
Charlize

Charlize put the letter in an envelope and pushed it under her parents' bedroom door. Then she went back to her room. She didn't always kneel when she prayed, but this time she did. "Lord," she prayed, "please let Mom and Dad love each other and please let them never get divorced. Show me what I can do to make life easier for them. Amen."

Is there also strife in your home? You can also pray for your parents, as Ephesians 6:18 teaches us.

And pray in the Spirit on all occasions with all kinds of prayers. Eph. 6:18

A RELIABLE GUIDE

When you pass through the waters, I will be with you. Is. 43:2

It was a beautiful day in Zimbabwe. The Carter family was delighted. They had been having a wonderful holiday at the Victoria Falls and today they were going to go white water rafting on the Zambesi River. Grandma Carter was also going along, even though the guide said that the trip was really only for brave and fit people.

Chris put on a red baseball cap. "That is so that everyone can see me clearly on the video," he explained. Someone was going to film the whole adventure on video for them so that they would always have a souvenir of their white water rafting experience. When everybody had taken their seats in the floating raft, the guide untied the ropes ... and off they went! The current first took them down the middle of the river at breakneck speed and then they continued downstream.

Suddenly the boat spun around and then made a beeline for a waterfall. Everyone yelled and screamed, but the guide didn't look worried at all. The men wielding the oars also didn't do anything to steer them away from the cliff. *Are they crazy?* Chris wondered. *It looks much safer on the other side.* The next moment they plunged over the edge into the depths. They all landed in the water and were sucked into the whirlpool right underneath the waterfall. It took a while before they reached the surface, rubbed their eyes, and got back onto the raft. Only now did they see what would have happened to them if they had taken the other route, the one that seemed so safe. There were dangerous black rocks on the other side. "Luckily our guide knew what he was doing," everybody agreed when they sat warming themselves around the campfire that night.

Sometimes the Lord takes us on routes that
seem to be dangerous. But He is a reliable guide,
who knows what He is doing. We can trust Him
completely. Read what Proverbs 3:5-7 says about this.

JANUARY 12

A TRUE ROLE MODEL

Roland really learned to respect the captain of the soccer team after a tough match against a rival school. Steve was definitely the man of the match. He had scored two goals and was everybody's hero. At a party at Leslie's house that night, some of the boys pulled out some bottles of beer. Leslie opened one and handed the bottle to Steve. "You were the greatest. Have a drink!" he said while everybody cheered Steve on. He held the bottle for a moment and then gave it back to Leslie. "Thanks, guys," he said, "but I'd rather have a soda."

On his way home, Roland talked to two of his friends about what their captain had done. "He could have taken one little sip," Dean said. "Why? We don't need to do things just to please other people. If it's against your principles, it's your right to say NO," replied Roland. Jacques added his piece. "My brother always says 'Test everything and hold on to what is good.'" Roland retorted quickly, "Yes, and see what happens when people think it means doing bad things. Lots of drug addicts thought it would be ok to just get high once."

"You can't go through the world all wrapped up in cotton wool," Sean said mockingly. "Well, I'd rather be under God's protection than the devil's wings!" was Roland's fiery reply.

"Calm down," Jacques said. "It seems as though Mommy's little boy can lose his cool real fast!"

Roland turned around and faced his friends straight on, "Who showed he had guts tonight?" he asked. "The kids who joined in the drinking were too cowardly to say 'No, thank you'. And they're going to be the ones who will regret it tomorrow morning!"

"I must admit, Steve gave us something to think about tonight!" Jacques said.

**Read Proverbs 1:17-18 to see
what advice Solomon gave his son.**

DANGEROUS GAMES

"The first one to move is a chicken!" yelled Felix. Some seventh grade kids were playing a very dangerous game. June and Helen refused to join in. "You can't force me to do something stupid," June said.

Their friends were standing on the white line in the middle of the road behind the school and watching for approaching cars. The winner of the game was the last one to run back to the sidewalk when a car came past.

"I won't do something so stupid!" Helen said. "You should have your heads checked by a shrink!" she warned. "Some cars drive very fast. There's going to be a bad accident here today." She had barely finished speaking when a green Toyota came tearing round the corner. The brakes screeched, and wild screams filled the air. Felix had slipped and fallen! He and Ian had been the last two on the line, but as they rushed out of the car's way, Felix had bumped into Ian and tripped. The car had stopped only inches away from Felix.

"Are you crazy or what?" shouted the woman who got out of the car. "You could have been killed!" She helped Felix to get up while his friends, standing on the sidewalk, were aghast. "I should report you to the police. Is life worth nothing to you?" Upset, she got back behind the wheel and drove away without taking down their names.

Felix brushed the dirt off his knees and the whole group started walking home in an embarrassed silence. One of the girls cried softly. Everybody thought of what had happened and could have happened. They were also thinking about the lady's words. Yes, life is too precious to gamble with!

Read Psalm 139:13-18 to see how precious you are to God and praise Him for the gift of life.

JANUARY 14

THE TEST

John was lying on his bed, stroking the head of the cute little beagle that was tucked in next to him. He looked at the shiny little nose and smooth hair and felt so much love for the dog that you would think they'd been together for years. But the truth is that he had only found him that afternoon, all forlorn, wandering the streets.

John knew that he had to go and find the dog's owner, but he'd always wanted to have a dog of his own! And this cute little dog had just showed up today. Perhaps this was an answer to all his prayers? Maybe the dog wasn't happy with its real owner. But the healthy, shining fur told another story. The dog was obviously well looked after and probably very happy with its owner. *But why didn't they look after it properly?* he thought rebelliously. *If I had a dog like this, I would watch it night and day!* The dog made a slight whining noise, as though he agreed with John.

John knew that his parents wouldn't let him get away with this. They were honest people who would do all they could to ensure that the pet got back to its real owner.

Reluctantly John got up and picked up the soft little body. He walked out the front door and turned toward the house where he had seen a PUPPIES FOR SALE sign a few months before. For the first time he admitted to himself that he actually knew where the dog had come from. For a few hours he had only pretended not to know.

When a boy in a wheelchair opened the front door, the dog jumped from John's arms and started licking his owner's face. John knew that he had done the right thing.

**Pretend that you are John and
read Psalm 119:9-16 as a prayer.**

January 15

The Torn Jeans

"Where are my jeans?" Theresa asked when she came home. "Lovey," her mom said, "you can't wear those jeans any longer. They are so torn I can't even fix them anymore. What on earth will people say if you walk around in jeans like that? Go and put on something else!" "But Mom," Theresa sulked, "I love those jeans and I really don't care what other people say about them. Anyway, I'm going to play monopoly at Helen's house this afternoon. I don't need to dress up for that!"

"Cherry said she's coming over this afternoon," her mother said. "Oh no!" exclaimed Theresa. "I can't always be looking after her. I'm going to phone her and tell her to come another time." She lifted the phone and began to dial.

"Theresa," her mom asked, "why don't you want her to come over?" "You won't understand. She can be so pathetic! And it's such a bore to push her round in that wheelchair all the time. Anyway, how would my friends feel about that?"

Theresa's mom looked at her quite seriously. "You don't care what your friends think of your torn jeans, but you think they'll be put off because you help a hurting friend? You know how lonely Cherry is and the two of you have lots of fun together. Remember, the Lord loves her very much. He wants us to be kind to her."

Theresa felt ashamed. "I've never thought of it that way!" she admitted. "Maybe my other friends will also like Cherry. Will you let me take some extra chocolate chip cookies to Helen's house so there'll be enough for the three of us?"

"That's my girl!" her mom said. She smiled and decided to write out a special verse and put it on Theresa's pillow that night.

**Read Matthew 25:40, the verse
that Theresa's mother gave her.**

NEVER GIVE UP

"Poor James fell down ninety-nine times tonight!" one of his friends joked as they were driving home in the minivan. "No, more than that!" James laughed. "I stopped counting when I got to a hundred. But eventually I got it right." He was quite pleased with himself. He had gone roller-blading with his friends and had his first encounter with the hard concrete surface of the skating rink. The first few hours had been torture. But by the end of the evening he was able to skate easily with his more experienced friends.

After James's father had dropped off his friends, he said, "You make me think of Thomas Edison." "Who was he?" asked James, while examining his bruises. "He discovered how to use electricity to improve our lives. He made 10,000 light bulbs that didn't work until he finally got it right."

"Wow!" James said. "I'm impressed." He knew what it had cost him that night to keep on trying.

"Yes," his dad continued, "someone asked him once how he felt after each failure. He said that he hadn't failed, because each time he had found one more way that didn't work."

They drove in silence for a while as James thought about Edison's perseverance. He watched the streetlights lighting up the road. "So it's thanks to him that we can just push a switch for a light to go on?" "Yes," his dad answered. "Many wonderful inventions like sound systems, CD players, and light bulbs can all be traced back to Edison's inventions."

"I hope I'll have that much guts one day!" James said seriously. "I think you've already got a good portion of it," his dad said proudly.

**Write Isaiah 40:29-31 on a piece of paper
and put it in an envelope. Write TO READ
THE NEXT TIME I FEEL DISCOURAGED on the
outside of the envelope and put it in your Bible.**

Those who hope in the Lord will renew their strength. Is. 40:31

COLOR BLIND

Ian was a really nice guy: he was polite and friendly and he was the school's best baseball player. But he was black. When he and his family moved to a house on Long Street, lots of people in the neighborhood were unhappy. Somebody spray-painted horrid words on their garden wall and some children dumped all their garbage right in front of the Moyo's doorstep. One night a group of young boys threw stones on their roof.

His father said, "There will always be people who are full of hate," he said. "Look what they did to Jesus. Many people didn't want to accept Him because He came from Nazareth. Other people looked down on Him because He was a carpenter's son. Nevertheless, He never allowed that to unsettle Him. We must go on with our lives and do what the Lord wants us to do. These people still need to learn that we were all made in God's image."

Patrick knew how Ian felt because he and his family were immigrants who had moved into that area only a year before. And it had taken him a long time to be accepted by the neighborhood kids.

One afternoon he decided to do something that would make his friends think about what they were doing. He took twelve cards and on each one wrote, **"Dear friends, since God so loved us, we also ought to love one another. If we love one another, God lives in us and His love is made complete in us"** (1 Jn. 4: 11-12). He put one in each of his neighbors' mailboxes. And he said to Ian, "We can walk home together in the afternoons, if you like."

Do you want to change your wrong
attitude and feelings toward people from
other races or countries? Ask Jesus to forgive
you and to fill you with the love He has for them.

Everyone who loves has been born of God and knows God.   1 Jn. 4:7

CAN WE TRUST HIM?

Rowan and Martin were going with their uncle to visit family in Montagu for the Easter holidays. But when they were nearly there, they came around a bend in the road, and saw that the bridge in front of them had almost been washed away. Big logs and debris had dammed up against the bridge until it finally collapsed.

"What now?" Martin asked anxiously. "We'll probably have to turn around," Rowan said. "I'm afraid we won't have enough gas to get back to Pine Town," his uncle said, worried. He thought for a moment and then said, "I will have to cross the river and get some help on the other side. I know there's a farmhouse just over that hill." "We're going with you!" the two boys said at once. "Not going to happen!" their uncle said. "The river is too strong for you guys. But don't worry. Wait here until I get back and then we can continue with our journey, taking a different route."

Uncle Neil immediately started walking. He struggled through the river, his clothes getting soaked through, until he reached the other side. Then he turned around and waved to them. After a while, he disappeared into the bushes. The two boys could think of lots of things that could go wrong, but they both decided not to talk about them. "One thing we can be sure of!" Rowan said. " Uncle Neil will never let us down." "And neither will the Lord," Martin said.

Two hours later, the boys saw a truck on the other side of the river. The friendly farmer had brought their uncle back. He was carrying a can of gas. Now the boys knew that they would get to Aunt Edith before night, where a hot supper would be waiting for them!

**Read the Psalm that Uncle Neil read to
the boys from his Bible that night: Psalm 91.**

God has said, "Never will I leave you; never will I forsake you." Heb. 13:5

MOANING MARY

It wasn't her real name, but because she always moaned about everything, everybody called her Moaning Mary. Every morning she would start with, "No! No! I don't want to get up so early!" And then at the breakfast table it was, "Yuck! I didn't want cereal for breakfast!" Then she would usually go to school mumbling, "Stupid school again!"

The worst was at nighttime when she had to go to bed. Then you could hear her complain loudly, "No! No! I don't want to go to bed so early!"

"It can't go on like this," her dad said one day. "I'm going to do something about it." The next day he went into Mary's room and sat down on her bed. "Mary, if you can manage not to complain about anything until your birthday in six months' time, we'll buy you the keyboard you want so badly." "Deal!" she replied.

The next few months were very tough for her. But because she wanted the keyboard so badly, she stopped her whining and tried to think differently about things. She gradually learned that it's possible to turn bad thoughts into good ones. And then it wasn't difficult to be cheerful rather than miserable.

The morning of her twelfth birthday her parents were up early. They were eager to hear what she would say when she unwrapped her present. But what did they hear? "No, no! That's not what I wanted!" They felt discouraged. Hadn't their daughter learned anything? But when they opened her bedroom door, Mary jumped up and gave each of them a hug. "Got you!" she exclaimed. "Thanks for the lovely gift and don't worry! From now on, I'll be Merry Mary. You taught me that it's much nicer to laugh than to complain!"

**Read Philippians 4:4. Don't you
think it goes well with this story?**

THE INVITATION

Penny belonged to a youth group that got together every Monday afternoon. In Sunday school, they learned all about the Bible and what Jesus taught us to do. But at Radikids they got a chance to do something for the Lord. They had already visited an Old Age Home and a Children's Home, collected money for AIDS orphans, and often wrote letters of encouragement to people who needed it.

One day their youth leader gave them each an assignment. "I want you to go and pray about it and then decide which of your friends you could invite to join Radikids. We need more helpers, especially now that we want to help at the soup kitchen in the homeless shelter." "None of my friends would want to come!" Penny said. "You won't know until you have actually asked them," Donovan laughed.

Penny didn't really feel like doing this. She was shy and hardly ever spoke to the other children at church. But she did try. The first few kids weren't interested at all. Penny was just about to give up when she found herself next to Sue at the bicycle shed. "Don't you want to come with me to Radikids on Monday afternoon?" she asked hesitantly. "I'll think about it," Sue replied. Then she raced off home. Penny followed slowly and prayed with her eyes open, "Lord, please work in her heart and make her want to come!"

Six months later on a Monday afternoon Penny and Sue were together at the bicycle shed again. "Remember that this was where you invited me to join Radikids?" Sue asked. "Well, I just want to tell you: these six months I've had some of the best times in my life! It's fantastic to do something each week that really matters." "And to think I nearly didn't ask you!" Penny said.

Look at what John says in his gospel: John 20:21.

A SPECIAL EXPERIENCE

The sixth grade class couldn't believe their eyes! What was Mrs. Roland doing? They were just about to go home and she was giving each child in the Sunday school class a $10 bill. "It must be a really important lesson she wants to teach us," Dianne thought. "It's going to cost her one hundred dollars!"

"Children," their teacher said, "I want you to give this money to someone who really needs it during this coming week. You may not spend it on yourself. And next Sunday each one of you must report back about who you gave the money to and how it made your feel."

"We're going to give ours to each other," the McFarlane twins joked. "Don't even think about it," Mrs. Roland warned, glaring at them over her glasses.

The next Sunday all the children were in class earlier than usual. They were all very excited to explain what they had done with their money.

"The woman who cleans our house was so happy that she started crying!" Thozi said. "And the guy from our class who lives in the trailer park brought me a chocolate to say thank you," Franklin told them. John replied, "I put my note in a sealed envelope and pushed it under Mrs. Ferreira's door." The children all knew that she was going through a very hard time. Everyone had stories to tell about the surprise and joy of the people who so unexpectedly received this money.

Then Mrs. Roland asked them to open their Bibles at Acts 20:35. She read: "Listen to the words of Jesus. He said: 'It is more blessed to give than to receive.'"

"Do you agree?" she asked the children as she closed her Bible. "It is so true!" they all replied together. Everyone was thinking about the special experiences they had had that week.

To whom would you give the $10?

THE THREE TREES

Three pine trees grew on the slopes of a high mountain. They were very happy, because they could see everything that was happening in the valley and the birds sang loudly in their tree-tops. In the evenings, the cool night wind rustled softly through their pine needles.

"I wish someone would come and get me and make a bed out of me fit for prince to sleep in," the one tree said. "I want someone to make a big sailing ship out of me, so that I can cross all the big oceans," was the second tree's wish. "Oh, I just want to keep standing here and feel God's sun on my branches each day and watch His moonbeams shine on me each night," was the third tree's wish.

But not one of the trees' wishes came true. The first tree was chopped down and a farmer made a feeding trough for his animals out of it. The second one was sawed up into planks of wood, and made into a fishing boat. The third one was chopped up and its branches were stored in a heap near a prison.

But one night a baby slept in the manger, and He was called the Prince of Peace. His Mother, Mary, wrapped Him in cloths and laid Him gently on the hay. Some years later, a Teacher climbed into the fishing boat, and spoke words that are still heard all over the world today. And the pieces of wood outside the prison became a cross on which the Savior of the world died.

Not one of those trees' wishes came true, because they were destined for bigger, more important tasks.

Maybe your wishes also do not come true because the Lord has other, better plans for your life.

**Read 1 Peter 2:9 and see if you can
understand what the Lord had in mind
for you when He called you to be His child.**

Many are the plans in a man's heart, but the Lord's purpose prevails. Prov. 19:21

A PEACE PLAN

There was always fighting and bickering in the Mallory's home. "We will have to work out a peace plan," Mrs. Mallory said one morning when there was once again a huge squabble in the kitchen. She prayed, "Lord, You said in Matthew 5:9: *'Blessed are the peacemakers, for they will be called children of God.'* Help me to be a peacemaker in this house today. Amen." When she walked into the kitchen, she saw Vernon and Frank wrestling each other. They had both grabbed the box of cereal at the same time and were tearing it apart. The whole kitchen floor was covered in rice crispies. When they saw their mother, both started cleaning up the floor in a hurry.

"I am going to give $20 to the person in the family that can think of the best plan for peace," she announced. Everyone came up with lots of original ideas during the week. Frank put a huge poster on the fridge that announced in big, black letters: NO TO WAR.

Yvonne wrote a song that said, " We will try not to fight with all our might; we will be sweet as honey and share the prize money!" She sang or whistled this song all the time.

Vernon drew a chart with blocks on it, in which black dots and gold stars could be pasted to keep track of who was really trying to keep the peace.

Unfortunately, all these efforts did not mean that there were no more arguments in the house! By Thursday the two brothers had started fighting again, but that evening Donna had the chance to put her plan into action. She played the tape on which she had recorded the heated argument her brothers had had that afternoon. They hung their heads in shame as they listened to it.

Would you like to know who won? Well, Mrs. Mallory decided to divide the prize money equally among the children.

To whom would you have given the prize money?

THE LESSON

André didn't really know why he didn't like Nick. Maybe it was because he never seemed to do anything wrong. "He's a real pain in the neck!" he said one day and got quite a fright when he saw his grandpa came into the room. "Who are you talking about?" Grandpa wanted to know. At first André didn't want to say anything, but then he admitted, "About Nick. He always does the right things and he thinks he's better than us. He never wants to join in when we play tricks on people." "Who do you play tricks on?" Grandpa asked. "On old deaf Danny!" he said. Grandpa quickly replied, "Oh, so Nick is like a conscience to you!" Suddenly André felt ashamed. But he was also annoyed. It was Mister Nick Goody-goody's fault that Grandpa was upset with him.

Two days later at school, André's teacher announced that Nick Bradford was seriously ill. He said that Nick would really appreciate a visit from his classmates. André didn't really bother much about Nick's misfortune. He really didn't feel like doing something special for Nick.

That night his grandpa read from the Bible, as usual. He read Matthew 25, and when he came to verse 40, he said: *"Whatever you did for* Nick Bradford, *you did for me."* André was stunned. He knew why his Grandpa had read the verse in that way. Jesus had said that if we visit the sick, or give food or clothes to the poor or do good to those who suffer, it is just as if we're doing it for Him personally. And if we do not do these things, it is just as if we're not doing anything for Him.

The next morning when he said goodbye to his mother, he said, "I'll be a bit late this afternoon. I'm going to go to Nick's place." Grandpa smiled contentedly as he sat drinking his morning coffee on the verandah.

**Read the chapter in Matthew
that Grandpa read to André.**

MEDICINE MAN

Albert Schweitzer grew up in the little town of Alsace in France. From a very young age, he had compassion on people who suffered. One day, when his parents took him to a city close to their hometown, he saw a big statue of a black man from Africa. There was a sad expression in the man's eyes. He never forgot that picture.

Albert did very well in all his studies, first at school and then at university. He earned two doctorates before he was thirty years old. He was also a great organist and wrote a famous book about the life of Bach.

But still he felt restless. He had heard many sad tales about Africa: how the people were dying of malaria, leprosy, and sleeping sickness. "I want to become a doctor and go and help those people!" he decided.

Everyone was surprised when he went back to university to study medicine and even more surprised to hear that he wanted to give up his brilliant career to go and work in Africa. But that is exactly what he did. When he finished his studies, he went to build a hospital at Lambarene in West Africa and treated the sick people from that area.

The "Medicine Man", as he was called, also taught his patients not to be afraid of evil spirits. He and his wife taught them about Jesus. From time to time Schweitzer went back to Europe for a while to raise funds for his hospital. He would give organ recitals and tell people about the needs in Africa. Then he would return to his simple life in the jungle.

All over the world people heard about him and he was awarded the Nobel Peace Prize for his life of service.

**Read 1 Corinthians 10:24 to see the kind
of life Jesus says His disciples should live.**

Let us do good to all people, especially to ... believers. Gal. 6:10

JANUARY 26

THE TWO BELLAS

Bella Griffin was always friendly at school. She even received an award for helpfulness. But at home she was grumpy and lazy. Bella's mom was worried. How was it possible that her child could lead such a double life?

Then her mother came up with a good idea. She knew that Bella really admired her Social Studies teacher. She phoned Miss Murray and asked, "Would you like to come and have dinner at our house on Friday?" Miss Murray said she would love to come. But Bella's mom didn't tell Bella about it.

On Friday, when Bella came home after softball practice, her mother asked her to set the table. "Why do I always have to do it?" Bella asked angrily. She grumbled all the while. She threw the tablecloth on the table and banged the crockery down.

"Please set an extra place," her mother said. "Someone is joining us for dinner tonight." Bella complained loudly, "Why do you always invite guests? It just means I have to do extra chores!" "Shhh!" her mother whispered. "Our guest has already arrived. You can go and call her for dinner now," she said.

Bella dragged herself out of the dining room. Suddenly she stopped dead in her tracks: Miss Murray was waiting for her in the lounge! She blushed. *How long has my teacher been sitting there, and how much of my complaining had she heard?*

"You should have told me that there was an important guest in the sitting room," she told her mother later that evening. "But there is always an important guest in our house," her mother said. She pointed to a framed cross-stitch picture on the wall. Her grandmother had made it years ago. The words on it were: *Jesus is the invisible guest at every meal.* After that, Bella tried to be just as friendly at home as she was at school.

Why don't you learn Philippians 4:5 by heart? That will help you remember that Jesus notices our behavior wherever we are!

CAUGHT IN THE ACT!

Mr. and Mrs. Brown had a mulberry tree in their garden and Christi had silkworms. That is why she rang their doorbell one afternoon and asked nicely, "Mr. Brown, can I please come every day and get some mulberry leaves for my silkworms?" "Certainly!" Mr. Brown replied. "As long as you don't eat my mulberries." "Thank you, sir, I won't!" she promised.

She walked to the corner of the garden where the mulberry tree grew. She climbed the tree and started picking some of the leaves. All around her were delicious looking juicy mulberries. *Now I know how Eve felt when she looked at the fruit tree in the middle of God's garden,* Christi thought. She really felt like taking just one berry before she went home. She only wanted to taste it! And yes, it tasted delicious. *Well, now that I have had one, I might as well eat a few more,* she thought. She ate and ate. But, oh dear! Now her hands were red all over. She tried to get rid of the red stains with a green mulberry. Then she walked home quickly, trying to look innocent.

But when she got home, her mother saw the purple smears on her face and asked, "Have you eaten some of the Brown's mulberries? If all the children who pick leaves there do that, Mrs. Brown won't have enough mulberries to make jam for the church bazaar."

Christi felt really bad. She went to wash her face and brush her teeth. But she didn't feel clean even after that. She knew she had sinned. Mr. Brown had trusted her and she had lied to him. Then she knelt at her bedside and asked the Lord to forgive her. When she got up from her knees, she felt much better. First thing in the morning she would go and ask Mrs. Brown if she could help her pick the mulberries she needed to make jam for the church bazaar.

**Read Isaiah 1:18 to see how the Lord can
wash us clean if we confess our sins to Him.**

JANUARY 28

THE WHITE LIE

Neither Eric nor Fred's parents allowed them to watch movies and videos with age restrictions. They said that the people who set the restrictions knew what was appropriate for children, and what was not. Fred's parents also did not like him to go to parties that were not chaperoned by adults.

Eric had a problem. Ed had invited him to his party on Saturday, but Eric knew that Ed's parents would be away. Ed and his friends also often talked about videos that they watched – movies that were definitely not meant for children. But he really wanted to go to the party. The other kids often called him a nerd because he wouldn't do everything that they did.

On Thursday night at dinner, his dad asked, "What are you going to do at Ed's party?" "I'm not quite sure," he replied. "But I'm sure Ed and his parents have everything very well planned." At first he thought that that was a really clever answer, because he hadn't actually told a lie.

But that evening he didn't sleep well. He felt guilty. That white lie was really not so innocent. It would be really bad if he lost his parents' trust in him just for one silly party!

Early the next morning he confessed everything to his parents. They responded just the way he thought they would. "Thank you for admitting your dishonesty," his father said. "I think you should phone Ed and tell him that you can't be there on Saturday, because you and your dad are going fishing!"

"Yippee!" shouted Eric, very relieved that he had told the truth to his parents. "Can Fred come too?" "Of course!" his dad said.

Read Genesis 14:10-20 to see what happened when Abram told a lie. Remember that dishonesty always has consequences.

January 29

The echo

A group of Boy Scouts went camping in the Drakensburg Mountains over the Easter weekend. Grant was tired but happy when he got home, and couldn't stop talking about all the great things they had seen.

"What was the best experience of the weekend?" his mother asked. Grant thought for a while and then answered, "We learned what is expected of a good leader. That was good. But I think the visit to Champagne Castle was the best! The view is absolutely magnificent from there. It really took my breath away. And, Mom, I've never heard such a clear echo before. Everything we said came back to us perfectly! If we shouted *hello*, then we got three clear *hellos* back."

But by suppertime his excitement had begun to wane. He was thinking about school the next day and the tests and assignments that were coming up. "After this weekend everything at home seems so boring," he said. "Bo-ring!" echoed his younger sister from the opposite end of the table. "And I hate school," he added. "Hate school!" she repeated.

He didn't pay much attention to the way she repeated everything he said until his mom gave him a bowl of stewed fruit with custard. He pulled a face and said, "You know I don't like this, Mom. It tastes horrid!" "Tastes horrid!" mimicked his little sister and knocked the bowl from the table.

"Oh boy! It seems we've got a little echo here that's nearly as clear as the one in the Drakensberg!" he said while helping to clean the mess on the floor. "Yes," his mom said. "Maybe we should watch our words more carefully if we want to be good leaders!"

Do you realize that younger children watch you carefully and often repeat what you say? Read what 1 Timothy 4:12 says about the example we should set.

PRAY WITH EXPECTATION

Rex was gone! That was the worst thing that had ever happened to Harry. The little fox terrier was his best friend. Just the previous evening they had gone for a run in the park and he had thrown sticks for him to catch. But now his little kennel was empty and there was no trace of him. *Could someone have stolen him? Could a car have run him over? Could he have run away?*

Harry searched the whole neighborhood. He asked all his neighbors if they had seen his little black and white dog. But all in vain! That night he returned home, very sad indeed. His mom tried to console him, "Maybe he'll be back tomorrow!" But the next morning he was still gone.

Harry knelt next to his bed and prayed, "Lord, you know where Rex is. Please let him return home safely." And just before he said *Amen*, he added, "And, oh yes, please forgive all my sins. Don't let my sinfulness prevent You from hearing my prayer."

Then he got up and emptied his moneybox. The youth leader had told them that they didn't need faith as big as a watermelon when they asked God to answer their prayers. But they should do something to show that they trusted the Lord.

That afternoon he came home with a brand new leash he had bought at the pet shop. "But Rex is gone!" his sister said in surprise. "Yes, but he might come back," Harry replied with his heart full of faith.

Three weeks dragged by. Harry's father was thinking of buying him a new dog. Harry was trying to fight off the despair.

Then, one morning early, Harry heard the familiar whining at the back door: Rex was back!

"Thank you, Lord!" Harry said as he grabbed the leash and ran outside.

Learn Matthew 21:22 or James 5:16 by heart.

"If you believe, you will receive whatever you ask for in prayer." Mt. 21:22

YOU CAN IF YOU WANT TO

Look on a world map at the piece of land that connects North and South America. Well, today a ship coming from the Atlantic Ocean can sail quite easily between the two continents. It doesn't take a ship very long to move through the Canal and reach the Pacific Ocean on the other side. But it was not always like that. Years ago, ships had to sail right around the southern point of Peru – a trip that took two months – if they wanted to reach the coast on the other side.

Someone came up with a plan to cut a 300-foot wide channel through the land so ships could travel between the continents. Ship owners would save million of dollars and lots of time. But it was not an easy task. Thousands of men were employed to dig right through mountains and change the directions of rivers. Many of them died from malaria, TB, and smallpox. But they persevered and finally completed the mammoth task.

Today nearly five thousand ships pass through the Panama Canal every year.

"Are there rivers you cannot cross? Are there mountains you cannot climb? We are the men who can do the impossible, what no man has done before." That was a song sung by the men who built the Panama Canal. If you ever struggle with a difficult Math problem or find it hard to fix a puncture on your bike, think of the massive Canal between the two continents of America. Think of the men who persevered until they had finished the job, despite enormous problems. Also think of the heroes in the Bible who didn't flinch when faced with troubles: Moses at the Red Sea, David facing Goliath, Esther before King Xerxes. Remember how they relied on God and then accomplished the impossible. Paul wrote in Philippians 4:13: *"I can do everything through him who gives me strength."*

Write Paul's words on a piece of paper and place it above your desk to encourage you.

February

FEBRUARY 1

BEAUTY INSIDE

A jewelry shop in the Mall had a glass tank full of oysters. Customers could fish for an oyster, and if they found a pearl inside, it would be theirs to keep. Jolene decided to spend her birthday money there. She always wanted a pendant with a genuine pearl in it. The shopkeeper gave Jolene a pair of tongs so she could fish for one of the oysters. Jolene held the oyster in her hand. The shell was very ugly, but when Jolene opened it, she stared in awe at the beautiful pearl that was inside. The jeweler promised to set it in a silver pendant for her. She was so excited!

As Jolene and her mom were driving home, she remarked, "I have no money left to buy the really cool sweater and sandals I wanted."

"But you have a precious pearl," her mom replied, and immediately reminded her of the merchant in Jesus' parable who sold all he had to buy a special pearl. "Yes, but I will stick out like a sore thumb when I'm with my friends in their new clothes!" she replied. "You should see how poor Carla is treated at Sunday school, just because she always wears the same old clothes."

"What a pity!" her mom said. "I heard you say that Carla is one of the best friends you've ever had." "Oh yes!" Jolene replied. "She always comes and sits with me when I'm down and offers to help me when I really need it."

"She sounds like a precious pearl in a humble shell," her mother said. She added, "In 1 Samuel 16:7 God said, 'Man looks at the outer appearance, but the LORD looks at the heart.' We should do the same. And don't you think it would mean a lot to Carla if somebody else in your class didn't always have the latest fashions?"

Paste this verse above your mirror to remind you of which things are important in God's sight.

FEBRUARY 2

LESSON FOR A LAZY BOY

Everybody knew where John got his nickname from: He was called "lazy-bones" because he liked to wriggle out of his chores! When his mom asked him to help her, he would say, "I'm too tired!" When his dad needed a hand in the garden, he would say, "I'll come and help you later on." And when his sister asked him to help her in the kitchen, he'd say, "It's not a man's job!"

One day his family decided to teach him a lesson. When he came home from basketball practice, he was shocked to see that there was no supper on the table. "Where's supper, Mom?" he asked. "I was too tired to cook," his mom said. He cut a slice of bread and went sulkily to his room.

The next morning at breakfast he asked, "Dad, will you please drop me at school today? I have too much stuff to take on my bike." "Maybe tomorrow," said his dad calmly. "But I need it to-day!" he exclaimed. "I have to hand in my science project today or my teacher won't grade it."

Usually his dad helped him in such situations, but now he re-fused pointblank. "You will have to make another plan," he said. "I don't feel like leaving so early."

John was devastated. "Will you help me, Sue?" he asked. "It's not a woman's job!" his sister replied bluntly. Suddenly John re-alized what was going on. He remembered all the times when he had refused to help his family members. He was ashamed.

"OK" he said, somewhat embarrassed. "I can see that you are trying to teach me a lesson. If any one of you will help me to get my stuff to school today, I'll turn over a new leaf."

"Help me with the dishes, then I'll take you to school," his mom volunteered. "Sure!" he cried out and eagerly jumped up to collect the plates from the table.

**Which verse in Proverbs 6
has a special message for John?**

FEBRUARY 3

TELL SOMEBODY

Mr. Orland was a very kind teacher, and he often asked Nigel to help him after school. Nigel was eager to please him and often stayed to help him in his classroom.

But one day, Mr. Orland had an odd request. He asked Nigel to come and sit on his lap and to scratch his back. Nigel felt very uncomfortable. He quickly glanced at his watch and said, "I have to go! I must be at the dentist at three." Nigel felt guilty about the lie, but he ran home as fast as he could.

He tried to forget about the incident, but he wasn't keen to help Mr. Orland again. He noticed that Mr. Orland had started asking somebody else to help him after school. Nigel started worrying about his friend, Paul. *What should I do?* he wondered. What he had heard about sexual abuse put him on guard. But he was embarrassed to tell his parents about what Mr. Orland had asked him to do.

Nigel's mother sensed that something was wrong. One night, when they had their usual bedtime chat, she asked him about it. Then Nigel told her everything.

"Don't worry about it anymore!" she said. "I'm glad that you shared this with me. You're not supposed to handle things like this on your own. Dad and I will pray about it and then decide what to do. Ecclesiastes 4:12 says, *'A cord of three strands is not easily broken'*. If we tackle this problem together with the Lord, we will be as strong as a three-stranded cord and we will know exactly what to do." That night Nigel slept much better than he had for a long time.

Put three pieces of string in your Bible to mark this verse. It will help you remember that it's wise to talk to a caring grownup when it comes to serious matters.

FEBRUARY 4

THE VANISHING BACKPACK

If you ever come across the book *Pilgrim's Progress* by John Bunyan, you should read it. It is the story of a man who went on a journey to the Heavenly City. As you read it, you will find that many of the experiences he had are similar to what we go through when we follow Jesus.

At the beginning of the story, Christian carried a heavy bag on his shoulders. It was the burden of the sins that he had committed in his life. Along the way, he met Evangelist. He asked him, "How can I get rid of this heavy burden?" Evangelist gave him a Big Black Book and pointed to a certain passage in it. "It is written that the King sent His Son to us so that whoever believes in Him, shall not perish, but have eternal life." Evangelist continued, "Do you see that gate? It is the gate of Decision. If you go through the gate, you will find the cross just on the other side. If you kneel at that cross and honestly believe that the Son of the King died for your sins, you will be relieved of your burden of guilt."

The man walked up to the gate and stopped to read the inscription on it: *Knock, and the door will be opened to you.* He reached out his hand and knocked. Immediately the gate opened. In front of him, he saw the cross. "Thank you, O Prince of Peace, for what You have done for me!" he prayed as he knelt at the cross. At that very moment the burden on his back came loose and rolled away! He immediately felt light and free. Christian went through many adventures on his journey to the Heavenly City.

Have you ever gone through that gate of decision and have you knelt before Christ to thank Him for dying for your sins? Then the heavy load of guilt and shame has been removed from your back and you can travel burden-free along the adventurous road that leads to heaven.

Read Ephesians 1:7 and you will see why God takes away our burden of sin.

GANGSTERS FOR CHRIST

Oswald's mom found a note in his room that had been written in some sort of secret code. She frowned. The previous week the school had sent out a circular warning parents that many of the school children were involved in neighborhood gangs. "These gangs are involved in activities involving drugs, alcohol and fighting," the letter said.

That evening Oswald's mom asked him a few straight questions. "Mom, you needn't worry!" he said. "I do belong to a gang, but we call ourselves *Gangsters for Christ*. We want to make our school a better place. We all wear WWJD wristbands and we try to act the way Jesus would've acted today."

Then he lowered his voice so that his sister couldn't hear him. "The tree house in Rick's garden is our club headquarters and no one can enter without the right password. It is 'We do good for Christ!' We've done lots of good things already!" "What kind of things?" his mom asked curiously. "Well, we protected Steven when another gang tried to hurt him. And we stopped people from telling lies about Mr. Woods.

We also raised money so that Leonard could go on the Youth group outings. We have lots of ideas of things to do this year. There's a gang in our class whose motto is *Vengeance*! But ours is *Peace*!"

Oswald's mom was not only relieved, but she was also very proud of her son. "What do you gangsters eat when you have your meetings?" she asked. "Catgut!" he teased.

His mom smiled. "Well, if you ever feel like a change, I will make you some chocolate chip cookies." "Then we will make you an honorary member," he said with a laugh.

John 20:21 was written in the gang's tree house. Find out what it said.

FEBRUARY 6

ALWAYS CHEERFUL

Pete Williams could have spent a lot of time moaning, if he really wanted to. He was born with a very rare lung defect and he suffered severely because of it. He had to spend weeks on end in hospital. One year he missed sixty days of school! He couldn't run around with his friends or play any sports at all. He had to swallow twenty-five tablets every single day!

One day while he was in hospital, Pastor Adler came to visit him. The minister felt sorry for the pale boy who was connected to a breathing machine and to a drip that pumped medication into his body through his veins.

"Is there something special that you want me to pray for?" asked the minister. "Yes," Pete replied. " Please pray that I will get well again. And pray that, if I don't get healed, I won't moan about it."

Pastor Adler felt a lump in his throat. He could hardly speak. But he prayed for the things Pete had mentioned. Then he asked, "Pete, how do you feel about your disability?"

Pete thought for a while. Then he replied, "I don't know why the Lord allowed my body to be like this. I cannot do much to change things. But I can do what the doctor tells me and I can choose whether I want to be grumpy or cheerful."

When Pastor Adler went home, he thought about what Pete had said. In his mind's eye he pictured how upset Satan must be because this brave boy would not be discouraged.

He went to his office at home and wrote in his diary: *Rejoice in the Lord always.* That was going to be the theme of his sermon on Sunday. His first line would be: "Sometimes we find ourselves in difficult situations. If we can smile in tough circumstances, we have victory in the Name of the Lord!"

Read Habakkuk 3:17-18 to see what this prophet said when things went wrong for him.

POSSESSIONS

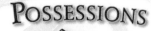

A rich man once went for a walk along the beach after a hard day at his office. Near some rocks, he saw a fisherman casually watching the fishing rod he had placed in the sand.

The fisherman was enjoying the sound of the sea and the cry of the seagulls. The rich executive started to chat with the fisherman. "Where do you work?" he asked. "Right here!" replied the fisherman. "Catching fish." "One at a time?" inquired the businessman. "If you buy yourself some nets you can catch a lot of fish at a time." "Why would I want to do that?" asked the fisherman. "Then you can buy yourself a boat and catch even more fish." "Why?" came the quick response. "Then you can buy even more boats and hire people to work for you and you could become very, very rich!" The fisherman smiled and again asked, "But why?"

"Stupid fellow!" the rich man muttered. "Don't you realize that you could become so rich that you would never have to work again? Then you could sit here on the rocks and enjoy the sunset without a care in the world!" "But that's exactly what I'm doing right now," the fisherman replied.

The rich man thought that happiness comes from lots of money. The fisherman knew that there are many other things that bring real happiness.

Why is this story included in this book? It is to remind you that the best things in life cannot be bought. As you grow up, don't be so focused on making money that you have no time to enjoy the wonderful things in the world, things God freely gives us.

Of course, when you are an adult, you do have to earn a living, because God expects you to look after your family, and to help others. But making money shouldn't be your goal in life.

Read Jesus' story about the rich fool in Luke 12:13-21.

February 8

GROUNDED!

Esther knew full well that what she was planning wasn't right. She knew that God expected her to be obedient to her parents. But she didn't feel like listening to them at all! She had been invited to Elaine's all-night party, but her parents had said she couldn't go. So she made a plan.

When they had gone to bed, she took two pillows and stuck them under her duvet on her bed. It really looked as if somebody was lying there. Then she got dressed and climbed through the window. Her room was on the top story of the house, but it wasn't the first time that she had used this escape route. She scrambled down the wall, clutching the ivy as she lowered herself.

Elaine's house wasn't far. When she arrived at the party, everybody cheered. Her friends were thrilled to see her and invited her to join them round the fireplace where they were toasting marshmallows.

Afterward they watched a video and drank hot chocolate. *My parents are far too strict!* she thought to herself, trying to silence the niggling in her conscience. But when she was on her way home in the early hours of the morning, she felt bad. *How will I be able to look Mom and Dad in the eye after this? And how can I do my best in the tennis match later on today?*

She started climbing up the ivy underneath her bedroom window. But suddenly the roots came loose and she landed amongst the roses with a thud! Her dad appeared on the verandah before she could get up. She knew exactly what her punishment would be: "Grounded for a month!" her parents declared in unison. But that wasn't what bothered her the most. It was the sad look in her dad's eyes that really upset her. *How can they ever trust me again?* she wondered.

Which one of God's laws in Exodus 20 did Esther break through her disobedience?

A NEW DAD

"Mom, will George be living with us forever?" Trevor asked when he and his mom were alone for a few minutes. His mom and George, whom he didn't really know very well, had got married the previous week, and Trevor was only just beginning to realize what that meant for him. They were busy moving into George's house, and for the first time the eleven-year-old boy saw that his mom's new husband could get cross. George had yelled at him when he dragged a box over the carpet, instead of picking it up.

Two months ago, George had asked Trevor if it was okay with him if he and Trevor's mom got married. At first he wasn't very happy with the idea, but later on he was quite glad that things turned out the way they had. After his own dad died, his life had changed drastically. There was nobody to fix his bike when it broke and there was nobody who could understand the stuff that boys were interested in. His mom knew nothing about football or motorbikes.

But now, after the incident with the box, he knew that George would be quite strict on him. There were bound to be ups and downs as they started a new family life together. His mom quietly asked, "Would you prefer to be the only man in the house again? Do you want to have a dad to take you fishing? Was it really better to be from a single-parent family?" Trevor thought about what his mom said. He was actually quite glad that his mom had someone to talk to about things. She had been very lonely after his dad had died.

He also knew that his own dad would have been just as cross with him for dragging a box across the carpet. "It's OK, Mom!" he said. "Do you think that if I say I'm sorry, George would shoot some baskets with me after we've fetched the rest of the stuff?" "Try it!" his mom answered with a smile.

Read Romans 13:1 carefully.

GOD IS TRUSTWORTHY

A clever man once showed a little boy his cupped hands. "In my hands I have a butterfly," he said. "You must guess whether it is dead or alive. If you guess right, I will give you a hundred dollars." Now the little boy had a problem! If he said, "The butterfly is alive," the man could crush it to death before he opened his hands and the boy would not get the money. But if he said, "The butterfly is dead," the man could open his hands and show that it was still alive, and he still wouldn't get the money.

The boy decided to take a chance, "The butterfly is dead!" he said. Immediately the clever man opened his hands to reveal a butterfly that was getting ready to fly away. "Now I've lost my prize-money," the child said. "I can't win whatever I do!"

Because the child could not trust the grownup, he found it difficult to make the right choice in life. Lack of trust always does that. But remember that God is completely trustworthy. We needn't feel that we are gambling away our lives if we follow Him.

One of the names that the Israelites gave to God was Jehovah-Tsidkenu. It means: *The Lord is just and reliable*. He will never try to trick us or confuse us when we have to make decisions. The Bible gives us all the guidance we need to make the right choices in life.

Underline the promise in John 14:2 in your Bible.
Isn't it great that we need never doubt the
trustworthiness of the One who made that promise?

He who is the Glory of Israel does not lie or change his mind. 1 Sam. 15:29

THE WINNING SHOT

Vera Simpson was the best squash player in the school. And she would represent the school in the State championships, if she won the match against Veronica Lee on Saturday. Veronica had won the district championships the previous year.

The atmosphere was tense when, after a grueling 45-minute match, the score was a draw and the two girls were fighting for the match point. The next few minutes would decide the championship. Could Vera beat the reigning champion? The spectators held their collective breath as Vera prepared to serve. She smashed the ball with awesome strength onto the front wall. Her opponent really didn't have a chance to hit that ball back. The referee shouted "Right!" and the line judge agreed that the ball was good.

But Vera hung back. She had seen something that the judges hadn't noticed. She hesitated for a moment and then shook Veronica's hand. "You win!" she said. Then she turned to the referee and said firmly, "The ball bounced twice."

Vera's friends were devastated. How could this have happened? Vera could have been the champion, but she disqualified herself by being honest!

"Why did you do it?" they asked her later. "Remember, I will have to live with my conscience for the rest of my life," she said.

What do you think of what Vera did? In Titus 2:10, Paul says that Christians *"should show that they can be fully trusted, so that in every way they will make the teaching about God our Savior attractive."* Let's always be 100% truthful, even though it might cost us dearly. People will then respect us and they will honor our Lord who gives us the strength to live holy lives.

You can also read 2 Corinthians 8:21 to
see what else Paul had to say on this topic.

HAPPINESS FROM A BOTTLE?

A guest speaker came to talk to the seventh grade class about alcohol abuse at their Sunday school camp. He asked the children why they thought some people drank alcohol. "It makes them happy," Adrian said. "That's a lie!" Beatrix blurted out. "In our home it brought only unhappiness. My parents got divorced as a result of it." "My brother says that he can communicate better after he has had a drink," said Esther. "Yeth, and then he lithps so much that nobody can hear what he thaith!" The kids laughed, but Conrad interrupted them, "It's not a joke! People drink to please their friends, but in the end it always leads to problems."

Then Fred spoke up. He was the cleverest kid in the class. "I think that people drink because they think it gives them self-confidence." "And what do you say?" asked the speaker. "I don't know!" he replied. "It looks like false confidence to me. Guys who drink too much get behind the wheels of cars with great confidence and then they cause tragic accidents."

The visitor then told his story. "I was one of those guys who drank to help me to relax. But in the end, my stress increased because of my drinking habits. I thought I could forget all my problems when I drank, but eventually my troubles got worse. I am here today to warn you. Alcohol can become a real enemy. And the earlier you start drinking, the greater the chance that you might become addicted to it. Make a decision today not to rely on alcohol to make you feel like you're having a great time at parties. And ask God to give you the strength to stick to your promise, and to help you really have a good time."

"I've already decided that I won't drink until I'm grownup. And then I might even decide never to drink at all," Conrad said. At bedtime their teacher told them to read Proverbs 23:31-35. Most kids agreed that Conrad's decision was the best.

What do you feel about this issue?

Let us behave decently ... not in orgies and drunkenness. Rom. 13:13

THE MIRACLE

Kids at school called her Winnie Wart because she had eight big warts on her hands. They hated it when they had to sit next to her on the bus, although her mom said that the warts were not infectious. She was glad when winter came because then she could wear gloves. She tried all kinds of treatments: the sap of raw aloe plants, ointments and plasters that her mom bought from the pharmacist, special vitamin supplements. She even tried to blow them away on a moonlit night, a remedy she found in an old library book. But every morning the warts were still there.

Winnie's parents weren't Christians, but she sometimes went to church with Mrs. Danvers, their next-door neighbor. One Sunday morning the pastor read Luke 17:11-19, the story of the ten lepers. Jesus had healed all of them, but only one came back to say 'thank You'. That night Winnie knelt by her bed and prayed, "Lord, You could make the skin of the lepers smooth and well again. Won't you please take away my warts? I promise You that I will tell my friends about it and I will thank and praise You always for what You do for me. Amen."

The next morning the warts were still there. But Winnie did not give up. Each night she repeated her prayer. And then, one day, when she dropped her gloves on the kitchen table after school, she saw it ... the warts were gone! "It's a miracle!" she shouted and danced around the table with her hands in the air. "Warts sometimes do that," her mom said. "They come and they go."

But Winnie knew that it wasn't just coincidence. She went to her room to thank God. She also started telling everyone she met what God had done for her. The kids at school started calling her Winnie the Saint, but she didn't mind at all.

Read the Scripture passage that the pastor read in church on the day when Winnie started praying about her problem.

FEBRUARY 14

ONE BIG FAMILY

It was a dreary day when George's mother was buried. But it was even drearier in his heart. How would he and his three younger brothers ever cope without their mom? Their dad worked long hours and their mom had done everything for them: cooking, cleaning, washing, and helping them with their homework. But then she had died in a car crash. *Who will look after us now?* he thought.

During the funeral service the pastor said, "Brothers and sisters, because we are all one big family through the blood of Jesus, we must stand by each other in times of need. The Smith family really needs us now." After the service, the pastor's wife came to George. "Don't worry," she said. "God will provide!" She hugged each of the boys.

The next day a friendly woman brought them a delicious casserole. She spent some time with George's father to find out how the women's committee could help the family. When she left, she gave each of the boys a bar of chocolate.

During the next few months, many women took turns to come and help the boys clean the house, do the laundry, make food, and wash windows. They also helped them with their homework and school projects. One day the pastor's wife came and sat with them at the kitchen table. Together they drew up a roster so that the boys could know when it was their turn to do what chores. In this way, they could keep things under control.

When George was grown up, he and his brothers never forgot how the congregation showed their love and concern for their family when things seemed so dark and hopeless.

Today George is a deacon in his church and he is always looking for ways in which he can help church members who are in need.

In Acts 2:44-45 you can read how the first Christians looked after each other.

A MESSAGE THAT CAN CHANGE HEARTS

Doctor Moffat was a missionary who worked in South Africa a long time ago. One young man often attended the meetings in which Doctor Moffat taught people from the Bible. One day he told the missionary that he wanted to become a child of God. Doctor Moffat helped him to confess his sins, to ask God's forgiveness and to commit himself to a life of obedience to Christ. From that day on, the young man was very keen to learn more about God and Doctor Moffat gave him a Bible to read.

A few weeks later, the young man came running to the missionary's house. "Papa, Papa Moffat, our watchdog has eaten a large part of my Bible!" he cried. The missionary felt sorry for the young man and promised to get him a new one as soon as possible.

But the young man was not easily comforted. "But think of the dog!" he said. "Don't worry, a few bits of paper will do him no harm. He's used to chewing bones, remember?" Doctor Moffat said.

"Papa, you don't understand!" the young man insisted. "I was once a very bad person. I loved no one and hated many people. Then the Bible came into my heart and I started loving my fellowmen. I didn't want to hurt anybody! Now the dog has the Book in his insides. Will he still kill the lions and the wolves and the wild dogs that hunt our sheep?"

What a wonderful story to help us remember the difference that God's Word can make in anybody's life.

Read what 2 Timothy 3:16 says about the Bible. Do you read your Bible regularly so that it can make a difference in your life?

FEBRUARY 16

WHO MADE IT?

Have you ever heard about Sir Isaac Newton? He was a famous scientist and is remembered today for his research and inventions. He invented the telescope and he discovered why a rainbow has seven colors.

He also discovered that when the sun, moon, and earth are in a straight line it causes a springtide at sea. Although he lived more than three hundred years ago, he predicted that people would one day travel into space by satellite. And in 1961, Yuri Gagarin orbited the earth in Sputnik! Yes, Isaac Newton was truly a great scientist.

He was a Christian, but had a friend who did not believe in God. One day Newton made a model of our solar system and displayed it in his workplace. He placed a ball in the middle to represent the sun, and all the planets circled around it without colliding.

When his friend saw this, he was amazed. "Who made this model?" he asked. "Nobody," Dr. Newton replied. "What nonsense!" the other scientist exclaimed. "Somebody must have made it, someone quite brilliant!"

Newton stood up from his desk and put his hands on his friend's shoulders. "This is merely a toy. It is only a copy of a system with complicated laws that you and I would spend many years studying before we could fully understand them. And yet you believe that the universe, which is a thousand, thousand times more intricate than my model, had no designer or maker!"

Have you ever thought about the wonders of the universe God made?

**Read Psalm 8 to see how David
felt about the Creator and His Creation.**

WILMA RUDOLPH

She was born prematurely, and weighed only four pounds at birth. She had polio when she was four years old and for eight years she had to walk with crutches and iron clamps around her legs. But when she was 20 years old, she won three gold medals at the Olympic Games.

Did she have a rich family who could afford the best hospitals? No, her mom was a washerwoman who did the laundry for rich people. There were 22 children in the family that she had to bring up.

Did she have the best coaches to prepare her for the track events in which she competed? No, she was a black girl who grew up in Tennessee before black and white children had equal opportunities in that state. Who was this remarkable girl?

Her name was Wilma Rudolph and she was born in Clarkesville in 1940. In 1960 she became the first woman to win three gold medals at the Olympics: for the 100-meter sprint, the 200-meter sprint and for the 400-meter relay. Two books have been written and a film has been made about the life of this extraordinary woman.

Her life was certainly not without problems. When she started running, she always came last. But she never quit. Her mom taught her that people can do anything if they put their hearts into it. She was also a believer who got her courage from the Lord.

Have you got a dream that you would like to see come true in your life? If it is something that will glorify God, put your heart into it and start working towards that goal.

Paul was also somebody who, like Wilma, knew how to persevere. Read what he said in Philippians 4:13.

February 18

THE ACCOUNT

One day a Christian man visited his Jewish friend at his hardware store. He began talking to him about the Jewish religion. "I understand that you also believe in the Old Testament of our Bible?" he asked. "Yes," the shopkeeper answered, "but we do not believe your New Testament. We don't believe that Jesus was the Son of God and that He died on a cross to pay for the sins of the world."

"Do you still offer animal sacrifices, as commanded in Leviticus?" asked the Christian. "No," replied the Jew. "Neither do we," said his friend. "We don't sacrifice animals to settle the debt of our sins. We believe that Jesus, the Lamb of God, paid with His blood for all our trespasses. That is why we believe we no longer have to offer the sacrifices commanded in the Old Testament law."

"Well," replied the Jew, "we do not make sacrifices, but we do read the parts of Scripture that refer to the sacrifices and then ask for God's forgiveness." "That's interesting," the Christian said.

Before he left the shop, the shop owner added up what his friend owed for his purchases. The Christian then picked up the invoice and read, "One hammer – $2.50, one screwdriver – $1.75 and a pack of nails – $1.00. That comes to $5.25. Thanks very much!" And he turned to walk out the door.

"But you must still pay me!" said the owner of the shop. "I read my debt out loudly to you. Isn't that enough?" answered the Christian, as he put the money on the counter. The shopkeeper definitely had something to think about: It is not enough to admit our sin: Somebody has to pay for it. Jesus did that once and for all on the cross. If we believe that, then our debt has been paid for and we do not need to be punished for our sins.

**Read Colossians 2:14 to find out
what Jesus did with the list of our debts.**

Having canceled the written code … he took it away, nailing it to the cross. Col. 2:14

CARRY EACH OTHER'S BURDENS

"The command in Galatians 6:2, *'Carry each other's burdens'* isn't about carrying each other's sports bags!" Mr. Oliver told the seventh grade class. "It means that we must support and encourage our friends when they go through tough times. You've all heard that Enrico's mother died last week. I want you to think of a way in which you can help him."

Arnold was Enrico's best friend. "I'll have to go round and see how he's doing," he thought after Sunday school. "But what can I say to him?" He had never experienced such a loss in his own life, and so he prayed, "Lord, give me the right words so that I can comfort my friend."

There were lots of people at Enrico's house. They were bringing flowers and food for the family. Arnold found Enrico in his room. He was sitting on his bed and staring out of the window in front of him. Arnold sat down next to him without saying a word. After a long time, Arnold started talking. He spoke about things at school and Sunday school, and he talked about the people who had come to the funeral. Later on, when Pastor James asked everybody to come to the lounge for prayer, Arnold stood next to Enrico.

Later that evening, when he was getting ready for bed, he stood in front of the mirror and told himself, "You did nothing to help your friend today! Is that what 'Carry each other's burdens' is all about?" He wondered why the Lord hadn't helped him to think of something really encouraging to say to Enrico. But two days later Arnold got an e-mail from Enrico. "Thank you that you came to sit with me on Sunday when I felt so down. It meant a lot to me. I don't know what I would have done without you."

Do you know of somebody who is going through a rough time? Remember that there are many ways in which you can show that you care.

FEBRUARY 20

SCOOP UP AND DRINK

Elizabeth Olivier told the story of a big fishing trawler that once ran aground near the mouth of the Amazon River. Luckily, the crew were all able to get into the lifeboat. Day after day, they floated on the vast expanse of the ocean. After a few days they had very little water left, so they sent out messages saying, "Come and help us! We are dying of thirst!" Eventually they received a message from another vessel. It said, "Scoop up and drink!" Were the people who sent the message joking or did they perhaps not understand their situation? They knew that they could not lessen their thirst by drinking seawater!

They repeated their signal: "We have no water!" But again, the same answer came: "Scoop up and drink!"

One of the men in the lifeboat put his hand into the water around the boat and tasted it. "It's fresh!" he exclaimed. Quickly all the men scooped up water and drank. All the while they had been in fresh water, and they hadn't realized it! The mighty Amazon River thrusts its fresh water deep into the ocean.

Can you guess which part of Scripture matches this story? Yes, it is the words of Isaiah in Isaiah 55:1: "*Come, all you who are thirsty, come to the waters; and you who have no money, come buy and eat!*"

Sometimes people are unhappy and dissatisfied because they don't realize that joy and peace are all around them. A Bible full of the rich promises of God might be lying under dust on their bookshelves or they might be living near a community of loving Christians. And above all, God Himself is as near to them as a whispered prayer, if only they would "scoop up and drink"!

See what Jesus said in John 4:14 about the water that He can provide for people who are thirsty.

YELLOW RIBBONS FOR JESUS

Brenda is a pretty twelve-year-old who lives in White River. She organized a very special week at her school. And she wishes many more schools would follow suit. It all started like this:

Her mom was driving her to school when the radio announcer started talking about charity organizations, and the special days set aside to support different organizations. "Why can't we have a *Week for Jesus* at our school?" Brenda asked. "There's an AIDS week and a STOP SMOKING week and a CANCER AWARE-NESS week. I would love to have a week for Jesus!"

Her mom said, "That sounds like a good idea to me, Brenda. Why don't you do something about it? See if you can speak to the principal and explain your idea to him." So Brenda went to the principal and asked him if the children could wear little yellow ribbons for the last week in February. "It will be a symbol of light," she explained. The school board liked her idea and Brenda started making posters to let everyone know what was going to happen. She also asked their pastor to come and give a talk at the school. He thought that it was a good opportunity to help people think about Jesus and to encourage Christian children to talk about their faith.

On the Monday of the *Week for Jesus*, most of the kids and the teachers were wearing little yellow ribbons. People made a special effort to be helpful and kind. Children shared their lunch with one other and looked for ways to encourage others. Many children decided to keep wearing their ribbons, even after the Jesus Week was over. "We should make every day a Jesus-day," they realized. And Brenda said to her mom, "We will keep living out the message of the Bible so that people who do not have one will know what it says." Don't you think that she had a great idea?

Read Matthew 5:16 and think how you can let your light shine for Jesus.

FEBRUARY 22

MORE THAN CONQUERORS

Dr. Adler was a famous psychologist. In one of his books he wrote about two patients who came to him for help. Both of them had lost an arm in an accident. He saw them regularly and made notes on the way they each handled their disability.

After a year, the one man was bitter and rebellious. He could see no reason for living and gradually withdrew from friends and relatives. But the other man was cheerful and positive. He even joked about his condition. "I wonder why we were born with two arms? I find one arm sufficient for all my needs!" he would say with a grin. Why did these two people experience life so differently? It had a lot to do with the way they looked at the world.

There is always more than one way of looking at a problem. And we can decide what our point of view will be. David's brothers said, "Goliath is too big! We can never fight against him!" But David said, "The giant is so big: I can hardly miss him!" He trusted the Lord and then the enemy seemed easy to defeat. So he picked up some pebbles, loaded his slingshot, and hit the giant head-on.

Some people look at a job that must be finished, and say, "We are only halfway", and then give up. Others choose to see it differently and say, "We are already halfway!" and carry on bravely. Can you see the difference? Christians ought to be the happiest, most positive, courageous people on earth, because we have God as our Partner. With Him by our side, we can tackle any problem. The apostle Paul experienced trouble, hardship, persecution, famine, and danger and yet said, *"In all these things we are more than conquerors through Him who loved us"* (Rom. 8:37).

Read Romans 8:35-39 carefully and then underline it neatly in your Bible for future reference.

FEBRUARY 23

WITHOUT A WORD

A missionary went to a faraway island to tell the people there about Jesus. But when he got there, he discovered that the language these islanders spoke was very difficult to learn. It had never been written down and, as the missionary was partially deaf, he could not follow the words or try to copy what they were saying. At first he thought that he should go home again. What good would it do to stay with these people when he could not communicate with them? But he felt a deep concern for them: they worshiped evil spirits and knew nothing about God.

So he decided to stay on and live among them. He helped them wherever he could. He especially cared for sick and elderly people. He stayed on the island until the day he died. Everybody was sad when he died and they buried him on the island.

Years later other Christians came to the island to teach the inhabitants about God. They studied the language and started telling the islanders about Jesus: how He loved people and cared for the sick and the weak. "Oh!" the listeners exclaimed. "We also know Him! He lived among us for many years." Then the missionaries found it easy to explain Jesus' message of redemption to them. They had already learned a lot about Jesus, just by watching one of His followers.

People can learn much about Jesus if we, His followers, act as He would've done. Many people do not own a Bible. Our lives should be like an open book through which they can get to know our Lord.

There is a verse in Matthew 5 that tells us to live good lives so that God can be glorified. Read up to verse 16 and find out which verse it is.

BRING THEM ALONG

There once was a doctor who really loved the Lord. He took Mark 16:15 to heart and so decided to go to a foreign country and tell the people who live there about Jesus.

He started working at a hospital in a small Chinese town where he could teach his patients about the Living God. Often he had to remove cataracts from the eyes of patients. After such an operation, patients could see much better than before.

One day a man who was almost blind came to the hospital. When the missionary doctor told him how Jesus lived and died for his sins, the man said that he also wanted to follow Jesus. "If you confess your sin, God will forgive you and make you His child," the doctor said, "because Jesus has already paid for your transgressions with His blood."

A few days later this man went back to his hometown: a new person! Not only was the operation to his eyes a great success, but he was also a Christian now who wanted to tell everybody about his new faith.

But that was not the end of the story. Six months later one of the nurses called the doctor to a window on the second floor of the hospital. "Doctor, come and have a look!" she said.

From the window they could see a strange procession in the valley below. Up front was the man whose eyes had been healed. He was holding a thick rope that twenty-eight blind men also held onto as they followed him. Their friend had led them miles to the hospital so that their eyes could also be healed and so that they could also hear about Jesus.

Maybe there are some of your friends you could lead to Jesus. Why not invite them to join the youth group at your church?

"Go into all the world and preach the good news to all creation." Mk. 16:15

JESUS' ARMS AND HANDS

War is dreadful. In countries where wars are fought, people are killed, buildings are ruined, and normal life ceases to exist. About sixty years ago, during the Second World War in Europe, millions of people died and houses, schools, cathedrals, museums and other buildings were bombed and destroyed.

In a town near the German border, a beautiful little church was bombed when the town was attacked. A statue of Christ had stood in front of the church, but the head, arms, and hands were ripped off in the blast. Most people fled from the town, and returned only after the war was over. Then they had to start from scratch to build houses, make gardens, and get things going again. They planned to restore the church so that worship services could again be held there. They found the head of the statue in the rubble, but the arms and hands had completely disappeared. They repaired the statue as best they could, leaving out the missing parts.

Today tourists often go to that town to see how the inhabitants reconstructed everything with love and dedication. Then they also visit the little church. Most people stand still for a while when they see the statue of Christ that has no arms and hands. They thoughtfully read the inscription on the pedestal. In bold letters, someone engraved the words: **"You are my arms and legs."**

Jesus says those same words to us, His followers, today. He wants to put His arms around people who suffer and He wants to reach out and help them with His hands. But because He is not on earth any more, He must use the arms and hands of His children in order to reach other people.

In Luke 10:25-37 you can read about someone who acted like Jesus. Think how you can be Jesus' hands and feet to somebody during the next week.

HOW DID THEY BECOME FRIENDS?

There was once a farmer who loved all his animals. But all his animals weren't so fond of each other! The turkey used to chase the hens and the cat often caught a chicken for dinner. But two of the farmer's animals had an excellent relationship: his crow and his dog were best friends.

One day when the farmer wanted to feed his dog, he could not find him anywhere. He whistled and called his name, but the dog was gone! So he went into the kitchen to fetch the raw meat the crow usually had for supper. As he went outside, the crow snatched the meat from the farmer's hands and flew away with it. A little while later, when the farmer was having his dinner, he heard the crow pecking against the window as he always did when he was hungry. "But friend," the farmer said, "I have already given you your food!" Even so, he cut another chunk of meat for the hungry bird. Again the bird behaved strangely. He grabbed the meat in his beak and flew away with it.

Then the farmer decided to follow the bird. Where would he take the meat? Guess what he found! The crow took him to a place where poachers had set a trap to catch wild animals. The dog was caught in an iron snare! If the farmer had not arrived then, the dog would have bled to death. The crow cared so much for his friend, the dog, that he tried to keep him alive with portions of his own food.

Can you think why the crow and the dog were so fond of each other? It could be because they had the same master who taught them to care for each other. Their example reminds us that all kinds of different people who all serve the same Master should love and care for one another. Our Lord Jesus expects us to love others as He loves us.

John 13:35 has a message for each one of us who wants to serve the Lord.

Dear friends, since God so loved us, we also ought to love one another. 1 Jn. 4:11

CAST YOUR BREAD UPON THE WATERS

"Give, and it will be given to you." Lk. 6:38

"Cast your bread upon the waters, for after many days you will find it again." Do you know this proverb? It comes from the Bible. You can read it in Ecclesiastes 11:1. It means that if you do good to others, good things will also come your way.

There is a story that illustrates the truth of this saying: A poor lady once wanted to give her sick husband something that would make him feel better. She knew that he liked apricot jam, but she did not have enough money to buy him some. If they had an apricot tree in their garden, she could have made some jam herself. But they only had a plum tree. So she picked some of the plums to sell at the market. Then she would have money to buy the apricot jam!

On her way to the market, she passed a group of children playing in the street. They looked poor and hungry. She felt so sorry for them that she gave them all the plums without thinking about the consequences. One little boy said, "Thank you ma'am!" and put a little lost kitten in her basket.

She started walking home with the kitten in the basket and decided to stop at a friend's house along the way. This friend had a disabled daughter whose beautiful blue eyes always looked very sad. When she saw the kitten, her whole face lit up and she begged, "Mommy, can I please have the kitten?" "She can have it with pleasure!" said the visitor and put the kitten in the little girl's lap. It curled up in her lap and began to purr immediately. "How kind of you!" said the little girl's mother. "Here, take this jar of apricot jam as a token of our appreciation."

Can you see how the truth of the proverb from the Bible was proved on that day?

**Also look up Deuteronomy 15:10
and see what it says about giving.**

THE LIGHT ON THE HILLTOP

A church was built on a hilltop in a little coastal town. The pastor of the church was a diligent man who always did his duty. One night, when he was preparing to leave for a prayer meeting, his wife said, "I can't see why you have to go to church tonight. I'm sure nobody else will attend the meeting. The storm will keep them at home. The rain is pouring down and a gale-force wind is blowing! Nobody will blame you if you stayed at home tonight."

But the minister wasn't put off so easily. He put on his raincoat and ventured out into the stormy night. When he got to the church, he switched on the lights and waited to see if anybody else would turn up. But none of his church-members had taken the risk of climbing the hill on that stormy night.

So the minister knelt down in front of the pulpit and started praying all on his own for the members of his congregation. He also prayed for people who were at sea in that terrible weather. When he had finished praying, he put out the light again and walked home in the rain.

The pastor did not know that on that very night some fishermen were out at sea in great distress. The furious wind and waves tossed their boat past the harbor and all around them it was pitch-dark. They could not tell which way to turn to get to land. But then they suddenly saw a light in the distance. "It must be the light of the church!" they cried out. With that light to guide them, they were able to find their way again and they sailed safely toward the harbor.

What would have happened if the pastor had not diligently done his duty that night? Remember that God expects us to be reliable and to let our light shine for Him. Who knows how He can use us to show people who are lost where to find Him?

Read Luke 16:10 to see what Jesus said about being trustworthy.

BE PREPARED TO BE THE LEAST

"That will be the day!" Danny shouted angrily. "I won't apologize to Miss Hayward. Colin broke the window, not me. I'm not going to say I'm sorry just to please everybody!" Danny's granddad listened patiently to what his grandson had to say. "You both played with the ball, didn't you?" he asked. "Yes, but Colin dodged on purpose when I passed the ball to him. It was his fault that the ball went through Miss Hayward's kitchen window."

"Remember, if you don't apologize, you will never be able to play near her house again," Grandpa reminded him. Danny thought about what his granddad said. Yes, that would be a pity. She had such a great stretch of lawn in front of her house, and she always let them swim in her pool in summer. But he decided, "No, Grandpa! Even if I have nowhere to play and even if I die of heat in summer, I will not go to Miss Hayward and say that I am sorry!"

Grandpa went to his desk and browsed through some newspaper clippings. "Come and have a look at this," he said. Danny looked at the cartoon that grandpa held out to him. Two goats were walking in opposite directions on the narrow ledge of a cliff, next to a gaping precipice. In the middle of the path, they came face-to-face with each other. What would happen next? Would they tackle each other until both of them fell down the cliff? No, the one goat went down on its knees and allowed the other to walk over him. And so they could both continue their journey.

"Why did you show me this picture?" Danny asked. "If you are prepared to be the least, like the goat in the cartoon who lay down, you and Colin can still play together in front of Miss Hayward's house," grandpa said.

Guess what Danny did the next day. Read John 13:5 and see how Jesus was prepared to be the least.

"Whoever wants to become great among you must be your servant." Mk. 10:43

March

COURAGE!

Two hundred years ago many parts of the world had not yet been properly explored. Details of continents like Africa could not be drawn in and were simply left blank on maps. Many people in Africa had also not heard anything about Jesus.

But in Scotland there was a little boy who dreamed of exploring unknown countries when he grew up. His name was David Livingston. He wanted to become a missionary, a doctor, and an explorer. His dreams came true! When he completed his studies, he decided to go to South Africa and then travel from there up into the unknown parts of Africa. He had many adventures as he traveled by wagon or on foot into the heart of the dark continent. He named the Victoria Falls on the Zambezi River and was also the first man to cross Africa from west to east. Sometimes he was sick with malaria, sometimes he was hungry or thirsty. Often he was in great danger. Once a lion attacked him and seriously injured his shoulder, but fortunately the African men who were with him killed the lion with their spears before it could do more harm. Everywhere that he went, he learned the language of the locals, gave them medical care and taught them from the Bible.

When he was sixty years old, he died on his knees while he was praying. The people with whom he had been living were very sad. They embalmed his body with special ointment and carried him for 300 miles to the nearest harbor. There they put his body on a ship, together with all his diaries and other possessions and sent him back to Scotland. After his death many young people were encouraged by his example to go to faraway countries as missionaries. Today, all over Africa, you will find schools, churches and hospitals that are testimonies of the work that was begun by the courageous pioneer, Dr. David Livingston.

Read Psalm 22:27-28. These words could have been a great encouragement to Livingston. It also has an inspiring message for you today.

You will receive power when the Holy Spirit comes on you. Acts 1:8

BE CAREFUL!

"Dad, can I go and play pool in the Arcade tonight?" Ryan asked. "I've finished my homework and Brian invited me to go along." "I don't think so!" his dad replied. "I've heard that they sell drugs there and that a group of youngsters ran riot there last weekend." "I know, but those kids got drunk and you know that Brian and I won't do things like that." "The answer is NO!" his dad persisted. Ryan went to his room and muttered beneath his breath, "Dad has obviously forgotten what it feels like to be young."

A little later his dad came to his room. He sat down on a chair. "Imagine you were a rich man who had to appoint a new chauffeur: Three men apply for the job. You want to know about their driving abilities and ask, 'How close to the edge of a cliff can you drive the car?'

"The first one says, 'So near that the gravel shoots over the side of the cliff.' The second one says, 'So near that the front wheels touch the edge of the cliff.' The third one says, 'Sir, I always try to keep as far away from a cliff as possible!' Which man would you appoint as your chauffeur?"

Ryan smiled. "Dad, you are trying to trick me!" he said. "You are right! I would rather trust my life to the cautious driver. And you're probably right about playing pool at the arcade, too! There are a lot of temptations there." "How do you know?" his dad asked suspiciously. Ryan blushed. "I went in there the other day," he said. "But before the gravel shot over the cliff, I came home again!"

His dad got up and hugged him. "Ask Brian if he feels like going fishing with us tomorrow."

Ryan rushed to the telephone. Maybe his dad had not forgotten what it feels like to be young after all!

Read Ephesians 5:15.

How can a young man keep his way pure? By living according to your word. Ps. 119:9

TO SIT WITH JESUS

"Trrrrrrrr" Eileen's alarm clock shrilled next to her bed. She switched it off and at the same time put on her radio. She liked listening to loud pop music early in the morning. She dressed quickly. She wanted to get to school early, because she wanted to watch the cheer leaders practicing for the game on Saturday. As she walked into the kitchen, she noticed her mom sitting on a bench in the garden. "Why are you sitting here all alone?" she called cheerily.

"I'm not alone!" her mom said as she gave her a good morning kiss on the cheek. "It is such a glorious morning. Just listen to the birds and watch how the first rays of the sun break through those leaves. I'm sitting here in the presence of the Lord!" she said. She watched Eileen go back inside to fetch her backpack, and continued, "It's a pity that you seem to be in such a hurry, otherwise you could also join us!"

When Eileen came to say good-bye, her mom said, "A great philosopher once said that there are three enemies of one's soul: noise, haste, and crowds. I agree. If I don't have a quiet time with the Lord each day, I feel empty and restless." "Maybe you need it, Mom! But I don't think that it's necessary for me," Eileen answered. "Well, even Jesus found it necessary to get away sometimes so that He could communicate with His Father without any hindrances. Come and sit here with me and I'll show you all the verses I have marked in my Bible that say that Jesus looked for quietness."

A little while later, when Eileen left for school, she wasn't sorry that she had missed the cheer leaders' practice. She and her mom had started their day with Jesus.

Look up the verses Eileen's mom showed her before they prayed together that morning: Luke 4:42; 9:18; 22:41.

THINK TWICE

"Stupid Roly-poly!" Helen said. She was furious because her sister Jeanette had borrowed her pen and then lost it. "I'll think twice before I lend you anything again. You are the most irresponsible, unreliable person I know!"

Jeanette fled to her room, sobbing her heart out. When her mom came to see what had upset her so, she found her with her face buried in her pillow. Bit by bit Jeanette told her mom what had happened. Her mom went to the kitchen and called Helen, who was still fuming. When she came into the room her mom handed her a bowl and an egg. "Please break the egg into the bowl," she asked. Helen did as she was told without interrupting the flood of words. "That pen was my most precious possession! Grandpa brought it for me from overseas. Now it's gone forever just because a pathetic dumb creature couldn't look after it!"

Her mom calmly said, "Please would you put the egg back into the shell again, just the way it was." Helen stared at her mom. "Mom, are you crazy? It's impossible to put the pieces of an egg together again! Remember Humpty Dumpty?" "Exactly!" her mom said. "And you cannot easily heal broken feelings either. I can fully understand that you are upset about your special pen that's lost, but people's feelings are more precious than any of your valuable possessions. Jeannette did not lose the pen on purpose. She was careless and for that she will be punished. But you really hurt her feelings with the things that you said. The Bible tells us in James 3 that a person's tongue can do a lot of harm. It can corrupt a whole person and can set the whole course of someone's life on fire." I think that you will have to think twice before you lose your temper like that again!"

Read James 3:6. Helen wrote those words on a card that night to remind her to think twice before she used such harsh words again.

BE WARNED!

Have you ever heard about Leonardo da Vinci, the world-famous artist? You might have seen his painting of the *Last Supper*. It is a beautiful picture of Jesus and His disciples sitting around a table. It took da Vinci many years to complete that painting.

Da Vinci used a different man as a model for each of the disciples in the painting. When he wanted to paint Jesus, he searched for a long time until he found someone who made him think of Jesus. The young man he chose had an open, serious face and people who saw the finished painting were deeply moved by his serenity and beauty.

Over the next few years, da Vinci continued to paint the disciples one by one. He left Judas for last. He was the disciple who betrayed Jesus, remember?

Legend has it that Leonardo da Vinci roamed the streets looking for somebody whose face was dark and bitter enough to represent Judas.

In a tavern he came across a man whose face was so villainous that he decided to ask him to model for Judas. When da Vinci asked the man to come to his studio, he asked, "Don't you remember me? You used me as the model for Jesus."

This story makes us think how badly someone can degenerate if he is not careful about the way he lives. Wrong friends and bad habits can change a beautiful person into an ugly villain.

> **Read Psalm 119:9-10 and ask
> God to help you stay on track.**

MARCH 6

THE MOST PRECIOUS

Once upon a time there was a king who did not know which of his sons ought to become the next ruler of his kingdom. So he called his three sons together and said to them, "Take enough food for the road and tour through the land to look for the most precious thing that you can find in my kingdom. Bring it to me and then I will decide which one of you will be my successor."

The three princes packed enough food for a week and started their search. The eldest son decided to go to the biggest city in the country. The second son visited all the castles in the country. But the youngest went to see one of his friends who lived in a rural area. He wanted to discuss the matter with his friend because he hoped that the two of them would be able to identify the most valuable article in their country.

At the end of a week the three sons returned to the king and appeared before him in his throne room. The first prince knelt before his father and gave him a casket full of glittering jewels and precious gems. The second son had found an exquisite cloth, hand woven with threads of gold and silver, to give to the king. But the third son hung his head and said, "I am so sorry that I have brought you nothing. But when I arrived at my friend's farm, he was busy plowing the fields. His father was ill, so I helped him. If the lands had not been plowed, he would not have been able to plant the wheat. That took all week, and I have not been able to search for anything of value."

The king stood up and took both hands of the youngest son in his own hands. He felt how rough they were from hard work and he said, "You will be the next ruler of my kingdom because you know the secret of hard work and service to your fellow country-men."

**Jesus said something similar
in Luke 22:26. Look it up.**

KAMBRO-KID

Anne felt very depressed when she got onto the bus. Her mom was ill and everything had gone wrong that morning. She and her sister had overslept and then she had burnt the breakfast toast. When she went to put out the trash, the bag broke and she had to clean the kitchen before she could do anything else. And on top of all that, she couldn't find her history book anywhere. "Today is going to be one of those days!" she said dejectedly. It always seemed that when days started so badly, things just got worse and worse.

But somebody who was sitting at the front of the bus apparently saw life very differently. He was whistling a happy tune and he greeted everybody with a warm "Good morning!" as they got onto the bus. His bright and cheerful conversation soon had everyone near him smiling.

When Anne got off the bus, her own mood had also changed. She turned to see who it was who had managed to brighten her day so wonderfully. And what did she see? A young boy wearing dark glasses and carrying a white stick sat there, chatting happily to everyone who got onto the bus. She felt quite ashamed of herself.

That whole day she thought about the young boy who was so joyful in spite of his disability. What was his secret? She talked to her friend Bonny about it. "Maybe he is a Kambro-kid," Bonny said. "My mom always say that people who can be joyous in spite of drawbacks, are Kambro-kids." "What is a kambro?" Anne wanted to know. "It is a plant that grows in the desert and even though it experiences severe drought, it can survive."

"I wish that I could be like that!" Anne said earnestly. Bonny smiled and said, "My mom says that all Christians should be Kambro-kids!'

Which verse in Psalm 23 makes you think that David was also a Kambro-kid?

MARCH 8

COUNT YOUR BLESSINGS

"Mom, can I go with Dawn to the Mall today?" Mary asked. It was a Saturday and it would be fun to browse through the stores. "All right," her mom said. "On one condition: You must be back in time to go and help me with the soup kitchen in Hillbrow." "Great!" said Mary and started dialing Dawn's number.

When she got home at half past one, she decided there would be time enough later to tell her mother about all the stuff that she had seen and the clothes she wanted to buy. For the moment she helped her mother put the heavy pots of soup into the car and to load the bread that they were taking with them. They drove to the rundown area near the center of the city. Her mom drove very carefully past the broken bottles and tin cans lying in the road. She didn't want to spill any of the soup.

When they reached the little church that functioned as a homeless shelter, a few other ladies were waiting for them. They all helped to serve the soup and bread. Mary was deeply moved by this experience. She felt compassion for the little children dressed in worn-out clothes who hastily gobbled the food that was offered. She was also touched by the toothless old people who thanked them profusely.

On their way home, her mom reminded her, "There was something you wanted to ask me." Mary thought of the nice things that she had seen in the shops that morning, but her worn jeans and sneakers suddenly seemed OK to her. Instead of asking for new clothes, she said, "Can I help you again next Saturday, and can I bring a friend along?" "Of course!" her mom said and praised God in her heart.

If you ever envy somebody who owns more than you do, think of those who have less than you and read Deuteronomy 15:10-11.

GRAY HEADS

"If you sit in our church and close your eyes into slits, you see gray all over the place!" Ruth said. She and Annie were sitting on their verandah and talking. "Yes, we live amongst the oldies!" Annie laughed. "The worst is that they are so forgetful! My grandpa can tell a story three times in an hour and each time I have to pretend as if I've never heard that one before." "That's nothing compared to my granny. She came by bus the other day, wet through and through because of the rain. Meanwhile she was clutching an umbrella under her arm. Forgot to open it!" "And mine put a plastic salad bowl on the stove and switched it on." The two girls were giggling at their own stories about the absent-minded elderly people in their community.

Ruth then started imitating the old lady next door: she tottered down the garden path with bent shoulders and dribbled spittle from her mouth. Just then she saw her mom at the window. She immediately felt guilty and straightened up. As she expected, her mom came outside.

"It isn't kind to make fun of people who are old and weak. When they were young, they did their share to serve the community. The least we can do is to treat them with respect. Ruth, go get your Bible and bring it here." When Ruth returned, her mom read from Leviticus 19:32: *"Show respect for the elderly and revere your God."*

"Sorry Mom!" "Sorry Mrs. Jacobs!" the two girls said simultaneously. Just then the bent figure of their neighbor appeared round the corner. The girls jumped up to go and help her with the parcels that she was carrying.

**Read Leviticus 19:32 to see how
God expects us to treat the elderly.**

Is not wisdom found among the aged? Does not long life bring understanding? Job 12:12

PEOPLE ARE NOT LIKE HORSES

More than three hundred years ago a court case in England was discussed in all the daily newspapers. A ship had sailed from Africa with a large number of slaves on it. They had been bought in Africa and were to be sold again in England. During the journey the slaves started getting sick. The captain of the ship solved the problem by throwing the sick slaves overboard.

In the court case that resulted from his actions, the judge ruled, "The slaves were the property of their masters and they could do with their property whatever they wanted. It's like throwing horses overboard!" he concluded. Many people were distraught about this ruling. They felt that people shouldn't even treat horses that way!

One person who heard the story decided to do something about it. He was William Wilberforce, a young man who was a member of parliament at that time. He was a very good public speaker, but his life had not amounted to much. It consisted of parties, gambling and drinking. But then he started studying the Bible. Soon he committed his life to Jesus Christ. He was tired of a life that had no meaning. When people started objecting to slave trading, he gradually realized that that could be the way in which he could serve the Lord. He decided to fight for the abolishment of slave trading.

He immediately started working for new legislation forbidding people to buy, trade or keep slaves. Many people hated him for what he was doing. Slave traders and people who used slaves in their businesses knew that they would lose a lot of money. But Wilberforce did not rest until every slave in England was free. When the legislation for the abolishment of slavery was finally passed in parliament, the other members of parliament gave this brave soldier of the faith a standing ovation.

One day Peter made an important discovery. Read about it in Acts 10:34-35.

Is Money Your Master?

Peter won the Town Council's competition for Junior Entrepreneur of the Year. He collected old newspapers, bottles and tins and sold them to a recycling plant. He also bought candy from a factory and sold it at a profit from his home. He kept a careful record of his expenses and his income.

Peter's dad was himself a successful businessman. He loved the Lord and he wanted to make sure that Peter did not become too fond of money. He printed a neat poster to put up in Peter's little shop. It had the words of Luke 16:13 on it, **"You cannot serve both God and money."** "Why did you do that?" Peter asked. "Because there are many people who spend so much time making money that they forget about the Lord," his dad said. "God knew what a huge temptation it is for businessmen to accumulate more and more money until there is no room for Him in their lives."

"But surely there's room for rich people in God's Kingdom!" Peter exclaimed. "Oh yes," his dad replied. "God helps people to become wealthy so that they can share their things with others and tell them about His love. That's why your mom and I calculated long ago how much money we needed to live comfortably. Everything that we earn above that, is for the Lord's Kingdom. And God truly blesses us. He helped us so that money never became our master."

When the City Council entered Peter for the nationwide competition for entrepreneurs, the judges were impressed to see that a twelve-year-old boy put away 10% of his income for charity.

Why don't you also start to give a regular percentage of your pocket money to the Lord? You could support a charity organization or a missionary of your choice.

MIRACLE AT LUIA

Antonio grew up in Luia in Mozambique. His village was a long way away from the big towns and cities of the region. One day, while Antonio and his friends were playing one of their favorite games in the dirt road, a man drove up in a jeep. It was the first time that Antonio had ever seen someone with a white skin and straight hair. The man had a thick black Book with him, and he talked to the grownup people of their village for a long time. That night he started a big machine and showed them pictures on the wall of one of their houses. It was about a baby that had been born in a stable and who did wonderful things when He grew up. But then wicked people nailed Him to a cross. After that He was put into a grave, but He came out of it again. In the end He left the earth in a cloud.

Antonio was amazed. Luckily he could understand everything that was said, because it was in Portuguese. Afterwards the missionary explained that the man in the film was Jesus, the Son of God. And He paid with His blood for all the terrible things that people do on earth. If anybody, including Antonio, believed that, his wrongdoings would be forgiven and he would one day live with God in heaven. All these things were written in the big black Book that the visitor brought along.

Antonio wished that he could go to school so that he could read the stories that had been written in that book, the Bible. And guess what? The very next year a school was built at Luia. The missionary brought a teacher to them who could teach them to read and write. Today Antonio can read the Bible all by himself because that missionary was prepared to go into far away places and take the message of Jesus to people who had never heard of Him before.

Would you be prepared to go to foreign places if God called you as a missionary? See what Isaiah said in Isaiah 6:8.

MIRROR-MESSAGES

One Saturday Bobby's father took him on one of his mountaineering expeditions. "Remember to flash the mirror at twelve o'clock!" his younger brother said as they started their trip.

The Italians who had built the mountain pass had planted a cross at the top of Nooncrest. While Bobby and his dad were climbing the steep footpath, they kept an eye on the cross. That was the goal that they wanted to reach before returning home.

"How do you feel about starting high school next year?" his dad asked when they stopped for a breather. "A bit nervous!" Bobby admitted. "I don't mind the schoolwork so much, but I'm not looking forward to encounters with the Seniors. Some of them can get pretty rough and wild!"

Just then Bobby looked at his watch. It was twelve o'clock. He took a mirror from his backpack and angled it so that the sun shone fully on it. He hoped that his younger brother would see the reflection from the farmhouse. Then he and his dad looked for a pleasant place to enjoy the delicious picnic that his mom had packed for them.

As they ate, his dad said, "Life is often like mountain-climbing. It's not easy, but it helps if you keep your eyes on the ultimate goal. When we reach the top and you see the beautiful view from up there, you will experience the joy of achieving something strenuous, but worthwhile. And one day when we are with the Lord, we will also be grateful if we've done things the Lord's way. Don't worry too much about the rough kids at school. Let your light shine among them. I know that Danny was very excited a little while ago when you flashed the mirror for him to see. He is already dreaming of the day when he can follow in your footsteps. At high school there will also be kids who will be glad that there's a role model like you around!"

Read Matthew 5:16 and Psalm 56:3-4.

The LORD is with me; I will not be afraid. What can man do to me? Ps. 118:6

MARCH 14

THE WORDLESS BOOK

A preacher who traveled from town to town to talk to children about Jesus, visited the children's club at church. He brought a whole stack of Wordless Books with him. Do you know the Wordless Book? It is a little book with brightly colored pages that can be used to tell somebody how to become a child of God.

The first page is a beautiful golden color. It reminds us that heaven is a beautiful place, and we can go there when we die. The next page is dirty and ugly. It shows us what our lives look like if we do not know Jesus – full of sin. If you do not clean up your life, you will never be allowed in heaven. Luckily Jesus can make you clean. That's why there is a red page that tells us how Jesus paid for our sin with His blood. The page after that is a spotlessly clean white sheet of paper. It shows what your life can be like if you ask Jesus to cleanse your heart. Then you become a child of God who will one day go to heaven. The last page in the book is green. It means that you have to grow up once you are born as a baby into God's kingdom. You have to go to church, read your Bible, pray and tell others about what Jesus has done for you.

The preacher explained all of this that afternoon when he visited the club. He also said that anybody who wanted God to be his or her Father and who believed the message of the Bible, could have one of the booklets. It would be a reminder of all the facts about becoming a child of God. If you were there would you have been one of the kids who took a Wordless Book?

Look for these verses in your Bible
and match each verse with each page in
the Wordless Book: John 14:2; Romans 3:23;
1 Peter 3:18; Psalm 51:7, 1 Corinthians 13:11.

THE SHELTER

Solomon's parents both died in the same month. Solomon moved in with another family, but they often drank too much and then they fought with him. So he decided, like many other AIDS-orphans, to go and live on the streets.

For a while things weren't too bad for Solomon. During the day he begged for money or food and at night he slept under newspapers in an arcade. But then winter came. His sleeping quarters got wet and the other street children who slept under a bridge, said, "There's no room for you here. We're already overcrowded!" Solomon started coughing a lot and there was a tight pain in his chest. *Will I ever have a home again?* he wondered.

One day Solomon heard about the shelter that the Salvation Army ran. Homeless children were allowed to sleep there. The people at the shelter were very kind. They gave him a bowl of soup and a blanket. A man in a uniform sat and talked with him. "Here," he said, "take some of this medicine for that cough of yours." Then he asked him, "Do you know the Lord Jesus?" Solomon looked away. He had heard about Jesus, but to *know* Him must be quite a different thing. "No, I don't know Him." he said sadly.

The kind man talked to Solomon for a long time. He told him that Jesus loved him and that He could take away his sins if he asked Him to. Then heaven could one day be his home where he could live with Jesus for ever. The man then helped Solomon to say a prayer and he tucked him in for the night.

The next morning when everybody at the shelter had already left after a warm mug of milk, one of the workers found Solomon. He was still wrapped in the blanket they had given him. "He's gone home," she said softly.

Read the words from the Bible that the Salvation Army officer read to Solomon that night. It was John 14:2-3.

MARCH 16

SCARED OF THE DARK

Theo wasn't scared of snakes and spiders. But at nighttime, when it was pitch-dark in his room, he was really frightened. He didn't want anybody to know how scared he was because he thought only girls and babies were supposed to be scared of dark rooms and stuff like that!

Every night before he got into bed, he would kneel and quickly say The Lord's Prayer. But it didn't seem to help at all. As soon as he put out the light, he was terrified. Often he would pull the sheets over his face, because it made him feel a little safer.

One day his granny came to visit him. She had a way of finding out what things bothered him. She hadn't been there long, when she offered to read Theo a passage from the Bible each night. The first night she read Psalm 139:1-12. She repeated verse 12: *"Even the darkness will not be dark to you; the night will shine like the day, for darkness is as light to you."*

Theo had never heard those words from the Bible before! Then his grandma said, "Isn't it wonderful to know that God, who watches over us, can see in the dark! Let's thank Him for that." *Does Granny know that I am scared of the dark?* he wondered. She prayed, "Lord, make Theo a strong and courageous person. Don't let him be afraid of anything. Let him remember that You watch over him by day and by night."

Theo hadn't ever prayed any prayer except The Lord's Prayer. But that night he prayed, "Lord, I am so glad that day and night are the same to You. Whether it's light or dark, it's all the same to You! Help me to trust You. Amen."

And guess what? That night Theo slept without a sheet over his head.

**Why don't you also read this
beautiful, reassuring psalm?**

POOR, BUT HAPPY

By now you probably know what a legend is. It is a story that is not true, but that has been told to children by their parents, who then told it to their children, who told it to their children. These stories are told over and over again, because they teach us lessons about truth and bravery and courage. Here is a German legend. See if you can identify the truth that it teaches:

One day, a very wealthy king became ill. One of his counselors said, "Your Majesty, if you could wear the coat of a truly happy man for twenty-four hours, you would be healed." So the king immediately sent messengers all over his kingdom to find somebody who was truly happy. They went to stylish noblemen, successful businessmen and wealthy farmers and asked them whether they were happy. But all these people just shook their heads. "We are not happy at all!" they said.

Then the messengers went to the most famous, the most beautiful and the most intelligent people that they knew of. But these celebrities also admitted, "Deep down we are not happy people!"

After a long while, one of the king's messengers came upon a poor and simple farmer who had a small piece of land where he grew wheat and corn and vegetables. He lived simply with his family and his animals, and he looked extremely happy. "Happy?" he said, when asked about it. "Of course I'm happy. But I cannot help you, because I could never afford to buy a coat!"

What lesson can we learn from this legend? Yes, money and possessions and fame cannot make you happy. Jesus once said, "Do not worry about your life, what you will eat: or your body, what you will wear ... consider the ravens: They do not sow or reap ... God feeds them."

Read Luke 12:22-34 and think about this question: What makes a person really happy?

MARCH 18

A SMALL SPOT IN THE UNIVERSE

Praise him, sun and moon, praise him, all you shining stars. Ps. 148:3

The grownups sat around the campfire in the camping grounds till late that night, but the kids had to go to bed early. Reginald and Stephen didn't mind, because they were allowed to sleep outside in their sleeping bags.

They lay talking under the starlit sky. They could see the Three Kings, the seven stars of Pleiades and Orion's Belt clearly. Reginald identified the constellations quickly. He knew a lot about stars and planets, because he had done an astronomy project at school.

"Do you know that the light that comes from those stars travels at a speed of 186,282 miles per second," he said. Stephen gasped in awe. He knew how fast it felt when his uncle drove at 75 miles per *hour* on his motorcycle. "And," Reginald continued, "the universe is so big that the light from some of the stars hasn't reached us yet!" "Do you mean to say that there are stars that sent out beams toward us thousands and thousands of years ago and we have still not even seen that light, even though that light travels at more than 180,000 miles per second?" "Exactly," his brother said.

That was too much for Stephen to comprehend. He listened to the waves lapping against the rocks. "Why would God think of us?" he thought out loud.

"Maybe it's because we're special!" Reginald said, as if he had come to that conclusion long ago. "He made the stars and planets and regulates the orbit that they have to follow. And then He made us in His image, the Bible says. We don't have to move in a set orbit. We can move around freely. We can choose where we want to go and how we want to live."

They continued to talk about the wonderful things in the universe for a long time before they fell asleep on the sandy beach.

Read Psalm 8. I think David must have written that psalm under a clear night sky.

SECRET AGENT

"Watch out! Here comes Holy Henry!" one of the kids called out as Henry Point entered the corner store. A few of his classmates were standing around the magazine racks. Without looking in his direction, they started loudly mocking their classmate who always objected when somebody told a dirty joke. "Poor little Henry! His mommy washes his mouthy with soap every time he says a little bad wordy!" one of the boys mocked. Andy did not want to make fun of Henry. He had great respect for him, but he could not muster up enough courage to defend his friend. He stood behind some of the others, so that Henry wouldn't realize he was there.

Andy was very upset by the way the others mocked Henry, and he decided to talk to his dad about it. That night, after dinner, he admitted to his father, "I don't seem to be able to tell my friends that I am a Christian." "A lot of people have the same problem," his dad replied. "Ever since Jesus was on earth, some people have tried to be secret disciples. The Bible says that Nicodemus went to Jesus at night because he didn't want others to see him there. And Joseph of Arimathea was also a secret follower of Jesus. He was scared of the Jews, who wanted to kill Jesus."

"It seems such a shame!" Andy said. "I feel like Peter when he denied that he knew the Lord," "Well, let's think of some ways in which you can tell your friends that you belong to Jesus."

"I can paste a little fish on my backpack and I can wear a What Would Jesus Do wriststrap," Andy said. "And I can read a Christian book or magazine in front of them all." "Good ideas!" "You can also lend one of your gospel CDs to a friend or invite someone to your youth group at church. But you must realize that you might also be made fun of, like Henry."

"Rather that than being a secret agent any longer!" Andy said with determination.

Read Matthew 10:32-33 and do something about it!

BE A BARNABAS

The Girl Scouts were camping at Rivers-End, the Raymond's family farm in Caledon. On the Saturday afternoon the teams were competing in an obstacle race. The third obstacle in the race was a rope-slide over a mountain stream. A cable had been fastened to the branches of an oak tree on the one side of the river and to the roots of a tree on the other side. Each girl had to take hold of a small rubber pipe that had been fitted over the rope, and push herself over the river by kick-starting against the tree trunk. They slid across the river at a tremendous speed and landed with a whap on the far bank. A pulley was used to get the rubber tube back to the first side. One of the camp counselors timed each team to see how long they took to get the whole group over the river.

The Cats had been doing very well in the obstacle course so far. Then came their turn at the slide. But Eleanor was terrified. She was afraid of heights and just the thought of crossing that rushing river made her tremble with fear. "You can go first," she told the others in a scared whisper. The girls yelled and screamed as they slid across the river. It made Eleanor even more nervous. Eventually it was her turn. She bit her lip and tears started running down her cheeks. Her team started chanting to encourage her, "Come on, Eleanor! You can do it!" they shouted. She still hung back. Over and over she changed her grip on the tube. Precious time elapsed. Finally she let go and rushed at an exhilarating speed over the ravine. On the other side her friends cheered with approval as she landed among them.

"Bravo! You did it!" they shouted joyfully. "I would never have been able to do it without you folks!" she said with a laugh.

Be on the lookout for friends who need encouragement. Be a Barnabas to them. According to Acts 4:36 Barnabas means "Son of Encouragement."

MARCH 21

THE BOOK

One Sunday morning Miss Jacobs brought a whole pile of books to Sunday school. "What are all those books?" asked Vernon. "These books are all regarded as holy by different people," answered Miss Jacobs.

"I thought the Bible was the only holy Book!" Len said. "Well, the Muslims believe that the Qur'an is holy, because they say an angel gave it to their prophet Mohammed. And the Hindu people see the Sanskrit as the true guide to life. Then there are things like the Book of Mormon and collections of teachings by Buddha and Confucius." As Miss Jacobs talked, she showed them the different books.

"But we believe that the Bible is the Word of God and that it is absolutely reliable," she said. "Forty authors wrote it over a period of about 1,500 years and yet it tells one story. No other book has ever been banned, burned, criticized or ridiculed as much as the Bible, and yet it is still read by millions of people all over the world, who find in it the answers to life. It has already been translated into more than a thousand languages."

"But shouldn't we study the other holy books as well?" asked Hester. Then Miss Jacobs wrote a Bible verse on the blackboard. *"Every Word of God is flawless ... Do not add to his words, or he will rebuke you and prove you a liar"* (Prov. 30:5-6). History and the lives of people have shown that the Bible is truly the Word of God," she said.

She continued, "Because we know that this book contains the words of the Living God, don't you agree that we should read and study it regularly? And don't you think it would be worthwhile to memorize parts of it?" The kids nodded their heads in agreement. Miss Jacobs then said, "I will give a $25 gift voucher from a Christian Bookshop to the class member who can repeat the most verses from Scripture by the end of the year!"

Why not memorize Psalm 119:105 for a start?

LENT

Doreen's friend, Pat, was a Roman Catholic. She was surprised when Pat told her that the people in their church fasted for forty days before Easter. "Does that mean that you're not allowed to eat a thing?" she asked curiously. "We do eat, but each of us decides for ourselves what we are going to sacrifice during this time." "What are you giving up?" Doreen wanted to know. "Chocolates!" Pat replied. Doreen knew how much Pat liked chocolates. "Why do you do it?" she asked. "It helps me remember what Jesus sacrificed for us. And it helps me start preparing for Good Friday."

Pat continued, "But on Ash Wednesday, we all eat pancakes!" Doreen had never heard of Ash Wednesday before, so Pat explained, "It is the Wednesday just before Good Friday, the day when Jesus turned His face toward Jerusalem and started walking toward His crucifixion. Long ago people used to put ash on their heads when they were really sad. Our Priest makes a cross on our foreheads on that day. Then we remember to grieve for the sins that we committed, and which caused Jesus' death." "But why do you eat pancakes on that day?" Doreen asked. "Oh, that's because we're not supposed to eat rich food like meat or fish."

Doreen explained that members of her church also spent time preparing for the Easter weekend. "Our minister preaches about Jesus' death every Sunday during Lent. And my grandma says that she fasts from the media for the month before Easter. She doesn't watch TV or listen to the radio or read magazines or newspapers." "Why would she do that?" Pat asked. "Well, she says that she can think much more clearly about spiritual things when she does that, and then she also has more time to pray!"

What are you going to do this year to commemorate Jesus' suffering? Maybe you can read the Easter story bit by bit from Matthew 26 and 27 during this time.

But God demonstrates his own love for us in this: ... Christ died for us. Rom. 5:8

A TRUE STORY

There's a railway bridge near the town of Mobile, where a terrible accident occurred in September 1993. One foggy night, a boat crashed into the bridge. Before any warning signal could be sent out, a passenger train started to cross the bridge at top speed.

There were 210 people on that train, and most of them were sleeping when the accident took place at 3 A.M. The unsteady bridge collapsed as the heavy train coaches began to cross over, and four of the eight coaches landed in the river.

Rescue teams rushed to the scene, but their task was almost impossible because the train had caught fire. Visibility was extremely poor because of the dark, the fog, and the smoke. Rescue helicopters were able to save some people from the water and the wreck. But 47 people died in that accident.

Many passengers acted heroically that night. One of them was Michael Dopheide, a college student who had been on his way to his home town. He swam in the icy cold water and brought many people to safety. Among those he helped was a little crippled girl, Andrea. Her parents had passed her to Michael through the train window. This was a deed of selfless love, because soon after they had helped her out, their compartment sank in the muddy water.

When the story about this unselfish act of the parents hit the front pages of the newspapers, many Christians were reminded of the saving love of Jesus. He chose to die so that we could live. Jesus Himself said, *"Nobody takes it (my life) from me, but I lay it down of my own accord."* You can read these words in John 10:18.

**Make an Easter card with a cross
on it and write Jesus' words underneath it.
Send it to someone you really care about.**

EASTER AND PASSOVER

For Christ, our Passover lamb, has been sacrificed. 1 Cor. 5:7

One day Evelyn and her Jewish friend, Rebecca, discovered something very interesting. It happened like this: On the Thursday just before Easter they were sitting together on the playground at school. Evelyn took out her lunch: she had a hot cross bun. Rebecca was eating matzos. "Let me taste that!" Evelyn asked. "OK, if you'll give me a bite of your bun!" Rebecca agreed. The two girls swapped pieces of their bread and both enjoyed the new tastes.

"Why do you eat such flat bread at this time of the year?" Evelyn asked. "Because we celebrate Passover this weekend," Rebecca said. "We remember when our forefathers fled from Egypt. The bread they had on their journey was flat like these crackers, because there wasn't time to make proper bread." Evelyn was very interested in Rebecca's story. "What else do you eat at Passover?" she asked. Rebecca was keen to share more, "Oh, many things. We eat parsley that had been dipped in salty water. It reminds us of the tears that fell while our people were slaves in Egypt. We also eat *charoset*, a mixture of chopped apples, nuts, honey, and cinnamon. That reminds us of the bricks that had to be manufactured for the Egyptians. Then we have grilled lamb. God told the Israelites that each family had to slaughter a lamb. The blood had to be painted above the door of each house. Then the Angel of Death passed over their homes when he came to take away the first born sons of the Egyptians."

Evelyn became very excited. "That's so similar to what we believe! We believe that Jesus was the Lamb of God who died for us on the cross so that we can live. That's why we eat buns with a cross at this time of the year!"

That weekend Evelyn and Rebecca read
Exodus 12:1-13 with great interest. They began
to understand why Easter and the Jewish Passover
are always celebrated on the same weekend.

THE THREE FRIENDS

For it is by grace you have been saved, through faith. Eph. 2:8-9

A certain man had three friends. He was very close to two of his friends, but he hardly spent any time at all with the third one. One day the king of his country sent a message saying he wanted to see him. The man was frightened because the king usually only summoned people who had done something wrong. *I'll take my friends with me so that they can defend me*, he thought. But the first friend absolutely refused to go with him. The second friend said, "I'll go with you up to the gates of the palace, but no further!" But the third friend, the one the man did not like as much as the other two, said, "I'll go with you!" When the king accused the man of the things that he had done wrong, his friend sincerely and openly defended him. Because of this defense, the king pardoned the man who had been accused.

This story is recorded in the Talmud. The Talmud is a Jewish book that contains many stories that teach valuable lessons. The lesson that Jewish children learn from this story is that we will all appear before our Creator one day to give account of what we have done during our lifetime. There are three friends that we probably would want to take with us on that day: Our money and property, our family and friends, and our good deeds. However, we cannot take our possessions with us when we die. Our family and friends can only escort us as far as the gates of death, then they have to leave us. But our good deeds can go with us when we have to stand before God.

This is what Jewish children are taught. But we know that not even our best deeds will be able to clear our name before God. The only Friend who can help us is Jesus. If you have accepted Him as your Savior, God will pardon you. Jesus will say, "Father, this is one of the children whose sins I paid for in full on the cross!"

Does this sound too good to be true?
Check it out in Colossians 1:22.

EASTER SUNDAY

Believers in countries like Russia have an interesting tradition. On Easter Sunday they greet each other in a very special way. When one believer meets another, he says, "The Lord has risen!" And the other person replies, "He has risen indeed!"

All through the ages there have been people who would not believe that Christ died and then rose to life again. But there have also always been others who believe with their whole heart: Jesus died on Good Friday, but He rose from the dead and He is truly alive today!

A Russian professor once presented a lecture to try to convince people that they were ridiculous to believe in the resurrection of Christ. After he had spoken for a long time, he thought that no one would still believe what he thought was nothing more than a fairy tale. But a priest got up and asked whether he could say something. "As long as you don't take too much time!" the professor answered. "I need only five seconds," the priest said.

He walked onto the platform, faced the audience, and said, "The Lord has risen!" And with one voice the people replied, "He has risen indeed!"

People who have a personal relationship with the Living Christ, cannot be misled. But nobody can believe all this on his own. The Holy Spirit has to convince people of the truth about Jesus. That's why we must pray for friends and family who find it hard to believe this miracle.

Do you believe that Jesus walked out of the grave alive on that first Easter morning? Thank God for that miracle, because it means that you too will overcome death one day – and live forever in heaven with Him. These facts are written in the Bible in 1 Corinthians 15:20-23.

Tell your family how Christians in Russia greet each other on Easter morning. Maybe you can start a new custom in your family.

"Then go quickly and tell his disciples: 'He has risen from the dead.'" Mt. 28:7

THE EMPTY TOMB

"Mom, did Jesus really come back to life after He was buried?" Donny asked. "Why do you ask?" his mom wanted to know. "Eric says that he doesn't believe it and that it doesn't matter whether we believe it or not." "The apostle Paul said that it made a big difference," his mom answered. "In 1 Corinthians 15:19 he said that if Jesus had not risen from the dead, then we Christians are to be pitied more than all people." "Why did he say that?" Donny asked.

"If Jesus did not triumph over death, we would have no guarantee that anybody could be raised from the dead. Then it would be futile for people like Paul to travel the world and preach the gospel, and endure all the pain and suffering he went through. Paul felt that it was worthwhile to suffer for a calling like that. He was beaten, stoned, and even thrown into jail. He didn't have an easy task, but he did it anyway. Why? Because he believed in the resurrection and he wanted to tell people about Jesus, who was powerful enough to break free from the hold of death. He wanted everyone to know that if they believed in Jesus, they could also one day rise from the dead."

"What would have happened if he did not believe that?" Donny wondered out loud. His mom thought for a while and then said, "Then he would have lived and died like everybody else and we would not have known anything about a man called Paul of Tarsus. And maybe our forefathers would not have become Christians at all!" "Wow, it does seem as if believing in the resurrection makes a big difference!" Donny exclaimed. "I'll have to tell Eric!"

You can read in 2 Corinthians 11:24-29 what Paul had to endure while he was traveling the world, spreading the good news about Jesus' resurrection.

For we know that since Christ was raised from the dead, he cannot die again. Rom. 6:9

TREAD SAFELY

Joshua's parents were very proud of him. He had been elected Class President. That night before the family started their dinner, his dad prayed a special prayer. "Lord, make Joshua a good leader among his friends. Let him realize that he now has a big responsibility." "Why did you pray like that, Daddy?" asked his little sister as they began eating.

Then their dad told them about his days in the army in Angola. He had been a lieutenant and he and his buddies sometimes had to perform dangerous operations. They often had to cross fields where landmines had been buried. If one of them stepped on a mine, they would all have died in the blast. Therefore, before they ventured into such a field, they prayed in the name of Jesus. They asked God to protect them. Then he could lead his battalion safely through that minefield.

"I didn't know where the landmines were buried," Mr. Crouse said. "But God knew! I talked to Him all the time and He saw to it that I put my feet on the right places. Then the rest of the troop could follow in my footsteps." Joshua listened attentively. "Weren't you scared?" he asked. "Just scared enough to cry out to God!" answered his dad.

He continued, "You have been chosen to be one of the leaders in your school. There are many dangers. The devil will try to mislead you, because, if you do wrong, a lot of other kids will follow suit. You will have to stay in close contact with the Lord!" "I suppose I will also have to call out to heaven regularly!" Joshua said as he started polishing his badge with his serviette.

**Read what Joshua's mom put on his
pillow that night. It was Hebrews 3:13-14.**

Then you will go on your way in safety, and your foot will not stumble. Prov. 3:23

BECAUSE I WANT TO

Betty grew up in a home where she was treated harshly. A social worker had taken her away from her parents because they could not provide for her. But her foster parents made her do all the housework and they weren't loving and caring. She had to get up at 5 o'clock in the morning, prepare breakfast and clean the house. In the afternoons she had to do the washing and prepare supper. Her life was miserable. When her foster parents weren't satisfied with her work, she was severely punished.

Eventually she left this home and found a job and a place to live on her own. After a few years she met a kind young man whom she loved and respected. They got married and Betty was truly happy. One day she was doing some spring-cleaning, when she came across a timetable that she had used when she was in high school. She read: *Get up at five o'clock, serve breakfast at six, clean the house before seven. Afternoon: washing and ironing; prepare supper.* Suddenly she stopped reading. With amazement she realized that she was still doing the same chores each day. And yet it was quite different, because she loved the man for whom she was doing all these things.

Many people see their religion as a burdensome duty and find no joy in it. They feel that they have to go to church and keep the Ten Commandments in order to escape God's wrath. These people act like Betty who obeyed her foster parents out of fear, but who was deeply unhappy. If they gave their hearts to Jesus and learned to love Him, things would change miraculously for them. Going to church and reading the Bible will then give them real joy, because they would do it out of love.

Jesus said, "I no longer call you servants, because a servant does not know his Master's business. I have called you friends." You can read these words in John 15:15. Do you serve the Lord because you must or because you want to?

THANKS, BUT NO THANKS!

Carl lay on his back on the grass under the oak tree in the backyard. He was having an inward struggle: Should he go to Jeff's party or not? He didn't want to be labeled a spoilsport, but he knew of quite a few things that had been planned for the party that made him feel very uncomfortable. Jeff and his friends often bragged about the questionable stuff that they found on the Internet and he also knew that the video that they had booked for the party was full of sex and violence.

Just the previous Sunday, the youth pastor had spoken about not giving in to pressure when things could pollute their minds. He had read Philippians 4:8-9: *"Whatever is right, whatever is pure, whatever is lovely, whatever is admirable – think about such things ... And the God of peace will be with you."* Then he gave them a stern warning: "Movies that break this command should not be watched by a child of God!" He continued, "We should be able to say, 'My relationship with Christ is so precious to me that I want nothing to come in between us.'"

While Carl was thinking about these things, he saw a cobweb in the branches of the tree. He was intrigued by the artistic way in which the web had been woven. But the spider was nowhere to be seen. Suddenly a tiny fly flew into the web. He tried to break loose, but the sticky coils of the web held him tight. Then an ugly fat spider came on the scene. He started to cover his prey with a creamy venom. Carl shuddered. *That little insect wasn't careful enough!* he thought to himself.

Suddenly he knew what he had to do about the party. He went to make a phone call, thinking how he could say 'thanks, but no thanks!' in a friendly way.

Read Matthew 6:22-23.

Can a man scoop fire into his lap without his clothes being burned? Prov. 6:27

THE BLUE MONSTER

Geraldine had a twin sister, Helen. They were identical twins and it was very hard to tell one from the other. At the beginning of seventh grade, their dad said to them, "The one who gets best results at school this year, will get a brand new bicycle in December." His plan worked well. The twins worked as hard as they could. All through the year their grades were very close. But when they received their final report cards, Helen had one percent more than Geraldine. That afternoon their dad came home with a shiny red bicycle on his truck. You can imagine how poor Geraldine felt when Helen started riding up and down the street on her new bicycle. She went to the river and sat on the bank for the whole afternoon, crying her heart out.

From then on the teachers had lots of problems with Geraldine. She lost interest in her schoolwork and she was sent to the school psychologist. After they had talked for a while, he heard the story about the red bicycle. "Do you know Jesus?" he asked. Geraldine nodded. "Listen carefully to what I suggest you do," he said. "Go home and look for a quiet spot. Then bring to mind everything that happened. But as you do, visualize that Jesus is with you: as you worked, when you got the results, when Helen got the bike, and when you ran down to the river. Talk to Him about it all and tell Him exactly how you feel."

That afternoon Geraldine went to sit on an old tree-trunk in the park. She did exactly as the teacher told her to do. Big tears ran down her cheeks. Eventually she said, "Thank You, Jesus, that You understand!"

Then she walked home with new courage to go and finish her homework for the next day.

If you ever have to cope with the blue monster
of despair, remember that Jesus had similar
experiences when He was on earth. You can
read about one such event in Matthew 23:37-38.

April

LOVING YOUR NEIGHBOR

At least three times a week, Matilda rang the doorbell of the Brown's home. "Can I clean your windows?" she would ask when Mrs. Brown came to the door. She could see that the windows didn't really need cleaning, but she thought that people wouldn't readily give her a job inside the house. "No thank you, Matilda!" Mrs. Brown would say. "Then can I sweep the garden path?" Matilda would persist, although she knew just what Mrs. Brown would say, because there was nothing to be swept from the garden path. "No thank you!" the reply would come. "But if you wait here I will fetch you some tea and something to eat." Then the woman dressed in old clothes and worn shoes would sit on the green bench on the verandah of the large house until Mrs. Brown brought her something to eat and drink. "Thanks a million, my good madam! May God bless you!" she always said.

One day after Matilda had left, Mrs. Brown thought of a way in which she could really help Matilda. She went to her wardrobe and took out all the clothes that she no longer needed. She sorted through piles of shoes as well. "Yes, these should be the right size!" she said and took out a few pairs from the bottom of her closet. Finally she had a large black bag full of dresses, jackets, and shoes that she could give to Matilda when she came around again.

Next morning, Matilda rang the doorbell. Mrs. Brown handed the bag to Matilda. Matilda opened it and peered inside. She looked through the clothes and shoes in the bag. Then a broad smile split her face. "Madam," she said, "do you know how pleased my neighbors will be when I give them these clothes!"

Read 2 Corinthians 9:7, then you will know how God felt about Mrs. Brown and about Matilda.

April 2

Lessons at a Birdbath

Veronica's grandmother was very fond of birds. In the back garden of her house she had a birdbath and a birdfeeder that she kept filled with birdseed. It was near her kitchen window so she could watch the birds that came to visit her garden. Although she wasn't rich, she always found enough money to buy seeds for the birds, and she filled the feeder every morning.

"Can you see how peaceful and happy the birds in my garden are?" she often said. "That's because there is always enough food for them all. If it weren't so, they would fight each other." Veronica noticed that the finches waited patiently until the turtledoves finished in the birdbath, and then they would go for a splash. Veronica's granny used the opportunity to illustrate a truth from the Bible. "John 10:10 says that Jesus came to earth so that we could have life in abundance," she said. "Because He looks after us so well, we need not fight each other!"

Next to the window in Granny's kitchen, she has hung a beautiful wooden frame that contained a Bible verse written in exquisite calligraphy.

> *"Do not worry about your life. Look at the birds of the air: they do not sow or reap or store away in barns, and yet your heavenly father feeds them. Are you not more valuable than they?" Matthew 6 verses 25 and 26.*

Veronica wondered whether that was why her granny was always happy and content, even though she didn't have much money.

When she asked her about it, Granny laughed and said, "Go see what is written in Psalm 147:9 and remember: The Lord even listens when the older ravens call!"

Read the verse to see what Granny was referring to.

The Lord Will Provide

When gold was discovered near Johannesburg in South Africa, people rushed to the city, hoping to become rich overnight. But not everybody found gold and became rich. Thousands of people lived in great poverty. A woman who lived in the area at that time felt great compassion for the poor people. Her name was Maria Kloppers, and she especially took pity on the children who lived in families who could not feed or clothe them. She bought a big house and, with a few helpers, she started to care for those children. The house became known as the Maria Kloppers Children's Home.

All the ladies who helped her look after the children were Christians. They decided not to ask people the give them the various things they needed for the running of the home. Instead, they just prayed about each need. Each day they got together and talked to the Lord about the food, clothing, furniture, money or assistance they required. And the Lord always provided in a miraculous way.

One day there was no milk for the babies. It was an enormous problem, because there were many babies and they were hungry! The ladies prayed about it and what do you know! The Lord persuaded a farmer who lived nearby to donate one of his cows to the home. In this way the home not only had enough milk for one day, but also enough milk for each day afterwards.

In Philippians 4:19 we read: *"And my God will meet all your needs according to his glorious riches in Christ Jesus."* We, too, can talk to God about the things that we need and we can trust Him to provide for us, just like He provided for the children at the Children's home.

**Is there a Children's home near you?
Ask your parents whether there might
be something that you could give to them.**

Phil. 4:19

God will meet all your needs according to his glorious riches in Christ Jesus.

April 4

Michelangelo

Maybe you know Michelangelo, the Ninja Turtle. But do you know where he got his name from? Michelangelo was one of the greatest artists who ever lived. His father was a rich merchant in Italy who hoped that his son would follow in his footsteps. But from an early age Michelangelo wasn't interested in making money. He wanted to become an artist. He was always busy with paint and a brush, or with clay out of which he made all sorts of figurines. At first his father took away these "toys", but eventually he realized that his son would never become a merchant. When Michelangelo was thirteen, he was sent to Florence to be apprenticed to a famous painter. This artist immediately recognized that the boy was an exceptionally gifted artist.

A man who liked to help artists also lived in Florence. Michelangelo's teacher took him to Lorenzo de Medici and showed him some of Michelangelo's paintings. "He's brilliant!" the rich man said, and he promised to give the young artist a regular income, so that he could carry on with his painting.

At that time there was also a monk in Florence who preached the Word of God with zeal and sincerity. People came from all over the word to listen to Savonarola. His words also made a deep impression on Michelangelo. From that time on, Michelangelo's work portrayed a special relationship with God.

I hope you will one day be fortunate enough to see the beautiful works of art that Michelangelo produced. Perhaps you will visit Rome and see the majestic scenes from the Bible that he painted on the ceiling of the Sistine Chapel. For four years he locked himself in the chapel and lay on his back on the scaffolding in order to complete the mural. Although he died in poverty, his paintings and sculptures live on to the praise and to the glory of God.

Read Mark 8:36. Michelangelo lived to glorify God and not to make lots of money. Do you agree with him?

What good is it for a man to gain the whole world, yet forfeit his soul? Mk. 8:36

GREAT HEART

When Elmo was born, he was so small that he could fit into a shoebox. When he started school, his mom could not find a school jacket small enough for him. But she always told him, "The size of your body is not so important. What is important, is the size of your heart." At first Elmo did not understand what she meant, but later on began to understand that how much you love others and how much faith you have, are much more important than the size of your jacket.

Elmo's grandfather encouraged him to play rugby. He really wanted his grandson to represent the school in a match. Elmo practiced diligently and he also ate lots of bananas to try to gain weight. And one day Elmo finally ran onto the field as the school's scrumhalf.

At the end of the second half of the game, Elmo got a chance to show what he was worth. The fullback of the opposing team broke through the defending line and came straight at Elmo. He was a huge fellow, but Elmo clasped his skinny arms around the muscular legs of the storming giant and clung like a leech. The muscular opponent dragged Elmo along the ground. *Where are my teammates?* Elmo thought in desperation. But before they could stop the fullback, he dived over the line, and scored.

Elmo felt hot tears prick his eyes. He had let his team down. But when the final whistle blew a few minutes later, his coach and lots of spectators ran onto the field. Everybody praised him for having the guts to try to stop the fullback. That evening his granddad brought him a brand new rugby ball. On the parcel was written:

Small of physique,
but great of heart!
We are proud of you!

Read Psalm 147:10-11 to see
how God looks at a person.

April 6

I'LL NOT WANT

Many years ago a farmer suffered great loss as a result of a severe drought. He decided to pack all his belongings on a wagon and to take to the road with his family. One afternoon a severe storm broke and he realized that they would have to find shelter for the night. Luckily there was a farmhouse in sight. He walked to the front door and knocked. An unfriendly man opened the door. "What do you want?" he asked. "Could you perhaps give me and my family a place to spend the night?" he asked timidly. "No!" the owner said firmly. "I have no room for vagrant people!" He closed the door in Uncle Albert's face.

The family had to sleep in the cold and wet under their wagon that night. Before they went to sleep, they prayed, and then sang: "The Lord's my shepherd, I'll not want!" The rich farmer and his wife heard the singing from where they were sleeping in their warm bed.

As time went by, things took a bad turn for the rich farmer. He had so many bad harvests that he also had to pack his belongings to go and find greener pastures. On his journey he came across a farm where the grass was green and where there was enough water for his cattle. He decided ask the owner whether he could make use of his grazing-ground. To his surprise the owner invited him and his wife to spend a few days on the farm. When he and his wife got into bed that night after a hearty meal, they heard their host and his family singing: "The Lord's my Shepherd, I'll not want!"

Suddenly the man and his wife realized who their benefactors were. Yes, it was Uncle Albert and his family. The Lord had provided for them and they could help the very people who once turned them away.

Jesus probably had this kind of thing in mind when He spoke the words in Luke 6:27-28.

WILD SHEEP

Johnny was visiting his uncle who lived on a farm. One morning he went with Uncle Charles in his Land Rover to one of the outposts. John loved driving along the stony road. They saw animals that Johnny never saw in the city where he lived.

Uncle Charles drove along the dirt road to see where Samuel, the shepherd, was looking after his flock of sheep. They found him near one of the small hills. He had made a fire and was cooking a stew in his three-legged pot. The sheep were grazing peacefully around him.

"Is everything all right, Samuel?" asked Uncle Charles. "Yes Sir!" said the old shepherd. "Although three of the sheep have been missing since the day before yesterday, I'm sure I will find them today." They chatted for a while and then Uncle Charles drove further. He still wanted to check how much water the wind pump had pumped from the underwater stream.

As they stopped at the dam, three sheep suddenly appeared from behind the bushes, shaking their heads restlessly and bleated loudly. When Uncle Charles moved toward them, they got a fright and ran down the hill. "I didn't know that you get wild sheep!" Johnny said, surprised. His uncle replied while he shook his head, "It's being away from the shepherd's care for two nights that has made them wild and confused! Did you notice how peaceful and contented the sheep who stayed with Samuel were? His caring presence made all the difference."

On their way home, Uncle Charles continued. "You probably know the parable of the lost sheep in Luke 10." Johnny nodded. He knew that story well. "I think that the Good Shepherd was not only concerned because of the external dangers that the sheep could face. He also knew how the sheep's character would change if he left the Shepherd's care." And then Uncle Charles added, "That's why we must always stay close to our Shepherd!"

Read this parable again to refresh your memory.

April 8

The Two Brothers

Do you ever fight with your brothers or sisters? That's a pity because God wants families to live together in love and harmony. Read Psalm 133 to see what David said about this. Here is a story about two brothers who loved each other very much:

Once upon a time there were two brothers. One brother was married and had a big family. The other brother had never married and lived on his own. They both stayed on the farm their father had left them when he died, and shared the workload equally. They worked hard and when the wheat was harvested, they divided it fairly between them.

One day, the older brother, who wasn't married, thought to himself, *It isn't fair that I received the same amount as my brother. He has a big family to care for.* So every night he secretly carried one bag of wheat from his barn and put it in his brother's barn.

In the meantime, the younger brother was also thinking about his brother. He said to himself, *It isn't fair that my elder brother earns the same amount that I do from the proceeds of our harvest. He is a single man and I have children who will look after me when I'm old one day. There will be nobody to look after him in his old age. He will need more money than I do.* So he decided to take one bag of wheat to his brother's barn every night.

This continued for quite a while, and both brothers were surprised when their didn't seem to be any difference in the number of bags of wheat in their barns.

But one night the two brothers carried their bags of wheat at the same time. They bumped into each other halfway between the two barns. What do you think they said to each other?

**Think of some way in which you can
give your brother or sister a nice surprise.**

FAITHFULNESS

All the Youth Club kids were upset. Bert had just told them that Craig, the youth leader, was going to leave them. "Guess what?" he said. "He's going to China to sell nuts!" "Well, if he's leaving, I'm quitting!" said Cedric. "He was the best guy we ever had at church and now he's dropping us."

"Shhhhh!" Beth warned them, "here he comes!" Craig Fisher greeted the group of kids cheerfully. "Come and sit here around me!" he called. "Do you remember that I told you how I had made a promise to God when I was about your age? At a youth camp I said, 'Lord, I want to do what You want me to do and I want to go where You send me!' And now God had made it clear to me that He wants me to go to China. There are lots of home churches there who want to be taught more about the Bible. I have joined a missionary organization that is training people to go and work over there."

"But what about us?" Cedric asked. His tone of voice clearly showed how upset he was. Craig put his arm around Cedric's shoulders. "You have so many opportunities to study the Bible and a student friend of mine said that she would love to lead this group next year. Christians in China are not allowed to meet openly like we do, and distributing Bibles is prohibited. That is why I am going there as a salesman. I'll be a contact person for Operation Missions. Young workers will bring Bibles to me so that I can give them to people who are really interested in God's Word. Will you pray for me?" Craig asked. "Only if you will send us e-mail regularly!" Beth said.

Then Bert spoke up, "Let's form a circle and pray for Craig now. And let's promise the Lord that we will also be faithful to His call, whatever He asks us to do."

See what the Lord promises in Revelation 2:10 to those who are faithful to Him.

A HARE CAN'T SWIM

Louis Ford loves the Lord and he loves children. Nearly every school holiday he takes a group of kids on an adventure camp. They go river-rafting and abseiling and do all sorts of fun things. But in the evenings around the campfire, he encourages them to talk about serious topics. Louis knows that a lot of kids feel inferior because they are not as smart as their friends.

"One day all the animals got together to start a school. The subjects that had to be taught, were running, climbing, swimming, and flying. It was agreed that all the animals had to take all the subjects. But when the school started, they discovered that Duck could swim very well, but he could not run or climb trees. Squirrel, on the other hand, was good at climbing and running. But flying? He failed miserably at that. Eagle was a champion when it came to flying, but he struggled with the other subjects, while Hare couldn't swim to save his life, even though he was the best sprinter around."

After Louis tells this story, he says, "The Lord created each one of you in a unique way. Maybe you're not very brainy, but you may be a good athlete. Or maybe you can't speak as fluently as your friends, but you can make things with your hands that they can't. You might be handicapped in one way or another, but you are extremely good at encouraging others. So let's not be jealous of each other and let's not think of ourselves as superior because we have certain talents. Each one of us was created in a special way, and as God's children we should stand together and serve our fellow Christians with the gifts that God has given us."

After that Louis usually gives the campers an opportunity to become really quiet and to thank God for the unique way in which He made them. You can also do that right now.

Read 1 Corinthians 12:12-26. It describes how we as Christians can use our gifts to serve one another.

Now you are the body of Christ, and each one of you is a part of it. 1 Cor. 12:27

WITH JESUS ON A SURFBOARD

Sydney was a surfer who had been invited to give his testimony at a Youth Service. He started by saying how cool it was to be a Christian. At first he hadn't been interested in the Bible or church or Christian friends at all. But then two kids, who were witnessing for Jesus, joined the surfing squad. When the other surfers smoked or swore or told dirty jokes, they never joined in. They were always cheerful and kind, and frequently asked the other surfers to go to youth meetings at their church.

The other guys really pushed these *saints* to the limit. They often deliberately blocked them in the tube and made it impossible for them to reenter. Yet they never lost their cool. It was clear that they had something really special in their lives. Eventually Sydney went with them to one of their youth meetings.

Sydney really enjoyed the meeting, and gave his heart to Jesus there and then. After that, surfing took on a new meaning for him. He realized that just as each wave is born somewhere in the ocean and it comes to break on a particular beach somewhere, each person is also born with a particular purpose in life. He also realized that he would never fulfill the purpose for which he was created if he did not have Jesus to help him. Sydney compared his Christian life to a huge wave: it carried him in the same way that a wave carried him on the ocean, and if he did not concentrate on what he was doing, he would end up on the rocks.

"I think walking with Jesus is better that riding the greatest wave!" he said. After the service that night, quite a few kids stayed behind to talk to him about their relationship with Jesus.

Do you know Jesus as your personal Savior and Friend? Remember that you have also been created with a destiny and Jesus can help you to find it. He knows all the tricky waves, currents and tides in the dangerous ocean of life.

Read Psalm 37:5-6. Maybe you would like to talk to the Lord about these verses.

Yet to all who received him ... he gave the right to become children of God. Jn. 1:12

GOING FISHING

The last Saturday of each month was always a highlight in Adrian's life. He and his dad had a regular fishing date. Adrian learned a lot about fishing and about life on these expeditions. His father pointed out that there are some rocks that are too dangerous to go onto, even when the sea looks calm. It might look like a perfect spot for fishing, but rocks that are too close to the water's edge can be deceptively dangerous. Many careless fishermen had lost their lives on these rocks. Concrete crosses marked the spots where these people had been swept into the sea. Adrian had had a few narrow escapes when he had ventured too close to the edge. He quickly learned to respect the mighty waters of the ocean.

Adrian's dad taught him which kinds of bait were suitable for catching various kinds of fish and he also learned which sinkers were right for the different angling areas. He soon knew exactly how to make fishermen's knots and how to unravel tricky knots in his fishing lines.

But Adrian wasn't always keen to take his dad's advice. When his dad showed him how to bait his hook, he said that a little piece of the hook should always stick out, but Adrian thought otherwise. He thought it logical for the bait to hide the hook, so he ignored his dad – but after quite a few days of catching nothing, decided to follow his dad's advice. When he did so, he started catching really big fish – and his mom was delighted with the fresh fish she could cook for supper.

Adrian gradually realized that it pays to listen to people with experience and knowledge of dangerous places. He also realized how stupid it was not to listen to his dad who gave him precious advice free of charge!

**You can read Jesus' invitation
to fishermen in Mark 1:17.**

A REAL MISSIONARY

Nerina's parents were missionaries in Thailand. They lived in Nakon Sawan and the people in the area were Buddhists. The Thai people do not believe in God, but they do worship many spirits. They make sacrifices to these spirits in the hope that they will ensure their goodwill and blessing. Each home has a family altar where they place food and flowers for the spirits.

Nerina wanted to make friends with the Thai children in the neighborhood and she wanted to tell them about Jesus, but they didn't really want to become friends with her. She had blonde hair, blue eyes, and a light skin, while they had black hair, dark eyes and a golden skin. She also could not speak the Thai language, but she discovered that if she stood at their garden gate and sang, then the little girl next door would come to visit her. That is how Nerina and Awd had become friends. Nerina's mom, who could speak Thai, could then invite Awd's family to come to their house. Nerina and Awd played together, even though they could not understand each other's language.

One day, when Nerina's dad went to Bangkok to fetch Thai Bibles and tracts to distribute in Nakon Sawan, Nerina asked him to bring her a Thai Children's Bible. She wanted to give it to Awd. She was very excited when he came back from his trip. "Did you bring the Bible?" she asked. "Yes," he said and he gave her a little Thai book with Bible stories in it. "Can I take it to my friend now?" she asked. She ran over to the house next door and gave it to Awd. When she came back, she was grinning from ear to ear. "Now I'm also a real missionary!" she said proudly.

Are you a real missionary? You are one if you are obedient to Jesus' command in Acts 1:8 and if you are prepared to talk to your friends about Jesus.

HE IS ALWAYS NEAR

When boys from a certain tribe in India turn thirteen, they have to spend the night on their own in a nearby forest. The next morning, when they return to the village after their night of solitude, they are regarded as adult men. One young boy was quite brave when he entered the forest on his thirteenth birthday, but as the darkness fell he became really scared. He sat under a tree and waited for the long hours to pass. Every twig that snapped, every animal that moved, every leaf that fell made him tremble with fear. He did not sleep at all that night. He sat bolt upright against the tree waiting for the dawn to break. When he heard an animal growl not far from where he was sitting he very nearly jumped up and ran home. But he managed to stay calm and stay where he was. He remembered that his dad always said, "The night is darkest just before the dawn!"

Eventually he noticed that the sky was becoming lighter in the east, and he heard birds start to chirp in the trees around him. With stiff legs he started walking back home to his village. But as he turned a corner in the path, he saw something very interesting. A man holding a rifle was sitting under a tree. It was his father! He had kept watch all night long. His father would have protected him from anything that might have threatened to harm him during that long night.

The boy ran to his dad. "If I had known you were here, I wouldn't have been so scared!" he said. "But now you are a man!" his dad said proudly.

Sometimes we feel as if nobody cares for us, as if we are all alone in the world. But remember, God is always near to watch over us and to keep us safe.

Read Psalm 7:1 David calls on God to protect him. He knew that God would keep him safe.

God is our refuge and strength, an ever-present help in trouble. Ps. 46:1

APRIL 15

THE SEARCH

A woman was absolutely heartbroken after her husband and her son both died straight after each other. "Why must I endure so much sorrow?" she cried. She was so depressed that a friend of hers decided to do something to help. She took her friend to an old, wise man, who lived just outside the village. "Please help this poor woman to cope with her sorrow!" she pleaded.

After the wise man had heard the story of the grief-stricken woman, he said, "Woman, go into the village and bring me a mustard seed that comes from a home where there is no grief. I will use that seed to take away your misery."

The grieving woman started to look for a home where there was no sorrow. First she went to the house of the richest man in the town. *He won't know what sorrow is*, she thought. But she was wrong. When she started to inquire about his life, he told her such a sad story that she was soon sobbing in sympathy. Next she decided to go to a home where a family, who seemed happy and contented, lived. But even there she heard about so many disappointments and setbacks that she was deeply touched by their difficulties. Day by day she heard similar stories wherever she went. By the end of the month she was so concerned about the trouble that other people were facing that she was planning how she could help them. She had no time to think of her own grief, and she didn't need the wise man's mustard seed after all.

The lesson we can learn from this story is that when we feel sorry for ourselves we should reach out to others around us who are also going through hard times.

We will soon discover that everybody has a measure of grief with which they have to cope. And when we help others, our own burden seems lighter. Jesus knew that when He said, *"Blessed are the merciful, for they will be shown mercy"* (Mt. 5:7).

**Think of someone who needs comforting
and decide how you can help that person.**

"Blessed are the merciful, for they will be shown mercy." Mt. 5:7

Plant a Tree!

Antoinette's grandfather lived in a little guest cottage in their garden. Even though he was getting quite old, he still loved gardening. He planted a vegetable patch in one corner of the garden. Then Antoinette and her family could eat fresh tomatoes, beetroot, carrots, and lettuce from her grandfather's garden. From time to time he employed a gardener to help him.

One Monday afternoon, when Antoinette got home from school, she heard a hustling and bustling in the backyard. "What are you up to, Grandpa?" she asked. "I asked Peter to come today to help me plant a few fruit trees," he answered. Antoinette looked at her grandfather and then at the tiny trees that came from the nursery in Hessian bags. "Do you mean to say that you will be able to eat fruit from these trees one day?" she asked curiously.

Grandpa smiled. "Probably not," he said. "But I am planting them for you and for the people who might live here one day after you have left! My whole life I have eaten fruit from trees that other people planted. Now it's my turn to do something for the next generation."

"Oh, Grandpa, how I love you!" Antoinette said and gave her grandfather a big hug. Then she went to her room to start her homework. Suddenly she blushed. She remembered something that had happened at school that morning. Miss Morris had asked the seventh grade class to help her to cover the library books. "Why must we do it?" they complained. "In another two months we will be leaving for High School. Shouldn't the smaller kids be doing this?" Now her grandpa had helped her to see things in a different light. She closed her eyes and prayed, "Lord, please help me to be as unselfish as Grandpa!"

Read 2 Corinthians 9:13-14 to see what Paul had to say about unselfish people.

A FAMILY WITH A DIFFERENCE

The people on TV were drinking a toast. "Mom, why don't we ever drink wine with dinner?" Anne asked. "Even in the Bible people often drank wine. We drink wine for communion, and Jesus turned water into wine. So what's wrong with it?" Anne's mom switched off the TV and came to sit next to her. She always did that when she wanted to say something of great importance.

"Sweetheart, I am so glad that you asked me this," she said. "I've been planning to talk to you about it. You see, Dad is an alcoholic." Anne was shocked. She never knew that! She had never seen her dad with a drink before, let alone getting drunk.

"When you were small, Dad was treated for alcoholism and the doctor said that he should never again drink one sip of alcohol. Someone who's addicted to alcohol doesn't easily overcome his addiction. Once you're an alcoholic, you remain one, even if you do not drink. We must always make it easier for Dad not to drink. That's why we do not keep alcoholic drinks in our home. That's also why your dad and I go to a meeting every Wednesday evening. There are other people with the same problem at Alcoholics Anonymous and we support one other."

Anne's mom continued, "We have learned that it isn't necessary to serve wine or beer or other alcoholic drinks at a party. With tasty things to eat and enough sodas or fruit juice around, we can have a festive get together without strong drink. The Bible doesn't say that drinking is bad or sinful, but it is wrong to have too much of it. And some people, like your father, get addicted to the effect that alcohol has on them. Then God must help them to live normal lives."

Anne now understood many things that she had wondered about before. She heard her dad coming through the front gate and she jumped up to go and make him a cup of coffee.

Read Proverbs 20:1 and think about it.

NOT EASY

For drunkards and gluttons become poor. Prov. 23:21

Arnold and his dad were great buddies. Sometimes they played golf together. After the game, his dad usually bought a beer for himself and a soda for Arnold. Then they would sit outside and enjoy the nineteenth hole. One day Arnold asked, "Dad, when can I also have a beer? Many of my friends have started drinking already." "Not before you reach the legal age!" his dad replied. "It is a proven fact that the younger you are when you start drinking, the more the chances are that you could become a habitual drinker." "Dad, you're a doctor. Why would a young person become addicted more easily than a grownup," Arnold asked. He really wanted to know this so that he could tell his friends. Arnold's father explained, "Well, strong drink has an ingredient, ethyl alcohol, which is addictive. When your body gets a regular amount of it while you are young, you start craving it. Many alcoholics admit that they started drinking at a very young age."

Arnold's dad was glad that he had a chance to talk to his son about this subject. He continued, "During your teenage years you are often highly stressed. That's because your body is undergoing some major changes. If you start drinking alcohol and it seems to help you relax and forget the hard realities of life, your body begins to want more of it, and you can become addicted.

"Can I give you some advice?" his dad asked. "Of course!" Arnold said. "Do not experiment with alcohol at this stage of your life. Too much is at stake. Tell the Lord about your reluctance to be different from your friends and ask Him to help you to swim against the tide. Who knows, your example may also keep somebody else from ruining his life."

Read Proverbs 23:29-35. It is one of the 15 passages in the Bible that says that drunkenness is wrong.

BE PREPARED!

The Bright family was singing joyfully on their way to a holiday resort. When they grew tired of singing, Mom said, "Let's play the 'what-if' game! I'll ask a question and the one whose answer is best gets a toffee!" She started, "What if you are at a beach party, and the kids start passing a soda around. You discover that it has been laced with alcohol. What would you do?" "I'd take the can but only pretend to drink it!" Andrew said.

"I'd say: Thanks, but no thanks! This is a dangerous game. Stop it!" was Angela's plan. Harry said, "I'd walk away from the group and phone you to come and fetch me." Little Nell had a simple solution, "I'd just say NO, and that's that!"

Mom gave each of them, except Andrew, a toffee. "Why don't I get any?" he asked. "Because your answer didn't clearly show what you really believe," his mom replied. "Remember, your friends watch you. They are interested to know whether you have principles or not. Some might admire you. Some might tease you, but deep inside they might be touched by your courage to do the right thing. And once you say NO, more kids might follow your example!"

Then Dad said, "Always remember that if you end up in a situation like that, Jesus knows about it. He is praying for you to be able to resist the temptation. And furthermore, Satan is also watching. He wants to see whether his plans to tempt you are successful. When he sees that you stand firm, he will buzz off."

Later that week their dad drove the children to a party on the beach. "Remember our conversation in the car the other day!" he said. And he read Deuteronomy 31:6 to them, *"Be strong and courageous. Do not be afraid ... for the Lord your God goes with you; He will never leave you nor forsake you."*

Think ahead: What will you do if your friends ask you to do something wrong?

The Lord your God goes with you; he will never leave you nor forsake you. Deut. 31:6

Being Together

Miss Stewart had a problem with her Sunday school class. She had eight pupils, but only three of them came regularly. The others came and went as they pleased. Often five of the girls would stay away on the same Sunday. *They can't all be sick at the same time,* she thought. She talked to the other girls about it and they said, "It's Anita! When she does something, the others follow her."

Miss Stewart went to visit Anita to find out what was going on. She knew that Anita was a kind and joyful girl, who probably didn't realize that it is important to be faithful at church. When Anita opened the door, Miss Stewart said kindly, "Hello Anita. We missed you at Sunday school and church on Sunday. Were you ill?" "No," Anita replied. "It was such a nice day, so I took my friends on a picnic." "I'm sorry to hear that," her teacher said. "The church and the Lord needed you!" "Why?" asked Anita. "We don't sing in the choir or have duties!" "I know, but the church isn't only made up of choir and board members. Bring me a broom, then I'll show you what I mean," she said. Anita fetched a broom. She looked puzzled when her teacher pulled out a few bristles. "Can you sweep the floor with these?" she asked. "Of course not!" Anita laughed. "Exactly!" her teacher exclaimed. "But with a lot of bristles you can sweep the floor beautifully. In the same way, we are all important at church. The Lord's Name is not exalted when only a few members attend."

Anita had never thought of it like that and she appreciated Miss Stewart's creative way of explaining it to her.

"All right, you've made a good point!" she said. "We won't stay away so quickly in future." "Jesus will be glad!" said Miss Stewart.

Write Romans 12:11 in your Sunday school workbook to remind you how important it is to be faithful on a Sunday morning.

BEWARE OF WRONG FRIENDSHIPS

Everybody liked Casper, the new guy who had moved into a house near the school. Bernie felt flattered that Casper had been especially friendly to him. They soon became great friends. But, unfortunately, Casper came from a home where his parents allowed him to do whatever he wanted, even if it was wrong. Slowly Bernie was beginning to act offensively too. One day his mom said, "I wonder whether Casper is influencing you to be cheeky and disobedient. You have changed for the worst since the two of you became friends." But Bernie replied, "Casper is OK, Mom. You have nothing to worry about!"

One day Casper and Bernie went shopping together. "I want some chocolate but I have no money with me," said Casper. "Keep the storekeeper busy, then I'll grab some candy!" Bernie wasn't keen to do this, but he didn't feel like arguing with Casper. He went up to the manager of the drugstore and asked him when the fresh bread would be coming in. But just as Casper was taking the chocolates from the shelf, the man looked around. He shouted, "You thief!" and Casper started running. Bernie went with him. In the park around the corner, they came to a halt. Casper laughed and unwrapped the chocolate that he had in his hand. He offered Bernie a piece of it. Then Bernie realized that he had been misled. "Casper," he said. "I'm going back to the shop to pay for the chocolates. And I'm going to apologize to the manager." Casper looked surprised. "Are you going to give me away?" he asked. "No, you must decide for yourself what you are going to do. But I am a Christian and I believe it's wrong to do things like this."

It took a lot of courage to go and talk to the shop owner, but Bernie asked the Lord's forgiveness and he asked Him to help put things right again.

Read what Solomon had to say
to his son in Proverbs 1:10.

April 22

Somebody Loves Us

Grecia lived in Zimbabwe. Neither of her parents had a job. Many people in the village where they lived were looking for work. They had planted corn and vegetables, and some villagers kept goats. But Grecia's family had no food or money left. Her mom had already slaughtered their last chicken.

One night there was absolutely nothing to eat for supper. Grecia asked, "Mama, is there nobody who cares about us and who will bring us some food?" Her mom was sad when she answered, "There's nobody, my child!" The next day her dad once again went out to look for a job. But he came home late that afternoon with a worried look on his face. He couldn't find work anywhere and there would once again be no food for his family.

Suddenly a big truck drove up the dusty road in front of their house. It stopped nearby and a few people got out. The people of the village came from their houses to see what was going on. The driver turned to them and said, "We brought you some food from a church in South Africa," he said. All the faces of those nearby lit up. "The people who sent this food have heard about your troubles. They asked me to bring you these parcels. They also asked me to give you a message. They want you to know that God told them to send you the food. He loves you very much, and so do His children in South Africa." The visitors started to unload the parcels of corn, milk powder, and flour. The villagers, who had been hungry for so long, rushed forward to receive their food parcels.

That night Grecia and her parents ate as they hadn't eaten for months. When they went to bed that night, Grecia said, "So all along there was Someone who cared about us, Mama!"

Read about God's love in John 15:9-14.

GOING TO CHURCH

It was Sunday morning. The church was filled to capacity, but Brenda, who loved the Lord very much, was disturbed by some things that went on around her. While the minister was preaching and praying, some kids were busy with other stuff. Two of them were whispering and giggling all the time. Another one wrote a note and passed it on to his friend. One of the boys was pulling the hair of the girl in front of him. And a young boy was sleeping soundly with his head on his mom's shoulder.

Then the minister read from the big, black Bible on the pulpit: "Today's reading is from Luke 19:45-46," he said. *"Then he (Jesus) entered the temple area and began driving out those who were selling. 'It is written,' he said: 'My house will be a house of prayer, but you have made it a den of robbers.'"*

Just at that moment a boy in front of Brenda took out a stick of gum and started chewing it loudly. *What would Jesus say if He saw this crowd?* Brenda wondered.

When the minister announced the closing hymn, he read Psalm 29:2: *"Ascribe to the Lord the glory due to his Name; worship the Lord in the splendor of his holiness."* But when the congregation started singing, some kids tried to be funny and pushed each other around. Very few of them joined in the singing.

Is this how God should be praised? Brenda thought. She decided that she was going to tell her friends at Sunday school what had gone through her mind during the service. "Help me, Lord, not to keep quiet about this matter, for Your holy name's sake!" she prayed softly.

**Paste the words from Psalm 29:2 on
your hymnbook to remind you how God
should be honored when we go to church.**

WHITE GARMENTS

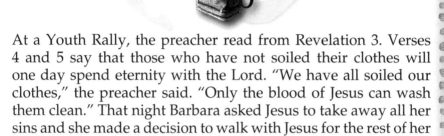

At a Youth Rally, the preacher read from Revelation 3. Verses 4 and 5 say that those who have not soiled their clothes will one day spend eternity with the Lord. "We have all soiled our clothes," the preacher said. "Only the blood of Jesus can wash them clean." That night Barbara asked Jesus to take away all her sins and she made a decision to walk with Jesus for the rest of her life, wearing clothes that were clean and white.

As the preacher had recommended, Barbara then started each day with Jesus. She read her Bible and prayed to Him before she did anything else. At first she was thrilled about her new commitment, but then one morning she overslept and skipped her quiet time. After a while she only read the Bible when she felt like it and she prayed a quick prayer on her way to school.

As time went by, Barbara started doing the same ugly things that she had been doing before her conversion. She made crib notes when she had to write a test, she watched TV programs that her mom had forbidden her to watch, and some Sundays she even pretended to be sick so that she didn't have to go to Sunday school. But she became more and more miserable with herself, and some nights she lay awake for hours.

Then one night when she opened her Bible again, it fell open at the same place the preacher had read from on the night of her conversion. "My clothes have become soiled again!" she realized. Next to Revelation 3 she had written in pencil: 1 John 1:9. She turned to that verse, read those words again and fell on her knees. "Please, Lord, wash away my sins again!" she prayed.

Then she got into bed, pulled the clean sheets over her, and fell soundly asleep.

Why don't you underline these verses in your Bible to remind you to visit God's laundry regularly?

THE TANDEM

It was Whitsunday and a lot had been said about the Holy Spirit at church. But Harold still did not understand where the Holy Spirit fitted into his life. "What does the Holy Spirit really do?" he asked his father. "And what did the pastor mean when he said that we should keep in step with the Holy Spirit?"

They were walking home from church. Harold's father did not answer immediately. He was thinking how he could best explain the work of the Holy Spirit to Harold. Then two kids passed them on a tandem bicycle. They were peddling very fast. The elder boy, who was at the handles, encouraged the younger one by saying, "That's the way, buddy! Keep it up!"

"That's it!" Harold's father exclaimed. "That's exactly how the Holy Spirit works in our lives." Harold wasn't sure what his dad meant. Then his dad explained, "You see, at the beginning of your life, you are in control. You go where you want to go and you do what you like to do. You are like the boy on the front seat of the tandem. But when the Holy Spirit comes into your life, you take the backseat and you allow the Holy Spirit to make the decisions. He takes you where God wants you to go."

"But surely it's nicer when you can hold the handles yourself," Harold said. "Oh no!" his dad answered. "I have allowed the Lord to lead me for many years. I was still in seventh grade when I committed my life to the Lord, and the Holy Spirit took control. The times in my life when I tried to grab the handles were disastrous. It was only when I followed His lead and let Him sit in front that I found true happiness. Life with the Spirit is always a great adventure: never boring, often risky. But when my courage begins to fail, I hear a voice deep inside that says, 'That's the way, buddy! Keep it up!' And then I can carry on with new strength."

**Read Galatians 5:25 to see what
Paul said about the Holy Spirit.**

Those who live in accordance with the Spirit [are] set on what the Spirit desires. Rom. 8:5

THE BURGLAR

The news spread like wildfire: There had been a burglary at number sixteen, Union Street. The Brand family came back from a weekend at the sea and found that their back door had been damaged. The burglar must have fled before he could finish the job. "He probably heard somebody coming and ran away." Felix said. "Wow! He did ruin our back door!" his mom said as she gathered the pieces of wood that had been ripped from the door. "It seems as if the burglar used a chisel."

"A burglar often returns to the scene of the crime," a neighbor warned. "All of us should be on our guard for the next few weeks." Two days later the Brands heard a loud chopping sound at the backdoor. They were all terrified. Mr. Brand took his pistol and went to the kitchen. Mrs. Brand quickly phoned the police. But when the children looked through the kitchen window, they saw who the burglar was! It was a woodpecker that was pecking away, determined to get every beetle that could possibly hide in the wooden door! The whole family heaved a sigh of relief.

There's a lesson we can all learn from this: We are often terrified of an imaginary threat without checking on the facts. Think how often people have wrong ideas about God and how scared they are of Him! Although the Bible teaches us that we should fear the Lord our God, it does not mean that we should be terrified of Him. It means that we should have a holy respect for Him.

Some people do not love God and they want nothing to do with Him, only because they haven't got all the facts straight. If they read the Bible diligently, they would soon discover how to get rid of their terror about God. The truth will make people free of fear, just like the Brand family of Union Street discovered that day.

Read John 8:31-32 to see what Jesus promised.

Whoever trusts in the Lord is kept safe. Prov. 29:25

APRIL 27

LOVE CAN GROW

Something was bothering Sally. Their pastor had said that it was very important that each person should love the Lord more than anything else in the world. *How do you know whether you love Him enough?* she thought to herself.

In the kitchen her mom was feeding her baby brother. It was very difficult, because every now and again he put his hands into the bowl or he spat out all the food. Her mom was very patient, though. She cleaned up after each spoonful and tried again.

"Mom," asked Sally, "what if a person doesn't love God enough. Will God still love that person?" Sally's mom put the bowl of porridge aside. "Do you think that I love Tommy?" she asked. Sally nodded. Anybody could see that her mom loved her little brother. She looked after him with so much care! Her mom spoke again, "Do you think that Tommy loves me?" "I don't think so!" Sally said. "He often keeps you up all night. And he cannot even say 'thank you!'" Then she added, "But I love you!"

"Thanks, dear!" her mom responded. "Well, it's the same with our love for the Lord, you know," her mom continued. "He doesn't wait till we care about Him before He loves us! As we realize how much He loves us, the love that we have for Him will grow steadily. The Bible says in Romans 5:8 that God loved us while we were still sinners. Through the Bible we learn more about God. And the more we know about Him, the more we love Him."

Sally went to her room and cut a piece of cardboard in the shape of a heart. On it she wrote: I love Jesus. She put it next to the little palm tree that she was growing in a pot on her windowsill. She prayed that her love for the Lord would grow along with the plant.

You could follow Sally's example, or try to think of another way to encourage yourself to love the Lord more and more each day.

THE BAT

A fable is a story that teaches us a lesson. Here is one of Aesop's fables. He was a Greek teacher from long, long ago. His stories are still told all over the world today because their messages are still relevant.

Once upon a time the animals and the birds were involved in a war against each other. Bat didn't want to take sides. So when the birds were winning a battle, Bat would fly around with them and say that he was a bird. But when the animals were victorious, he would creep on the ground and pretend to be a mouse.

After a while the animals and birds discovered how dishonest he was and nobody wanted to be his friend. They were so disgusted with him that he decided to hide from them. He only came out at night to look for food and to give his wings some exercise. Even today, Bat keeps hiding from the scorn of both animals and birds.

We can learn a lesson from his experience. We shouldn't try to please everybody. We ought to decide who our friends are and then we must show where our loyalty lies! There are good things and bad things in this world. When we choose to serve Jesus we know that we are on the right side. But we have to be brave enough to show whose side we're on. Matthew 6:24 says, *"Nobody can serve two masters."*

When you are with friends who don't know Jesus, don't act as if those things aren't important to you. The Bible says that our light must shine in the dark. Everything we do and say should clearly show whose side we are on.

**Read the rest of the verse in
Matthew, together with Philippians 2:15.**

"No one can serve two masters ... he will hate one and love the other." Mt. 6:24

BETTY AND THE BUGS

Tom and Betty Young were missionaries in South America. They lived in a grass hut in the jungle. One summer they were plagued by millions of tiny insects that had invaded their home. The bugs especially seemed to like Betty. Her whole body became infected with itchy blotches, and it was so bad that she could hardly sleep at night. During the day Tom went through the jungle, teaching their neighbors about Jesus. And at night, Betty told him how the insects bugged her all day. She became miserable, and neither of them knew how to handle this situation.

But suddenly one day the plague stopped! Betty wrote in her journal: "Problem with insects miraculously solved!" From that day on there were no bugs to be found anywhere near their hut. She was, as you can imagine, very relieved.

A few weeks later she received a letter from a friend back home. "Dear Betty," she wrote. "Last night I woke up and felt an urgent need to pray for you. I don't know what your needs are, but I have asked the Lord to help you with whatever challenge you are facing at the present moment. When you receive this letter, try to remember what happened on November 15. I believe that God helped you in a special way on that particular day." Betty took her journal from a drawer. On November 14 she had written, "These insects are driving me crazy!" On November 16 the entry was, "No more bites, no more bugs! Praise the Lord!"

With tears in her eyes, Betty realized that a friend had prayed for them in their distress, and God had heard her prayers! Then she closed her eyes and said, "Thank You, Lord, for friends who pray for us. And thank You that You answer their petitions."

This story comes from a book that records the many and various ways in which God answers the prayers of His children.

Read 1 Samuel 12:23 to see how seriously Samuel saw his work as an intercessor. Ask God to remind you to pray for other people.

I urge ... that requests, prayers, intercession and thanksgiving be made. 1 Tim. 2:1

APRIL 30

SEVEN WONDERS

If you made a list of the things that you want to see in your lifetime, what would be on it? Long ago people made a list of *The Seven Wonders of the World* but many of these wonders no longer exist and many new and wonderful things had been discovered and built since then. That is why a teacher once asked his class to draw up their own list of The Seven Wonders of the World. This is what they put on their list: 1. Egypt's Great Pyramids 2. The Taj Mahal in India 3. The Grand Canyon in North America 4. The Panama Canal in South America 5. The Eiffel Tower in Paris 6. St. Peter's Cathedral in Rome and 7. The Great Wall of China.

While the teacher was counting the votes, he saw that one of the students had not handed in her list. He asked her, "Are you struggling with this assignment?" "Yes!" she said. "There are so many wonderful things on earth. I cannot decide which are the most important." "Well, let's hear what you have written down so far," the teacher prompted.

And here is what the girl said, "In my opinion, The Seven Wonders of the World are 1. To be able to see 2. To be able to hear 3. To be able to touch 4. To be able to taste 5. To be able to feel 6. To be able to laugh 7. To be able to love."

Maybe you will one day be able to travel the world and visit all the wonderful places that the students listed as *The Seven Wonders of the World*. But if you cannot afford it and have to satisfy yourself by looking at pictures of all these places in *The National Geographic* magazine, remember the list of special things the girl made that day. And remember to thank the Lord for all the precious things in life that He supplies free of charge.

**Read Psalm 17:14. Here David praises
God for supplying his needs so abundantly.**

The heavens declare the glory of God. Ps. 19:1

May

MAY 1

TOO BAD

Carrie couldn't sleep. Her sister had been rushed to hospital because she had passed out in the bathroom. For months Esther had not eaten properly. She had never been fat, but a friend persuaded her to go on a diet. At first she just ate less than usual, but later on she didn't want to eat at all! She became thinner and thinner.

Her parents tried to get her to eat. "Esther," her mom said, "you are at a stage in your development when your body really needs proper nourishment. If you skip meals now, you will regret it when you are older. You could develop some serious long-term health problems." But Esther didn't want to listen. When her mom forced her to eat, she would secretly stick her finger down her throat in the bathroom later. Carrie blamed herself for not telling her mom about those episodes. Now her sister was lying in hospital and she was being fed through a tube. The doctor said that she was suffering from anorexia and that some of her organs had already been seriously damaged.

Suddenly the lights in the kitchen went on. Carrie found her mom there. "Do you feel like a cup of tea?" her mom asked. They both sat at the kitchen table drinking tea. "I hope you don't ever get yourself into such trouble!" her mom said. "The doctor says that Esther has very low self-esteem and that she thinks that she can get others to admire her if she can look thin and seem to have a lot of self-control. Always remember that you are precious to us and to the Lord and that it's better to be a little plump than to have such an obsession about your weight!" "You needn't worry about me!" Carrie said as she took another cookie. "Be careful," her mom warned, smiling. "You also don't want to end up at the other extreme!"

**Isaiah 43:1-7 explains how
precious you are to the Lord.**

MAY 2

THE SNOWSTORM

Titus 3:8 says that people who trust in God should devote themselves to doing what is good. Once in a while a special opportunity to do good arises, and in the end we discover that we actually benefit from what we did. That is exactly what happened to a man who went mountain climbing in the Alps one day. This man and his friend found themselves in the middle of a terrible snowstorm. On their way home they bumped into another mountaineer, who could not go any further. He was lying in the snow and had already lost consciousness. The two men realized that if they left this man where he was he would die. But they had to make sure that they themselves could reach shelter, otherwise they would not make it either!

"We cannot help this man! It will cost us our lives," the one traveler said and walked on in the direction of the nearest hut. But the other man sat down next to the frostbitten man and started to massage his hands and feet. It took hard work to try to get life back into the dying man's body, and the kind helper found that the blood in his own body flowed faster because of the strenuous effort of helping the fallen man. By the time the half-frozen man came to his senses and was able to start walking again, his helper was thoroughly warmed-up. But what had happened to his friend? A search party found him the next day, buried under the snow.

"Do not forget to do good and to share with others, for with such sacrifices God is pleased," says Hebrews 13:16. This is why we can know for sure that the Lord was pleased with this man's unselfish behavior. And as a bonus, his own life was saved!

**Why not underline these two verses
from Titus and Hebrews in your Bible
to remind you to do good at all times?**

WHY?

Usually Gerald didn't watch the news on TV, but that night he sat with his parents when the news was broadcast. He shivered. There was so much bad news! Locally there were droughts, crime, and overcrowded hospitals. From overseas there were newsflashes about war in the Middle East and scenes of people that had been brutally wounded in bomb attacks. The news bulletin also showed pictures of the ruined houses that had been struck by a hurricane.

When his father switched off the TV after the weather forecast, Gerald asked, "Why are there so many bad things going on in the world, Dad? Can't the Lord put a stop to it all?" For quite a long time it was quiet in the lounge. The whole family was thinking about Gerald's question. Then his dad said, "God is not responsible for all the bad things that happen on earth. People are often selfish and cruel and they simply don't care how they treat others or the environment. In that way wars, droughts, and famine occur. God appointed us to look after the earth and each other. If we don't do that, things can go horribly wrong. We cannot blame God if people choose to fight with each other or vandalize the earth."

"But what about innocent people who suffer as a result of these things?" Gerald wanted to know. He was thinking about the neglected children he had just seen on the news. "Sometimes calamities strike and people who had nothing to do with the cause of it, suffer. Or children become sick even though their parents looked after them in a responsible way. We haven't got answers to these questions," his dad admitted. Gerald's mother put her arms around his shoulders. "All that we know for sure is that God loves us and that He will help us when bad things happen to us," she said.

Read what the Bible says about
this topic in Psalm 34:15-22.

WE HAVE AN ENEMY

"How do we know that a creature like the devil really exists?" Aaron asked his mother. She answered, "The Bible mentions him quite often! Go and fetch your Bible and I'll read to you from 1 Peter 5:8." Aaron brought his Bible. His mom read, *"Be self-controlled and alert. Your enemy the devil prowls around like a roaring lion looking for someone to devour."* She added, "There are many other places in the Bible where the devil is mentioned. Jesus Himself often referred to him. And apart from that, I can see for myself that an evil being like the devil is at work in the world." "Why do you say that?" Aaron wanted to know. "Well, who else is influencing people to do such dreadful things as stealing and fighting? Certainly not God! Just look at all the things that are happening in the world. I believe that when people do not obey God but allow themselves to be influenced by the devil they become dishonest and cruel. He doesn't want people to serve God and be happy."

"But where does he come from?" Aaron asked curiously. His mom replied, "The Bible doesn't say much about it, but it seems that there once was a war in heaven and the angels who rebelled against God were thrown out. The Bible says that Satan and his helpers are doing their best to ruin all God's beautiful plans for the world. That is why everything around us isn't good and right and wonderful!"

Aaron seemed worried: "What will happen if the devil wins the war against God?" "That can never happen!" his mom assured him. "He was defeated when Jesus died on the cross and rose again from the dead. But he can still do a lot of damage and we must resist him fiercely! He is like a vicious dog on a chain that can do a lot of harm, but who can never go further than his master allows him to go. One day he will finally be taken away from the earth and then everything will be fresh and beautiful!"

Read the reassuring words of Romans 16:20.

CHURCH IN AN IGLOO

From early childhood, Archibald Fleming wanted to become a shipbuilder. But the Lord had other plans for this gifted Scottish boy. One day his sister came home with the news that she had seen an Eskimo. She told Archibald how Eskimos lived in the snow and he was very interested. She also told him that at that time only one person had ever gone to the Eskimos as a missionary. That night, when Archibald said his prayers, he told God that he would like to go to the Eskimos with the Good News about Jesus.

Later in his life Archibald had forgotten about this resolve, until one day when he saw an article in a magazine that described the life of people living in Greenland. Suddenly he remembered his prayer of long ago. He decided there and then to finish his studies and go to Battin Island as a missionary. Many people thought that he was foolish to give up his promising career as a shipping engineer to go and live among the Eskimos. But he knew that he would never be happy if he wasn't obedient to God's calling. He firmly believed that God wanted him to go to the icy Arctic to take the gospel to the people who live there.

Archibald had to study hard before he could speak the language of the Eskimos. He lived among them in their igloos and he learned to eat thick chunks of blubber to survive in that icy weather. The Eskimos of that region believed in more than fifty different spirits that they served out of fear. Archibald told them about the one, true God who loved them.

In Romans 10:15 Paul wrote, *"How beautiful are the feet of those who bring good news."* Archibald didn't mind treading in the ice of those faraway regions in order to take God's message to thousands of Eskimos who needed to hear about the Creator – God who loved them.

Pray for the churches in Greenland, Canada, and Iceland where the Eskimos live.

THE BEEKEEPER

Rita heard a strange sound outside. When she went to investigate, she saw an unusual sight on the porch. A whole cluster of swarming brown bees was hanging there! She called her dad and he phoned Mr. Burke, who was a beekeeper. Soon a truck drew up in front of their house. "Good grief! What a lovely swarm!" he said. "Thanks for letting me know!"

Mr. Burke had a wooden box with him. He climbed a ladder and slowly put his hand into the cluster of bees. The bees buzzed dangerously close to him, but he kept his cool. He lifted out a huge bee between his forefinger and his thumb and put her into the box. She was the queen and all the other bees quickly followed her into the box. Mr. Burke put the new hive onto his truck and then came inside for a cup of coffee.

Rita was very excited because she had never met a beekeeper before. He answered all her questions patiently. She learned many things from him. He hoped that the swarm of bees that was in their new hive on the truck would build a whole honeycomb city in the box. The bees would store honey in some of the cells and the queen-bee would lay an egg in each one of the others. Mr. Burke also told her that when it gets too hot, the cells start to melt, as they are made of wax. But the whole swarm of bees then starts fanning the air with their wings at top-speed. This cools the air even better than an air-conditioner can!

When Mr. Burke left, Rita said, "To think that a small bee brain could think out such clever plans!" Her dad laughed. Then he said seriously, "It's hard to understand how some people can think that everything on earth came into being by chance! To me it is clear that behind all the wonders of nature there is a Creator-God, who designed and made all the wonderful things that we observe around us."

Read Romans 1:20. Paul obviously had the same thoughts about creation as Rita's dad.

THE HERO

In Pinelands, Cape Town, there is a beautiful bronze statue of Wolraad Woltemade and his horse. Wolraad Woltemade was an ordinary young man who worked as a soldier in Cape Town. Under normal circumstances he would have lived and died and nobody would ever have known about him. But then something extraordinary happened, and today his name is found in almost all the history books of South Africa.

During the month of May, 1773, a Dutch ship, *De Jonge Tomas*, sailed into Cape Town harbor. That night a terrible storm struck the Cape and the anchor lines of this ship broke loose. The ship was smashed against the rocks nearby and the frightened screams of 205 people on board could be heard far and wide.

Officials hurried to the scene of the disaster. But unfortunately they were more interested in the cargo that came adrift than in the people who were drowning. They wasted time erecting a miniature gallows on the beach, warning people that anyone who tried to steal the cargo that washed ashore would be hanged. Nobody was allowed to go near the beach.

But one man wasn't put off by all these regulations. Wolraad Woltemade took his horse and set out to save the desperate people on board. Seven times he went to the sinking vessel and seven times he returned with two people on his horse. He rescued fourteen people this way. But when he went in for the eighth time, his horse, who was getting tired, was unable to keep going, and both he and his horse drowned.

When we hear about this man's courageous efforts, we cannot help thinking of Christ. He wasn't put off by the people who wanted to prevent Him from going to Jerusalem. He was willing to die there, so that we can live for all eternity.

Read about this in 1 Thessalonians 5:10 and thank Jesus for His heroism on Calvary.

Christ loved us and gave himself up for us. Eph. 5:2

THE JESUS SUITCASE

When Dennis was still very young, his parents taught him to have a regular quiet time. His mom had given him a little suitcase with a yellow fish painted on it. Inside he kept his hymn book, his Bible, his journal, and his Sunday school workbook. Sometimes his mom would put a story or a newspaper article into it as well. He called this his Jesus suitcase. At first he also kept an egg timer in it. That was to make sure that he never spent less than three minutes on this very important part of his day! But later on Dennis found that three minutes gave him too little time with Jesus. He had many things that he wanted to share with the Lord in prayer and he was keen to learn more about his best Friend.

When Dennis turned twelve, he went to boarding school. He packed his Jesus suitcase into the car, along with all his other bits and pieces. His mom gave him a box of his favorite ginger cookies, and his sister gave him her tennis racquet to replace his old, broken one. Then his dad drove him to the famous school where he had also spent some good years.

But the first night in the dorm was quite a challenge for Dennis. The other boys were rowdy, and even when the bell rang for quiet time, they kept on talking and messing around. Dennis wasn't quite sure what to do. *Should I look for a private place to open my Jesus suitcase and have my quiet time?* he wondered. But he decided to kneel next to his bed and open his Bible. For a moment it was dead quiet in the room. Dennis felt like a goldfish in a bowl. And then the talking and shuffling started again as if nothing had happened.

But the second night, when he knelt at his bedside again, the other guys also took out their Bibles and spent time quietly with Jesus.

**Why is it important to have a
quiet time? See what Psalm 16:11 says.**

THE ACCIDENT

A few years ago, a tragic bus accident resulted in the deaths of a number of children who were returning from a football match. The driver of the bus lost control of the vehicle and it plunged over the railing of a bridge into a river. Rescue workers did all they could to free the children from the wreckage, but many children died that day. After the funeral, the school principal asked a pastor to come and talk to the children about what had happened. What could he say that would console them?

"Dear children," he began, "we cannot understand why God allowed this terrible thing to happen." He then took out a piece of material and showed it to the children. Colored threads ran through it, but they seemed all mixed-up and there was no pattern. It looked like a mess. It really seemed as if the person who worked on it knew nothing about needlework. "My mother created this piece of embroidery," he said. And then he turned the cloth over. On the other side was a beautiful design of flowers.

"Today we are thinking about the tragic accident that happened last week. We do not know how this could possibly fit into the plan of a loving God," said the pastor. "But we are looking at things from the wrong side. One day when we meet God face to face, He will show us the other side of the picture. And then we will understand how all this could fit into His design for the good of the world."

Then he prayed, "Lord, we are devastated by what happened to our friends on Saturday. We cannot understand why You allowed this accident to happen. But we trust You and we believe that You had a very good reason why You did not interfere. Please put Your loving arms around those who mourn and give them peace!" Amen.

Read Jesus' words in John 13:7.
They are worth remembering.

"You do not realize now what I am doing, but later you will understand." Jn. 13:7

YOU CAN'T HOLD ON TO IT FOREVER

A rich businessman told a story from his childhood to a meeting of people eager to hear about his business success. He grew up on a farm and he had to look after the cattle on weekends.

One Saturday he wanted to go hunting with a friend, so he persuaded his little sister to look after the cattle for him. "If you look after the cattle, I'll allow you to keep my wallet with you all day," he said.

She was thrilled with the plan. She carried the wallet everywhere she went, and played with the money while she watched over the herd of cattle. That evening, when her brother returned, she gave him back his wallet. She was completely satisfied with the reward!

After the man had told his story, he laughed about his little sister's naivety. But one of his friends, who was a Christian, had something to say to him afterwards. "My friend, remember we are also only allowed to hold on to our money for a little while. One day, when we pass away, we will not be able to take it with us."

These words gave the rich man much to think about. He realized that his money would stay behind when he died. From then on, he tried to live a life that wasn't focused only on making money.

We must be very careful not to allow making money to take up so much of our time and energy that there isn't any time left for God. In Ezekiel 7:19 the prophet said that people will one day throw their silver and gold in the streets, because it will be worthless. Riches can never save anyone's soul.

Read this verse in your Bible.

People who want to get rich fall into temptation and a trap. 1 Tim. 6:9

IN PARADISE

A TV program had all the kids at school talking! A man claimed to be able to talk to people who had died. Lisa was interested in what he said because both her parents had died in a car wreck. There were lots of things that she would've liked to ask them. Were they happy? Did they know what she was going through?

One night their minister came to visit Lisa and her grandma. He read a few verses from the Bible and then he asked, "Is there anything that you would like to ask me?" "Yes," Lisa said quickly. "Where did my parents go after they died?" The minister looked at her and said confidently, "I knew them well and I know that they were born again. They are in heaven. Revelation 2:7 says, *'To him who overcomes, I will give the right to eat from the tree of life, which is in the paradise of God.'*"

"Is it possible for people who are still on earth to talk to people in paradise?" Lisa wanted to know. "I know that there are people who claim that they can communicate with the dead. But the Bible warns us against such things." Pastor Scott opened his Bible to Leviticus 19:31: *"Do not turn to mediums or seek out spiritists, for you will be defiled by them."* Then he said, "Many people in our congregation are very curious about similar things and often ask me about it. They seem fascinated by programs on TV that show people supposedly talking to the dead. Then I read Isaiah 8: 19-22 to them. *'When men tell you to consult mediums and spiritists, who whisper and mutter, should not a people inquire of their God?'*"

When Pastor Scott prayed before he left, Lisa realized that he knew what had been bothering her. Before he said *amen*, he asked, "Lord, will You please give Lisa the assurance that her parents are safely in Your loving care?" That night Lisa read her mom's favorite passage, Psalm 23. The fourth verse was especially comforting for her.

Read this psalm, or recite it if you have been clever enough to memorize it.

BREAK WITH UNDESIRABLE FRIENDS

Chris wasn't sure what to do. He had hung out with a group of friends ever since grade school. But they had begun to do things that he thought were wrong, and he wasn't sure how to handle it. So he wrote a letter to a columnist in a Christian magazine.

I have friends who do things that bother me. We have been buddies for a very long time and I don't know how to end our friendship. Please give me some advice.

This was the sympathetic answer from the counselor.

Dear Chris, I can imagine how you feel. Who wants to be without the warmth and support of friends? But if you are a Christian you must sometimes be prepared to sacrifice certain friendships that can pull you away from Christ. Remember, true friends will not reject you if you say NO to them, because they will allow you to be yourself.

My advice to you is: ① Stay away from situations where you will be tempted to do wrong things. ② Be honest at all times. Do not act as if you are enjoying something just to please others. ③ Make friends with Christian young people, and then try to win your other friends to Christ.

May the Lord enable you to stand alone, if necessary. Do not harbor regrets for things you need to sacrifice for Jesus' sake. You will not hurt your friends' feelings if you refuse to do wrong things with them. Your friendship with Jesus is the most precious thing in your life!

Chris read the letter a few times. *Yes,* he thought. *I am tired of fighting against my conscience when I am with these guys.* Then he wrote down the names of two kids at school who loved the Lord and he decided to begin working on becoming friends with them.

Read the wise counsel found in Proverbs 18:24.

THE EGG

One day when Ada came home from school, she knew that something was wrong. Her mom had been crying. "What's the matter?" she asked. Her parents looked at each other. Then her dad spoke up, "I've lost my job. Our manager decided that some posts were redundant, and I was asked to leave." "Just like that?" Ada was shocked. "Yes, but they have given me a couple of months' pay, which will help until I find work again."

At first Ada did not realize what this redundancy would mean for the family. But slowly things started to change at home. Her dad was busy with application forms all day long, they no longer got ice cream on Sundays, and her mom never seemed to smile anymore. On her birthday Ada only got a new pair of school shoes. But the worst was still to come! One morning her mom announced, "We will not be going to the sea this year." "Why not?" Ada asked. Her mom said, "We had to sell our cottage at the sea because we needed the money. And don't cry about it. Remember, there are people who are much worse off than us!"

Ada went to her room. She remembered the advice that her Sunday school teacher once gave her, "If you are ever disappointed, draw an egg and write a request to God on it. Then wait for that egg to hatch!" She drew an egg with a crayon and wrote on it: *Please God, give Dad a job again!* Then she put the page in her Bible.

Three weeks later, when Ada came home from school, the whole family was eating ice cream in the kitchen. "What's going on?" she asked. Her brother answered, "Dad got a job at a firm that sells caravans and we're going to the beach this summer!" "My egg has hatched!" Ada shouted. And then her mom smiled again!

You can also draw an egg and write a prayer request on it. Place it in your Bible at Psalm 34:17 and wait for it to hatch!

Do not be anxious about anything, but ... present your requests to God. Phil. 4:6

USE IT!

One of the most famous books ever been written is *Les Miserables* by Victor Hugo. It tells the story about a young man who stole a loaf of bread because his family was starving, and he spent 19 years in jail because of this crime. He tried to escape many times, and finally succeeded.

But he was a fugitive and could not find work anywhere. Soon he was desperate and hungry. One night a priest gave him food and a place to sleep. But after the priest had gone to bed, Jean Valjean stole all the silverware he could find in the house and crept out into the night. But soon the police caught him. They recognized that the silver came from the priest's house, and dragged him back there. But the kind priest, Digne, acted as if he had given the silver to Jean as a gift. "I forgot to give you the candlesticks as well!" the priest said and handed them to the astonished man. When the police left, the priest said to Jean Valjean, "Go and sell the silver and use the money to live an honest life from now on."

Digne's kindness made a deep impression on Jean Valjean. He decided to spend the rest of his life in service of his fellowmen. He became known as an honest man who always helped others, especially the poor and suffering.

Jesus expects us to be like Digne and not to be revengeful. It isn't always easy to forgive, but we will never be happy while we bear a grudge against anybody. And when we forgive people we give them a second chance. Jesus has forgiven us our sins and we must use the freedom that forgiveness gives us to do good to others.

Read Jesus' parable on
forgiveness in Matthew 18:21-35.

For if you forgive men ... your heavenly Father will also forgive you. Mt. 6:14

THE FOOLISH MILLER

A miller and his son set off to market to sell their donkey. On their way to the market, they met a group of women. "Look at these silly men!" they said. "They are walking while they could just as well be riding on the donkey! How stupid!" The old man thought about what the women had said and then put his son onto the donkey while he led the animal. A little further on they passed a group of men sitting at the side of the road. One of them said, "See, that's exactly what I've just been saying. Today's children have no respect for their parents. Look at that boy, riding a donkey while his poor father must walk!" Immediately the old man asked his son to get off the donkey so that he could ride it.

But then they met a group of children. "Oh how dreadful!" they said. "The poor little boy must walk while his strong father can relax on the donkey's back!" Then the miller picked up his son and let him sit behind him on the donkey so that they could both ride further.

When they had almost reached the market, one of the villagers came up to them and asked, "Is this your donkey?" "Yes," replied the miller. "It's a disgrace that the poor animal must carry both of you! You should be carrying him instead." The man and his son got off reluctantly, fastened the donkey's feet together, hoisted him on to a pole, and tried to carry him. They had reached the village by then, and all the villagers who saw them laughed until tears ran down their cheeks, and their sides ached. They had never seen such a silly sight. And just as they carried the donkey across the bridge, the pole broke, the donkey fell in the river and drowned.

The moral of this story is that we should never try to please everybody, but should do what we know is best.

Proverbs 9:10 tells us whose advice we should take seriously.

THE PICTURE

Reporters milled around Geoffrey Neuland: they really wanted to get the story of this remarkable young man for their newspapers. Geoffrey had just received the highest award at university, in spite of the fact that he was a paraplegic. "What single factor was most important to your success?" one journalist shouted as he passed. "A picture!" he answered. "Which picture?" the journalists called out, trying to keep up with the wheelchair. "Was it a picture of a girlfriend?" one woman guessed, her pencil and notepad ready in her hands. But Geoffrey did not answer because his father lifted him into the car and quickly drove away.

One of the reporters later made an appointment to interview Geoffrey at his home. Almost as soon as the journalist sat down, he asked, "What picture did you refer to when we asked you what the secret of your success was?" Geoffrey smiled. "I was talking about a picture in my mind! On the day I left home to start university, my father called the family together. He prayed, 'Lord, please watch over our son as he embarks on this dangerous voyage on the vast ocean of life. Be the Captain of his ship, the wind in his sails and the compass that shows the way.'

"The picture of a ship on the stormy seas that he drew in my mind that day, helped me to persevere. When I needed advice, I consulted my Captain. He always supplied answers to my questions through His Word, my compass. He always inspired me to give my very best, like the wind that fills the sails of a boat to keep it moving forward."

"Remarkable!" said the young reporter. Apart from an interesting news item, he had also acquired a picture that afternoon that would stay with him for the rest of his life.

David had something similar in mind when he wrote Psalm 107:23-32.

He stilled the storm to a whisper; the waves of the sea were hushed. Ps. 107:29

JOHNNY APPLESEED

Some people said that he was crazy. Others thought that he was a genius: too wise for this world. But everybody was delighted when Johnny Appleseed was in the district. He had the most extraordinary habits! He always wore an upside down saucepan on his head and his clothes were made of sackcloth. He traveled up and down the river on two canoes that he had fastened together. And he carried a leather bag filled with apple seeds wherever he went.

When he came to a place where the soil seemed fertile, he would plant some of the seeds. And when he returned to places where his apple trees were already growing, he pruned them with loving care. Sometimes he built fences to prevent the wild animals plundering the young saplings. His only income came from selling young apple trees.

He loved animals and would often buy horses or cows from owners who neglected them. Then he gave these animals to people who would look after them properly.

Jonathan Chapman (that was his real name) was a devout Christian, and he saw it as his calling to look after God's creation and to try to make people happy. He also grew herbs that he used to make medicines. Children loved him, because he always told the most wonderful stories. They also loved listening to him as he joyfully sang songs of praise wherever he went.

Today, two hundred years later, nobody knows where he was buried, but people believe that his grave must be in one of the apple orchards that he planted, where the birds sing all day long and the squirrels play in the branches of the trees and the breeze spreads the sweet aroma of apple blossoms far and wide.

Read Psalm 104. It tells of the joy that you can experience when you spend quality time in nature.

How many are your works, O Lord! In wisdom you made them all. Ps. 104:24

THE MAN ON THE DONKEY CART

Lambert had to work the late shift one Saturday night at the restaurant. When he finally left, the streets were deserted and dark. Suddenly he was attacked by a gang of thieves who took his watch and his wallet and stabbed him with a knife. They thought that he was dead and dragged him into the bushes next to the road.

The following morning a minister drove past in his smart car. He saw the man, but he was already late for the early morning service so he drove on. Then a social worker came by, taking her dogs for a walk. But she thought, *If I touch this man, I'll have to be a witness in court again, and I have more than enough on my program as it is!* So she walked on as if she had seen nothing. The poor man lay beside the road and groaned. *Is there nobody who cares enough to help me?* he thought. Just then, a hawker drew near on his donkey cart. "Oh dear!" he said. "What happened to you?" He helped the wounded man onto his cart and made him comfortable among the sacks of potatoes and piles of pumpkins. Then he drove the wounded man to the emergency room of the local hospital.

It's good to know that there are many people who would not just walk past a wounded man and leave him there to die. But unfortunately some people never want to get involved in the lives of suffering people. They are too busy running their own lives. To which group do you belong?

If you know of somebody who needs help and you ignore that person, then you are like the minister and the social worker in the story. But if you forget about your own troubles for a while and reach out to someone in need, then you are like the kind man on the donkey cart.

**Does this story sound familiar? Read Jesus'
parable of the Good Samaritan in Luke 10:25-37.**

STANDING UP FOR TRUTH

Laura enjoyed helping in her uncle's store after school. Sometimes her cousin Dean also helped. "Come, come!" he would shout, "Cokes for blokes and cheese curls for girls!" Everybody enjoyed his funny remarks.

But one afternoon, as they were packing the storeroom, Laura noticed Dean slip a chocolate bar into his pocket. She was stunned that he could be so dishonest. *What should I do?* she wondered. She didn't want to betray her friend, but she couldn't pretend that she had seen nothing! She decided to wait and see what would happen. But that night she couldn't sleep. Her parents often talked about how corruption was widespread and that it often started when young people were dishonest with small things. If they were not corrected early on, they began to think they could get away with more serious offences. And eventually they could end up in jail for embezzling huge amounts of money. "Lord, please help me to do the right thing!" Laura prayed.

The next day she helped Uncle Robert with stocktaking. He stopped checking the items on the shelves, and scratched his head. "There's a mistake somewhere! The figures in the book do not tally with the stock in the storeroom," he said. Laura blushed. *Should I tell him what I saw? Will Dean still be friends with me if I do? What will happen if I keep quiet?*

""Do you have any idea how this could have happened?" her uncle asked. Laura couldn't lie to him. "It might be possible for someone who helps out in the store to slip stuff into his pocket," she mumbled. Her uncle understood exactly what she was saying. "Have you seen anything like that?" Uncle Robert asked. Laura looked down. "Yes," she said softly. Her uncle understood her embarrassment. "Don't worry about it," he said. "I appreciate your honesty. I'll handle the situation from here." Laura felt as if a heavy load had been lifted from her shoulders.

Read Proverbs 4:18-27 and think about it.

Do not swerve to the right or the left; keep your foot from evil. Prov. 4:27

STOP THE RACE!

"It's not fair!" Patrick muttered. His father had sent him to his room before dessert was served and it was all the dog's fault! His dad had been in a bad mood all day long. He had received a traffic ticket that morning and had been annoyed with everybody ever since. Patrick felt really sorry for himself. It wasn't his fault that Fido chewed up his dad's newspaper. He had left it on the rug, and now his dad had punished him and his dog. Poor Fido had to sleep outside tonight.

Patrick decided to work on his science project to get his mind off his disappointment. He would have finished the project long ago but his friend, Mick, had put his grimy lunchbox right on top of his open notebook and so part of the work had to be done all over again! While he was working on it, he grew angrier by the minute. He thought of ways to ruin Mick's book. Suddenly he was struck by a thought: This vicious circle could keep on forever. His dad had been annoyed with the police officer on traffic duty, and he had taken out his bad mood by punishing him and Fido. Now here he was planning to hurt Mick.

Just then the door of his room opened. His dad stood in the doorway with a plate piled with strawberry shortcake. "I'm sorry!" he said. "I was unfair." "And I will try to remember not to leave the paper lying around where Fido can get it," Patrick responded. At these words Fido rushed into the room, tail wagging. The vicious cycle had come to an end!

I'll have to forgive Mick! Patrick thought as he was getting into bed a little later. When he said his prayers, he ended with the words of the Lord's Prayer, "Forgive us our trespasses, as we also have forgiven those who trespass against us." It had new meaning for him that night.

You can also pray the Lord's Prayer (Mt. 6:9-13) and especially think of Jesus' words about forgiving others.

THE LION AND THE MOUSE

Here is another well-known fable by Aesop:

One day King Lion was taking a nap in the sun. Suddenly he was rudely awakened! A tiny field mouse had run over his front paws. The lion was furious: his rest had been disturbed! He caught the little mouse in his big paws. He licked his lips as he thought how tasty this savory morsel would be. But the mouse looked into his eyes and begged, "O Your Highness, King of the Jungle, please do not eat me! Let me go and then one day, when you need me, I can come to your aid!" The lion laughed out loud. "You arrogant little pipsqueak!" he said. "Do you honestly think that you can ever do me a favor?" But the lion was impressed by the courage of the tiny animal, and he wasn't really all that hungry, so he set him free.

And guess what? One fateful day the big Lion King was trapped in a hunter's net. The more he tried to break loose from the ropes that held him tight, the more he got entangled in the net. After much effort he was growing weak, and he groaned in pain and frustration. But the little field mouse heard his groans and came running to the place where he was caught.

"Have no fear, Your Majesty!" he said. "Just be patient. I will get you out of here! You saved my life once, and now it's my turn to help you!" He started to chew through the rope with determination. A few hours later the lion was free.

After all the exertion the lion and the mouse both lay down to rest in a nearby field. After a while King Lion opened his eyes and said to the mouse, "You taught me an important lesson today!" "And what might that be?" the mouse inquired. "I now realize that no one is too small to be of some consequence!" King Lion confessed.

Read Romans 12:6-8 to see how each person can play a significant role in God's Kingdom.

BE A WINNER, LIKE JESUS!

Today we take a glimpse into the life of a young boy who managed to say "No" to temptation four times in one day! While you read the story, note that he used the Bible to ward off all the attacks of Satan, just as Jesus did in Matthew 4:1-11.

Bert's first temptation came in Math class. He was struggling with an algebra problem, when Satan whispered in his ear, "Look over Wayne's shoulder. He has the answer in his workbook." But Bert remembered what was written in Exodus 20:15. So he decided rather to struggle and get the answer on his own.

At lunchtime one of the eighth grade boys pushed Bert aside so he could get to the counter before him. "Punch him!" the devil urged. Bert was just about to let fly when he remembered Matthew 5:38-39. So he waited patiently for his turn to get his lunch, as if nothing had happened.

Later on, when Bert was riding his bike home after school, he got to a traffic light just as it turned orange. "Go for it!" Satan said. But then Bert remembered Jesus' words: *"Do not put the Lord your God to the test."* The next moment a taxi whizzed past Bert. "What a close shave!" Bert exclaimed.

That afternoon Felix came to visit him. "I want to show you something on the Internet," Felix said with a mysterious smile on his face. While Felix surfed the websites, Bert suddenly realized what his friend was looking for. His parents had told him never to look at such things. Philippians 4:8 came to his mind. His mom had pasted these words above their television set. He didn't want to defile his thoughts, so he suggested that they rather go outside and play a game of darts.

That night Bert could go to bed with a clear conscience. He managed to resist quite a number of snares from the devil. "Thank You, Jesus!" he said.

**Look up the verses that
Bert used to chase Satan away.**

TAKE MY HANDS

"Take my hands and let them be, consecrated Lord to Thee!" The children at the Youth Club sang these words loudly. When they finished singing Rosalie said, "Let's look at our hands today and ask ourselves, 'Do my hands work for the Lord, or not?'"

Dale put his hands in his pockets. He was thinking of a couple of things that he had done during the past week that definitely didn't honor God. He had taken some candy from his sister's desk drawer and he had punctured William's bicycle wheels.

Carrie looked at her hands. She remembered how she had sketched Dan's face with special emphasis on his prominent ears and how the kids at school had roared with laughter. She knew that that wasn't a loving thing to do!

Amanda also felt guilty about what she had done with her hands. Although her mom had warned her that it is rude to point at people, she still often did so when she wanted to accuse or ridicule some kids at school.

Jack reflected on what he had done that day. He constantly struggled with a quick temper. That morning he had used his fists when one of his classmates had made him angry. He knew that he would have to ask God to help him to practice more self-control.

Then Rosalie asked for suggestions. "What can we do with our hands for the Lord that will make Him glad?" "We can help our moms in the kitchen!" Wilma volunteered. "I can take an old lady by the hand and help her across the street," Simon said. And Wendy added, "Or I can put my arms around someone who is sad." "And we can pray!" Helen said quietly.

"Then let's do that right now!" Rosalie agreed.

Look up the following verses. Decide whether each one refers to good or bad things that we can do with our hands: Proverbs 10:4; Ephesians 4:28; and 1 Timothy 2:8.

Whatever your hand finds to do, do it with all your might. Ecc. 9:10

OPERATION SUNSHINE

Doreen was very unhappy. Her family was poor and life was hard. Her dad sometimes had to work double shifts, which meant that he was seldom at home. Her mom also worked all day. Doreen had to stay at an aftercare center in the afternoons. They could never afford to take a vacation.

Doreen's next-door neighbor was a very kind woman. Sometimes she brought them cookies that she had baked herself. One Saturday afternoon Doreen went over to her house. "Do you want me to cut off the dead roses for you?" she asked. "That would be very kind of you!" said Mrs. Goring. "Here are the pruning shears. When you have finished, you can come to the kitchen for a cookie and a glass of milk."

Later on, when Doreen was seated at the kitchen table, Mrs. Goring asked, "Why do you look so sad?" Doreen poured out all that was on her heart. Kind Mrs. Goring put her arm around her shoulders and said, "Doreen, I understand what you are going through. Life isn't easy when you are struggling to make ends meet. But I want to share something with you: My parents were wealthy but they quarrelled all the time. Eventually they got divorced. My best friend came from a poor family, and I remember how I once asked God to rather make us poor like the Beacons. They were always so happy together. Your parents are going through a hard time. I believe God has given you a special gift to bring sunshine into their lives. Let's think of ways in which you can make things easier for them!" Mrs. Goring fetched a pen and some paper.

That night, Doreen glanced at the list, *Help Mom in the kitchen; thank Dad for working so hard for us; clean my own room; invite Mom and Dad to go for a walk with me.* "Tomorrow I will start Operation Sunshine!" she said with a smile.

**Read Proverbs 22:1-2. It has something
interesting to say about wealth and poverty.**

POISONOUS WORDS

James 3:3 says that it is easier to get a horse to obey you, than it is to control your tongue. What does that mean? Here is a story that illustrates this verse.

Elaine always did her best at school and she always got good grades. But there were other children in her class who were envious of her success. When the English teacher read one of her essays to the class, Muriel whispered to the girl next to her, "Her mom helped her with it."

Soon the rumor spread throughout the school. Later on kids started saying, "Elaine is dishonest!" All her friends started avoiding her. Poor Elaine didn't understand what was going on.

The slanderous stories reached the ears of the principal and he asked Elaine to come to his office. "It's not true!" Elaine said with tears in her eyes when he confronted her. He called in her parents and discovered that all the accusations were unfair. "Elaine does all her homework on her own," her mom said. "And she is always honest with us."

Although the teachers tried to stop the rumors about Elaine, many kids still didn't trust her. "There is never smoke without fire!" they said.

Can you see what damage Muriel did with her tongue? Now you can understand why James 3:5 says, *"The tongue is a small part of the body, but it makes great boasts."*

We all struggle to control our tongues, but we can ask the Lord to help us with this. Because, just as a snake's venom comes from inside himself, so our words come out of our hearts.

Ask Jesus to give you a heart full of love for other people, and then you will never feel like gossiping.

See what Matthew 12:34 has to say about this.

The tongue also is a fire, a world of evil among the parts of the body. Jas. 3:6

SHOW YOUR COLORS

A few days after Eric and his family had moved in to their house in a new town two boys came to visit him. "Would you like to go cycling with us on Sunday? We know of a great mountain bike trail. If you want to go, you can meet us at ten at the school gate."

This invitation put Eric in a tight spot. His family always went to church on Sunday mornings and he knew full well that his parents would not allow him to miss Sunday school and church without a very good reason. But he really wanted to make some new friends in the new neighborhood.

He thought of a plan. On Sunday mornings he usually went to Sunday school an hour before church and then met his parents again after the church service. He sat with his Sunday school friends in church so he could easily slip away for two hours. On Sunday he put on his church clothes, and then hurried to meet his new friends. While he was waiting for them, he changed into a bright orange sports T-shirt and black cycling shorts, and hid his smart clothes under a hedge.

Somehow Eric did not enjoy the cycling as much as he thought he would. He was feeling guilty. He thought about the Sunday school lesson from a few weeks back about Peter who was ashamed to admit that he was Jesus' disciple. And here he was too shy to tell his friends that he was a Christian who went to church on Sundays.

Eventually he gathered the courage to say, "Guys, I have to go now. I was supposed to go to Sunday school today. But I wouldn't want to miss church as well! I'd love to come with you again another day!" His friends were surprised. But not as surprised as the people in church! Because just after the second hymn was sung a boy dressed in sweaty sports clothes sneaked into church. He had a big smile on his face!

**Read Luke 9:26 and remember it
when you are with your friends.**

I am not ashamed of the gospel, because it is the power of God. Rom. 1:16

NIGHTMARES

Delia was plagued by nightmares. One night she cried out in her sleep and her mom rushed to her room to see what was wrong. When she turned on the light she saw Delia sitting bolt upright in bed. "Tell me what's wrong! Is something upsetting you?" she asked as she sat next to her daughter and put her arm around her.

At first Delia didn't want to say anything. But after a while the words rushed out like a torrent, "There are three kids at school who hate me. They go round telling lies about me. They tease me and push me around in the corridors. Yesterday one of them broke my ruler and they hid my math book!" She was sobbing. Delia's mom hugged her close to her. "Why do they treat you like that?" she asked sympathetically. "They were swearing and making fun of the Bible one day and I said that I didn't like it. Since then they have hated me!"

"Now I understand why you have nightmares every night," her mom said. "These girls have terrified you. But let's see what God has to say about this." She picked up Delia's Bible and opened it to Matthew 5:11. She read, "*'Blessed are you when people insult you, persecute you and falsely say all kinds of evil against you because of me. Rejoice and be glad, because great is your reward in heaven.'* Let's also read verse 44. Jesus gave some advice about dealing with people like this. *'Love your enemies and pray for those who persecute you,'*" her mom read these words and then suggested, "Shall we do that right now?" Delia agreed and they both knelt down to pray.

At that same moment three girls in different parts of town turned over restlessly in their beds. The Lord had heard the prayers of His children! He was going to be very active in the lives of three little girls in the next few months.

Are you also scared of certain people?
Pray for them and see what happens!

The LORD is with me; I will not be afraid. What can man do to me? Ps. 118:6

DISAPPOINTMENTS

Darla had been practicing for the swimming gala for weeks. She practiced before school and she used every spare minute in the afternoons to get as fit as she could. She ate healthy food and made sure she got enough sleep. She concentrated hard when her coach instructed her and she regularly prayed about the competition. Her goal was to make the swimming team, and that would only happen if she did well in the upcoming competition.

But one morning, a week before the big day, Darla woke up with a bad cough. She sucked some cough lozenges, but they didn't help at all. By the afternoon she had developed a bad headache and her knees were wobbly. She didn't have the energy to go and practice. When she got into bed as soon as she arrived home from school, her mom phoned the doctor.

"She has flu," he announced. "This virus is doing the rounds and you will have to be careful. Darla could get pneumonia if she doesn't stay in bed for at least a week." Darla started crying. She would have to miss the swimming gala!

"Darla," the doctor said kindly, "life is full of disappointments. The sooner you learn to cope with them, the better. There will be other opportunities for you to achieve your goals in swimming, and you will appreciate it so much more!"

After he had left, Darla asked her mom, "How can I handle this situation?" "In the same way that Joseph handled his disappointments," her mom replied. "Remember how he was put in jail although he was completely innocent? But he kept on believing that the Lord was right with him through his disappointments. Remember how God turned things around for his good and he became second in command to the king."

"As soon as I feel better, I want to read that story again!" Darla said as she took her medicine.

**Why don't you read this
fascinating story in Genesis 39-41?**

FIRE FROM HEAVEN

Big drops of rain fell on the roof of the little church in the Sudan. But the people inside were listening attentively to what the preacher was telling them. He was telling them about a God of love, and some of them had never before heard of such a possibility.

Suddenly a storm broke loose. Nobody could hear what the preacher was saying. Thunder, lightning, and sheets of rain bombarded the little building. Little children clutched each other and everybody was frightened. Storms like that can cause much havoc in that region.

The Christians in the church started praying out loud. "Lord, please keep us safe in this storm!" Just then a flash of lightning struck the building and set it on fire. Some people fell to the ground in terror. Others shuddered and screamed in fear. A few brave ones tried to stop the fire while others helped the injured.

When the storm subsided, the preacher suggested, "Let's sing a song of praise to the Lord! He has kept us safe through this storm!" The people started singing and dancing out of sheer joy. They couldn't help thinking about what would have happened if they had not known the Living God. Then they would have believed that Sango, the god of fire, caused the storm. They wouldn't have helped the injured, because that would have infuriated Sango even more. Neither would they have tried to put out the fire. Instead, they would have thrown valuables and livestock into the flames to pacify their angry god.

The preacher read from the Bible. He wanted to remind them of God's promise. *"I am with you and I will be with you wherever you go"* (Gen. 28:15). The congregation nodded in agreement. They had once again experienced the truth of these words.

**Don't you think these words would be good
to remember when you have to travel anywhere?
Why not paste them into your suitcase?**

DESMOND AND DUSTY

Desmond's uncle worked for the Leprosy Mission. He was traveling throughout the country asking people for donations so that children with leprosy could be properly cared for. One weekend Uncle Stephen came to stay at Desmond's house. He showed them all pictures of little children with leprosy. Some of them had lost fingers or toes and a few had to have their arms and legs amputated. Desmond felt very sorry for the kids in the photos. One little boy particularly caught his attention. "How much will it cost to buy him a wheelchair?" Desmond asked. "We could perhaps get a second-hand one for $300," his uncle replied.

On Monday morning, as he left, Uncle Stephen put $10 in Desmond's pocket. Desmond immediately began to figure out how many tennis balls he would be able to buy with the money. But suddenly the picture of the little boy with leprosy popped into his mind. He put the bill into his Bible and asked God to show him a way to multiply the money. That weekend his family went to visit friends on a small farm just outside the town where they lived. The farmer had a lot of piglets. Suddenly Desmond had an idea. "Mr. Brown, how much do you want for one of these piglets?" he asked. "They usually sell for a lot of money," he said thoughtfully. "But you can have one for $10."

Desmond bought the little pig and his dad made a place for it to live behind the garden shed. Desmond kept Dusty, the pig, there. He fed him with special mash and food that he cooked up in the kitchen. His friends helped him to gather peels and fodder in the afternoons. Dusty grew big and fat and after a few months Desmond sold him for $300!

And that is how a little leper boy one day got a wheelchair from a man who told him about Jesus. On that day he experienced the love of the great Physician who definitely has a special place in his heart for people who have leprosy.

Read Matthew 8:1-4 to see how Jesus helped a leper.

PRECIOUS THROW-AWAYS

One morning when Patience opened her door, she found a blue bundle on the ground in front of her house. She picked it up, and what do you think was inside the blanket? A little baby girl fast asleep! "Her mom probably didn't want her," she said. "Maybe she hasn't any money and cannot care for the baby." Patience's home was small and she didn't really have enough room for a child, but she took the little one inside. She washed her and made a bed for her in a suitcase that she usually kept under her bed.

The neighbors were kind: they gave her second-hand baby clothes, diapers, and bottles. She cared for the baby, whom she named Surprise, with great tenderness. But it wasn't long before another baby was left on Patience's doorstep. This time she made a bed out of an apple box. The news that Patience was looking after two abandoned babies quickly spread through the whole town. And little by little more and more babies were left in Patience's care. But she did not have the means to look after so many children. A social worker got to hear of what was happening, and came to investigate. She realized that a solution would have to be found for this problem. She went to Rev. Scheffler, the minister of a church nearby. After talking to him about what Patience was doing, he decided that his church would build a Children's Home in that area. Then these babies could be cared for and they could learn about Jesus.

Today the Macingine Children's Home is a haven where preschool children are lovingly cared for. They also learn to love the Lord at an early age just because one woman was obedient to the Lord's command to love our neighbors as ourselves.

Read what Jesus had to say about children in Matthew 18:1-6.

"For I was hungry and you gave me something to eat." Mt. 25:35

June

"WHO? WHO?"

Harold woke up to a loud twittering in the tree in front of his bedroom window. A flock of small birds fluttered noisily from branch to branch. *What is causing all the excitement?* he wondered. And then he saw it: an owl was perched majestically near the top of the tree. The huge bird opened and closed its eyes slowly, but otherwise sat completely motionless.

At regular intervals during the next day Harold checked whether the owl was still there. The old gray owl was sleeping and the other birds had subsided.

As night fell, Harold heard: "Who? Who?" He ran to the window. Yes, the big old owl was still sitting there, its silhouette etched against the twilight sky. *Why does the owl remind me of my grandfather?* he thought.

Probably because he was so calm and looked so wise. Then Harold remembered what his granddad had written in his Bible that he had given him on his twelfth birthday. He picked up the big black Book and opened it to the first page. He looked again at his grandfather's neat handwriting: *"Who will rescue me from this body of death? Thanks be to God – through Jesus Christ our Lord."*

Grandpa John had had a hard life. His parents had died when he was still young and he had struggled with poverty. As a young man he had worked in a factory with some rough characters and temptations had abounded in that place. Grandpa knew what he was talking about when he gave advice on life issues. At the last family get together before his death, he sat in a wheelchair while his grandchildren played around him. Later, when he said grace at the table, he mentioned each one of them in his prayer. "May they learn to live by your Book and to Your Glory!" he prayed.

The owl interrupted Harold's thoughts. "Who? Who?" the owl cried. "Who will help me?" the boy retorted. "Thanks be to God, through Jesus Christ our Lord!" he added softly.

You can read Psalm 119:9-16 as a prayer.

THE PLACE OF THE WILD DOGS

Do you sometimes wonder whether God can still do miracles like those in Moses' day? The following story from *Missionary Stories for Primaries* will make you think.

Mr. Swanson, a missionary in Central Africa, had led many people to the Lord. But near to where he lived, there was a village known as "The Place of the Wild Dogs." Nobody wanted to go there because as soon as strangers came close to the village, dogs would rush toward them, barking and growling. Mr. Swanson often wondered how, if all the Christians were too scared to go there, the people of that village would ever get to know about Jesus. One day he got a letter from his home church. The letter encouraged him to go to the scary place where the wild dogs lived. So, taking his Bible with him, he set off with a group of Christians who agreed to go with him. Before they left on their mission, they knelt down and prayed, "God, You once closed the mouths of lions when they wanted to attack Daniel. We are keen to go and tell the people who live on the other side of that hill about You. We want them to love and serve You! Please protect us against those vicious dogs!"

They started walking: over the hill, through the long grass, until they could see the huts of the village. But then they also saw the dogs! Mr. Swanson walked forward with determination. The others followed at a distance. The dogs came running toward them, barked and growled, but did them no harm!

And so the Good News about Jesus could be taken to people who had never even heard His Name.

Are you curious to know what was written in that letter? Read Psalm 91:14-15. A Sunday school class sent it to Mr. Swanson. "We are all praying for you!" they added and signed their names underneath.

HONESTY IS THE BEST POLICY

It is always better to be honest, although the devil often tries to convince us that honesty doesn't pay.

A young boy picked up a wallet on the sidewalk, and when he looked inside, he found $100! He was very excited about it and rushed home to tell his mom. But his mom said that they should take it to the police station. Imagine how difficult that was for the boy. He probably thought that "finders keepers" would be the best solution for this problem! He thought longingly of all the things that he could buy with so much money. But he went with his mom to the police station, and gave the envelope to the police. They took down his details and told him that they would let him know if the owner turned up. If, after a month, nobody had claimed the money, then they would give it to him.

That afternoon a man walked into the police station. "I've lost my wallet!" he said. "It was in my pocket and must have fallen out." The officer on duty said, "Somebody did hand in a wallet with money in it. How much was in it?" "$200!" said the dishonest man. "A boy brought in a wallet with $100 this morning, but that was probably not your wallet." "The little rascal probably stole the rest!" the man said. "Oh no! Then it probably isn't your money," the police officer corrected him. The dishonest man had to turn away in disappointment.

A month later, the police contacted the boy and told him that no one had claimed the money. Both the man and the boy learned interesting things through this. The man learned, "What goes around comes around!" And the boy learned, "Honesty is the best policy."

Learn these words by heart and use them to chase away the devil whenever he wants to tempt you into being dishonest

The LORD detests lying lips, but he delights in men who are truthful. Prov. 12:22

CHOOSE TO BE FRIENDLY

Do you know anyone who delivers newspapers to earn extra money? Then you will appreciate this story: A well-known writer, Albert M. Wells, did a paper round when he was young. But he did not like it at all! He had to get up early every morning and he had to keep out of the way of vicious dogs that chased him all along his route, barking all the while.

He tried everything to stop them, but nothing seemed to work. Stones, sticks, a water pistol, a bright flashlight: nothing made them leave him alone. He shouted at the dogs in the most threatening voice he could manage, but they simply ignored him.

One day an experienced newspaper deliverer gave him some excellent advice. "Don't chase the dogs away and don't run away from them. Feed them!" He took a bag of dog food with him every day on his rounds and he fed the dogs some of the pellets. Soon the dogs were much friendlier, and he could do his job hassle-free! Albert tried it for himself, and it worked wonders.

This story has something to teach each of us. When people make life difficult for us we can choose to moan and complain, or we can act as if they don't exist, or we can argue with them. But a much better solution is to become friends with them.

Paul said that kindness is a fruit of the Holy Spirit that dwells in us. That means that if we are children of God, we should prefer friendliness to fighting. Don't wait until people are friendly to you. Starting today, be kind to friend and foe alike. You will soon discover that people will respond in friendly ways.

In Proverbs 15:1, Solomon said, "A gentle answer turns away wrath, but a harsh word stirs up anger."

BEWARE!

Parents in Myanmar tell their children a story about a washer-woman and a potter to teach them not to be envious. The potter was jealous of the washerwoman because she made more money than he did. So he devised a cunning plan.

He went to the palace and told the king that he knew a wash-erwoman who was so good at her job that she could scour a black elephant until it was white as snow. "That I'll have to see!" the king said. He summoned the woman to his court and com-manded her to wash one of his black elephants until it was white as a lily.

This is exactly what the potter had hoped would happen. He knew that if she did not fulfill the king's command, she would be executed immediately. When the woman heard the king's com-mand, she realized that the envious potter had planned this to get rid of her.

So she also came up with a plan! She told the king that she could only wash the elephant if she had a bath that was big enough to hold the elephant. "No problem!" said the king. "I'll ask my friend the potter to make a bath that is big enough for the elephant."

What could the mean potter do? He had no choice but to obey the king, and so he made a huge pottery bath. But when the elephant got into it, it broke into a thousand pieces. He tried again, but the elephant stepped into the second bath and it also broke. And this is how it continued until he had no more clay.

It so often happens that when someone plans to harm someone else, the whole plot backfires, and the plotter ends up being harmed instead.

In Psalm 57:6 David writes about a time when Saul dug a pit in his path and then fell into it himself. You can read all about it in 1 Samuel 24:1-12.

They dug a pit in my path – but they have fallen into it themselves. Ps. 57:6

STANDING TOGETHER

The doctor told Tim and his parents that he had leukemia. This is a kind of cancer of the blood, and people who contract the disease need very special treatment. Tim had no idea what lay ahead for him. Every day his mom had to take him to the cancer clinic. On the way there she always bought him ice cream or chocolate. This special attention made him feel curious and excited about all the new experiences that awaited him. But after each treatment Tim started feeling worse and worse. Soon his arms were full of marks from all the injections that he had been given. He also fell behind in his schoolwork because he had to miss so much school. He began to feel nauseous a lot of the time too.

Tim's teacher was very kind. She encouraged his classmates to be especially kind to him as he went through this difficult time. She also told them that it was possible that the treatment Tim was receiving would make him lose all his hair. "Don't tease him about it!" she said. "Think how you would feel if you saw all your hair in the washbasin one morning."

The kids noticed that Tim's hair grew thinner and thinner. After a while, there were only a few strands on his head. Then one day Henry, the class president, announced, "I saw Tim on his way to the clinic this morning. He is completely bald!" At lunchtime Henry gathered the whole class under an oak tree on the playground. "Guys, let's think of a way in which we can support our friend!" "We can take turns to walk home with him in the afternoons," Rob suggested. "We can help him with his homework!" was Lucy's suggestion. Very soon they had an exciting plan for the day Tim was due to return to school.

When Tim's mother dropped him at school the next morning, he stopped in his tracks as he opened the classroom door: every boy in the class had shaved his head completely bald!

Read what Galatians 6:2 says about standing together.

Encourage one another and build each other up, just as ... you are doing. 1 Thes. 5:11

WHAT IS GRACE?

Barry was always in trouble at school, and his teachers weren't sure how to handle him. He had been punished over and over again. In fact, he couldn't keep count of the number of times that he been sent to the principal's office because of bad behavior.

One day he was once again in the principal's office. "Why were you sent to me this time?" he asked. "Because I hit one of the boys in my class," Barry answered sullenly. The principal looked at him quietly for a while, and then asked, "Why did you do it?" "I didn't like the way he looked at me!"

"Should I punish you again today?" the headmaster asked. The rebellious boy retorted, "Sure, I don't care. You can punish me as much as you like, but I'll keep doing what I like anyway!"

The principal was taken aback. What could he do to help this boy change? Gently he said, "Barry, today I want to teach you about grace." "I don't need grace!" Barry said. But the principal turned to the teacher who had brought Barry. "Here is a ruler. Barry deserves to be given six strikes on the palm of his hands, but I want you to give me the punishment he deserves." Then he turned to Barry. "Would you please count the blows?"

The principal stretched out his hands and the teacher started hitting him. One, two, three, four times the blows fell down on the outstretched hands. "Stop!" Barry shouted. "I'm the one that should be punished!" But the teacher kept on hitting the hands in front of him until the full number had been given. The principal's hands were red and swollen. Barry was crying like a baby. The principal took his face between his swollen hands and said softly, "That's how grace works, my boy!"

Do you now understand God's grace? Jesus bore the punishment for our sins. Have you thanked Him for doing that for you?

Read what Romans 3:23-24 says about God's grace.

For the wages of sin is death, but the gift of God is eternal life in Christ. Rom. 6:23

HELPING OTHERS

Every spring, swallows built a nest in the garage next to Sarah's house. She loved to sit on the garden wall and watch them. But this year there had been very little rain. The swallows couldn't find the mud they needed for building of nests anywhere. But, to Sarah's delight, she saw that one of the swallows had made a plan.

She watched amazed as it flew to the birdbath and sipped a little water into its beak. Then it flew to a patch of dry soil in the garden and mixed the water with the soil. Finally it flew back to the building site with the special mud in its beak.

Sarah realized what an immense task this little bird faced! She decided to help the little mother-to-be. She took the garden hose and thoroughly wet a patch of soil in the garden. Then she stepped back and wondered whether the swallow would discover the place where new building-material could now be found.

She wasn't disappointed. When the swallow came to sit on the side of the birdbath, it saw the wet patch glistening in the sunlight. With a musical trill that came from deep within her, she flew to the mud patch. From then on her task was much, much easier!

Sarah had a good plan to help the brave little swallow. From Proverbs 3:27 we learn that we should also be creative and help people who are having a hard time.

INNER BEAUTY

Gertrude was usually very cheerful, but one day something upset her very much. "What's wrong?" her mom asked when Gertrude came into the kitchen after school. Her usual smile had completely disappeared. "A TV crew came to film a commercial at our school and when I volunteered to be an extra, Jill said, 'Yes, they do need ugly ducklings as well!' It is true. I have such a big mouth and I'm covered in freckles."

"Come and sit down here, and I'll tell you a story," her mom said. A little smile appeared on Gertrude's face. "There once was a priest who didn't like the statue of Mary that stood in front of the church. It was an ugly statue and people nicknamed it *The Ugly Madonna*. But the people in the congregation wanted it to stay. Tourists came from all over to look at it.

Then the priest came up with a plan. Each year the statue was taken through the streets in a procession. One year it was his task to drive the truck on which the statue was placed. As he drove at the front of the procession, he stepped on the accelerator and then quickly slammed on the brakes, causing the statue to fall off the truck. "I hope that destroyed it!" he thought. But suddenly the watching crowds began to cheer and shout! When the statue fell to the ground, a lot of clay broke off and revealed a pure silver Madonna! Today people from all over the world visit the town to see this marvelous statue."

"Mom, do you mean this ugly duckling will turn into a beautiful swan one day?" Gertrude asked, pointing to herself. "Many people, including me, think that you are beautiful right now, because you are the most lovable, sweet, and kind freckle-faced girl we know! You see, we know what's on the inside!"

Gertrude hugged her mom and gave her one of her silver smiles!

**Read what Samuel said about
David's brothers in 1 Samuel 16:7.**

"The good man brings good things out of the good stored up in his heart." Lk. 6:45

WHOSE FAULT WAS IT?

One busy Saturday morning a man riding a motorbike knocked down a little boy who was crossing the street. The boy's legs were badly damaged and he would never be able to walk again. "It wasn't my fault," said the biker. "I was distracted by the students on the sidewalk!" "We were doing what the student leaders told us to do!" the students said. "They told us to protest and shout out slogans and march in the street because we are not happy with our lecturers." The leaders answered, "We had to do something, because our lecturers weren't teaching us." But the lecturers said, "We went on strike because we don't get enough pay!" "We can't pay you more because we have to spend so much money on crime prevention," the authorities responded. And the criminals replied, "We commit crimes because we have no jobs!"

"And we cannot give you jobs, because you want too much money!" the employers answered. And so it went on and on. In the meantime the little boy was struggling in the children's ward of the local hospital: he was learning to walk with crutches, which he would have to rely on for the rest of his life. Whose fault was it?

People always seem to blame others for their own mistakes. Ever since Adam first blamed Eve, people have reacted to wrongdoing in this way. Adam said, "The woman You put here gave me some fruit from the tree, and I ate it." Then Eve said, "The serpent deceived me, and I ate." Let's be different. Let's be like David and admit when we do something wrong. And let's then ask God to forgive us.

Read Psalm 51. It is a prayer that David wrote after he had murdered Uriah, and taken his wife.

GOD IS IN CONTROL

Sometimes God allows things to happen to us that are hard for us to understand. But we can be sure that God has a purpose when He allows bad things to happen.

Here is a story that illustrates how true this is: A man was a passenger on ship traveling from Australia to America. But the ship was wrecked in a storm, and the man was washed ashore on an island. He fell to his knees and praised God for saving his life. But he also said, "Lord, please help me to survive until somebody comes to rescue me." He set about building a shelter from wreckage of the ship that had drifted ashore.

He collected berries to eat and found crabs and small fish to cook. He was grateful that the Lord answered his prayers for day-to-day survival. But each day he scanned the horizon to see if a ship was on its way to rescue him. None ever came close enough to see his signals.

Then, one day, something terrible happened. He had been looking for food along the coastline and when he got back, he saw that his wooden shelter was on fire! *How could this happen?* he thought. *Why would God allow this? Where will I find material to build another house in this forsaken place?* He tried to extinguish the fire, but eventually all that was left of his dwelling was a heap of ashes.

He went and sat on a rock, in tears because of his loss. But suddenly he saw something on the horizon. It was a ship! He waved and shouted at the top of his voice. The ship came nearer and nearer and a rescue boat was launched to fetch him. "We saw your smoke signals!" the sailors said.

"Forgive me, Lord!" the man said. "You had a plan with my disappointment all along!"

Learn Romans 8:28 by heart and remember it when things do not work out the way you wanted them to.

In all things God works for the good of those who love him. Rom. 8:28

THE DANGEROUS ONE

Ps. 5:11   But let all who take refuge in you be glad.

"The dangerous one caught my lamb!" Tatama shouted in distress. Some Indonesians believe that you should never mention a dangerous animal by its name, because if you do, it might harm you. That was why Tatama called the tiger that had killed his lamb "the dangerous one". "We must kill him before he catches one of our children!" he exclaimed.

A missionary lived in Tatama's village. Tatama went to him for advice. "Let's pray about it," the preacher said. "And remember the Bible verse that I taught you from Psalm 2: 'Blessed are all who take refuge in Him.'"

When they had finished praying, they both knew what they had to do. "We must go to Wattima, the best hunter in the district, and ask him to find the one that is hungry!" Tatama said.

Wattima, who was also a believer, was willing to hunt the tiger. "The Lord will help us!" he said. He could track down any animal, even in that dense jungle. Suddenly he saw a movement in the long grass. Stealthily, he walked closer. And then he saw the orange animal with the black stripes!

Wattima threw a piece of wood toward the tiger. The animal leaped to its feet. A furious roar echoed through the jungle. As he lifted his head, Wattima fired a shot. The one that was beautiful, but also dangerous, fell to the ground, dead.

On the way home, Wattima said to the missionary, "Thank you for telling us about the One on whom we can rely!"

Look up the Bible verse that the missionary taught Wattima and Tatama.

BREAD FOR AFRICA

Six-year-old Calvin couldn't forget the picture that he had seen on the church bulletin board. It was a picture of little children from Malawi. Their legs were thin as sticks and their tummies were swollen. "They have no food to eat and they will die if somebody doesn't do something about it," the preacher said when Calvin asked him about it. Calvin thought about the heaped plates of food he ate every day and about the fridge and pantry at home that were always stocked with food. That night, when he got into bed after a good supper, he thought out a plan. He would take all the money in his moneybox and buy bread for those children!

On Monday evening at six o'clock, when the church board was meeting in the vestry, a delivery van from the town's bakery stopped outside. When the driver knocked on the door, the pastor opened it. "I brought the bread that Calvin Dearham ordered!" he said. The pastor called Calvin's father, who was an elder in the church, but he knew nothing about the order. He picked up his cell phone and called his son. "Did you ask the baker to deliver bread to the church?" he asked. "Yes, Dad. It is for the hungry children in Malawi!" Calvin replied. The members of the board heard the conversation. One man took a bill from his pocket. "I will buy a loaf of bread for fifty bucks!" he said. A deacon, who had a successful business, took out his checkbook. "I will buy three loaves for $3,000!" he said. Soon everybody opened their wallets and started buying the loaves of bread!

The next morning the church secretary had $8,000 to send to the Missionary Society that took food to the hungry people in Malawi. And all because a six-year-old boy took pity on a group of people in distress.

Read Psalm 41:1 to see what God promises to people who have regard for those in need.

He who is kind to the poor lends to the Lord, and he will reward him. Prov. 19:17

FATHER'S DAY

The Sunday before Father's Day, Mr. Smith asked his seventh grade Sunday school class a question. "If you were a father and you had a son or daughter, what would you do for him or her?" As the children responded, Mr. Smith made notes on the cardboard he had pasted on the board:

> **I'll protect my kid. I'll teach her what is right and wrong. I'll punish him when he is naughty. I'll give him whatever he needs.**

Isaac was the joker in the group. "I won't send him to school!" he said. Mr. Smith did not write that one down, though! He then asked the children to open their Bibles to Romans 8:15. Mr. Smith wrote ABBA at the top of the list that he had made. "Who can tell me why I did that?" he asked. "Because God is our Father!" "Abba means father!" "Because God our Father does all those things for us!" The children quickly gave these answers.

"That's correct!" Mr. Smith said. "Now let's thank the Lord for being such a good Father to us, and then each one of you can make a colorful card to give to your dad on Father's Day."

"What about Harry?" Sandy asked. "He hasn't got a father anymore!" Mr. Smith walked up to Harry and put his hand on the boy's shoulder. "You can make a card for God and put it in your Bible," he said. "Remember, God wants to do all the things that a father does for his children, for you! John 1:12 says, *'To all who received him, to those who believed in his name, he gave the right to become children of God.'*"

For a while it was quiet in the room: the kids were all praying. Then they got stuck in to the scissors, glue, and colored paper, making creative cards for their dads.

**Why don't you make two cards for Father's Day:
One for your dad and one for your Heavenly Father!**

JUNE 15

FURIOUS!

Freddie was furious! His mom had grounded him for the whole weekend. He wasn't allowed to visit his friends, he couldn't ride his bike, and he wasn't even allowed to watch TV! He sat moping in his bedroom.

His dad came in and sat on the bed next to him. "What's wrong, old chap?" he asked. "Mom thinks that I took money from her purse! I wasn't even near it! Sophie saw me in your bedroom and now they are accusing me of things I didn't even do!" He started fuming again as he thought of the false accusations.

His dad left the room and came back with a bag full of balloons. "What are you doing?" he asked his dad, who could sometimes explain things in the most unusual way! "I want to show you the different ways in which you can handle your anger," his dad said.

He blew up one balloon. "You can let it loose for all to see," and with those words he let the balloon float in the air.

He blew up another one. "Or you can moan and groan," his dad stretched the opening of that balloon and it made a whining sound. "You can, of course, also explode!" he said as he pricked the third balloon with a pin. "But these aren't good ways to deal with your anger. Let me show you the best way!"

His dad took another balloon that had been blown up, and let the air out slowly. "This is the best way to let go of your rage!" he said. "Let's go and talk to mom and see what we can do!"

Half an hour later Freddie rode off happily to see his friends. His dad's plan had worked and he was hoping that his mom would soon find the money that she had lost.

**Read Ephesians 4:29-32 and decide
which verse suits this story best.**

In your anger do not sin ... search your hearts and be silent. Ps. 4:4

JUNE 16

GOOD NEWS!

There was a new baby in the Grovers' house. What a joy! Dad contacted the local newspaper and arranged for them to publish the news in the classified columns. They let all the neighbors know. Grandma phoned everyone in the family. When Mom came home from the hospital with the baby, Dad put up a banner at the front door.

Joanne was fascinated by all the excitement. "Were you just as glad on the day when I was born?" she asked. "Of course we were," Grandma said. "Has your dad ever told you that the oak tree in the corner was planted on that day? We were all invited for the ceremony and we had tea and muffins right there in the garden!"

"Births are big events," Grandma continued while she knitted a baby jacket. "That's why God sent prophets ages before Christ's birth to announce that He was coming. And angels told people about His birth when He finally arrived!"

Grandma continued, "God told Mary all about the special Baby she was going to have, and He also sent angels to tell Joseph all about it. And when the Baby was finally born, angels announced it to the shepherds in the fields outside Bethlehem."

Grandma looked at her granddaughter, who was listening eagerly to every word. "But, there was a day that was far more important to me than the day your dad was born. That was the day he was born again. Ask him to tell you about it. The day when he acknowledged Jesus as his Savior was a red-letter day. The Bible says that there is a party in heaven every time a person on earth is born again."

"How do you know that?" Joanne asked, surprised. "You can read it in Luke 15:10," Grandma said, delighted to be able to share this with her granddaughter.

Check whether Granny Grover was telling the truth.

JUNE 17

FREE AT LAST!

Frieda lived on a farm. One day her dad brought home a baby squirrel that he found in the orchard. It was still too small to fend for itself, but its parents had disappeared. Dogs had probably attacked them. Frieda fed it with a feeding bottle and she made it comfortable in a wooden box. She became very fond of her new pet and she called him Smoky, because of his color.

But after a few months, he became restless and naughty. He ruined the curtains in Frieda's bedroom and climbed onto all the furniture with his sharp little claws.

One day, while Frieda was feeding Smoky, he bit her finger. Her mom said, "It's time to let the squirrel free. He must go back to where he came from. Squirrels are not supposed to be house pets. It is cruel to keep him cooped up like this."

That night Frieda cried herself to sleep. The next morning she left Smoky on his own in the garden and did not bring him in at bedtime. But he came in on his own. After a week he found his way to the orchard. Frieda only saw him once after that: he and another squirrel were chasing each other from tree to tree. Then Frieda realized that she had done the right thing by letting him go.

One night, while she was having her quiet time, she came across these words of the Lord in Psalm 50:10-11, *"For every animal of the forest is mine, and the cattle on a thousand hills. I know every bird in the mountains and the creatures of the field are mine."* The words comforted her. She prayed softly, "Thank You, Lord, that You will look after Smoky Yourself. And thank You that we could borrow him for a while to live with us."

If you are fond of animals, you can make a beautiful poster using pictures of animals and birds from magazines and then write the words from Psalm 50 on it.

God made the wild animals ... And God saw that it was good. Gen. 1:25

BIRDS OF A FEATHER

Conrad gave his heart to Jesus at a youth camp. For the first time he understood what Jesus had done for him on the cross. He confessed his sin and asked the Lord to make him a true disciple of Jesus Christ. But he had no idea what difference that prayer would make to his life.

After that weekend he started to read his Bible regularly and he prayed sincerely every day, but he hung around with the same friends he had known before he was born again. He never bothered to tell them what had happened to him at camp.

Then something happened that forced him to show his gang of friends that a real change had taken place in his life. Henry was planning to celebrate his birthday with a beach party, and he invited the whole gang, included Conrad.

Everybody knew that it would be a rough party, like all Henry's parties. And yet Conrad accepted the invitation. He thought that he might be able to be a quiet witness for the Lord at the party. *I needn't drink, smoke, or tell dirty jokes when the others do,* he thought.

When he joined the party on the beach, one of Henry's friends remarked, "I'm glad to see that you came along! Somebody said that you became a Holy Joe some time ago. I am glad to see that was a false alarm."

Conrad was taken by surprise. These guys had not expected one of Jesus' followers to turn up at a party like this. "What you've been told is the truth!" Conrad said. "I've become a Christian and I do not belong here." Then he turned around and went home. He realized that he would have to make new friends. Then they could also have fun beach parties, but ones where His new Friend Jesus would feel welcome.

Read Paul's warning in 1 Corinthians 15:33.

WHERE IS HEAVEN?

One Monday morning, a man met his pastor in town. "You preached a good sermon on heaven yesterday," he said. "But you forgot to tell us where heaven actually is." "Did I?" asked the pastor. "Then I'll tell you right now! Do you see that apartment block over there?" The pastor pointed to a neglected building on the street corner.

"In apartment number eleven there is a family who is having a hard time. Go and buy them some meat, a loaf of bread, and a bottle of milk. Take it to them and tell them that you bring it in the Name of Jesus. Ask them if you could read Psalm 23 to them, and then pray for them. After that, if you do not feel as if you have been to heaven, I'll give you back every cent that you spent!"

The next day the man knocked on the door of the parsonage. "Pastor," he said, "yesterday I experienced heaven, and I just want to thank you for showing me the way. I realize now that heaven is not only a place where God's children will spend eternity, but that we can already experience the joy of heaven on earth!"

"Come inside," the pastor invited. "I want to show you a verse from the Bible. I wrote it out and I keep it in my wallet. It is a map to heavenly joy." On the card which the minister took from his wallet, was written: Proverbs 11:25: *"A generous man will prosper; he who refreshes others, will himself be refreshed."* "That is so true!" the visitor said while writing down the quotation in his notebook. "When I saw the delight on the faces of that poor family when I gave them the food, my cup of joy ran over!"

**You could keep a similar card in your
pocket to remind you to be generous.**

He who refreshes others will himself be refreshed. Prov. 11:25

WIZARDS AND MUGGLES

"Who reads the Harry Potter books?" Miss Shaw asked at Sunday school. Quite a few kids raised their hands. "And what do you think of them?" she asked. "They're thrilling!" Danny said. "Have you learned anything from them?" "Oh yes, I know all kinds of things about witchcraft and stuff like that!"

"That's why some parents don't want their children to read those books," Miss Shaw said seriously. "Parents do not want their children to have an unhealthy interest in witches, sorcery, and spells. This kind of preoccupation can lead to involvement in the occult." "What does that mean?" Ann asked. "Occult practices involve magic and secret rituals that people use to honor Satan, and the devil lures people into his traps by making these things seem mysterious. People are naturally curious about the unseen world. But if they spend more time reading about witchcraft and sorcery than in serving God and studying His Word, the devil can easily trap them into Satanism."

Then Miss Shaw asked one child to read Deuteronomy 18:11-12: *"Let no one be found among you ... who practices divination or sorcery, interprets omens, engages in witchcraft or cast spells ... anyone who does these things is detestable to the Lord."*

"Wow! I never knew that was in the Bible!" Ann said. "But Harry Potter is only a story!" Danny reacted indignantly. "Yes, but it doesn't sound as if God is pleased with such stories!" Ann answered. "Here in verse 14 God says we shouldn't even listen to sorcerers." "You are a real muggle!" Danny said. "Let me give you two more quotes from the Bible to see what God thinks about sorcerers and then you can decide for yourself whether God wants us to have witches and wizards as our heroes," said Miss Shaw.

Here are the verses from Scripture that the kids had to look up that day: Micah 5:12 and Galatians 5:19-21. You should read them too!

JUNE 21

FEARLESS!

Mary Slessor was born in Scotland in 1848. She grew up in a very unhappy home. Her father was an alcoholic and they were extremely poor. She had to go out to work when she was only eleven years old. Every day she worked from six in the morning until six at night. Mary was a Christian and she loved to read her Bible. She had heard about missionary work in West Africa and she was very upset to learn about the cruel things that happened in that part of the world. "I wish I could go there to tell people about God!" she thought.

When she was 26, she went to Nigeria as a missionary. It is amazing to read about all the things that she had experienced there. She met cannibals, encountered wild animals, and clashed with slave traders. She found the terrible heat of Africa exhausting, and she often struggled with malaria.

Nevertheless, she did outstanding work for the Lord. She became renowned for standing up for the rights of twin babies. People in that area used to believe that twins should be put to death soon after birth, otherwise bad luck would come to the parents. Mary helped people to end this superstitious behavior. She even adopted a pair of twins when their father and mother did not want them.

The people of Kalabar grew very fond of her. Through her life and testimony, many people started to believe in the living God. At her funeral, a girl started to weep hysterically, but one of the men who attended the service said, "Let's rather sing a song of praise. And then the thousands of people, who came from far and wide for her funeral, sang praises to God for the life of "Our Big White Mama!" as they had called her.

Paul was also a fearless missionary for the Lord. Read 2 Corinthians 6:5-10 to see some of the things that happened to him.

"Therefore go and make disciples of all nations." Mt. 28:19

WHAT REALLY MATTERS

Paganini was probably the greatest violinist who ever lived. Many interesting stories are told about him, but the following incident from his life really makes us think.

One night, Paganini was scheduled to perform in front of a large audience, but something terrible happened. The curtain was raised, the audience applauded and he bowed. But as he placed his bow on the violin to begin playing, he realized that the instrument in his hand wasn't his own. He excused himself and went backstage to fetch his own violin. He soon discovered, however, that somebody had taken his famous violin and had put an inferior one in its place.

For a moment he was completely stunned. But then he walked back onto the stage with renewed enthusiasm. "Ladies and gentleman," he announced, "tonight I am going to show you that the instrument is not the most important factor when a master musician performs. The heart of the musician is what truly matters!"

That night he played as never before, and gloriously beautiful music poured out of that inferior violin. The audience was awed, and when he finished playing, they rose to their feet and gave him a standing ovation. All were convinced that he was truly the greatest violinist. He did not need a perfect violin to produce extraordinary music.

This incident shows us that even a simple life can be a beautiful life. If you put your life in the hands of the Master, He can make your life worthwhile. The people who know you will praise the Lord, who leads you. He can produce amazing results through your life, if you only let Him!

Read Isaiah 11:2 to see what difference the Sprit of the Lord can make in a person's life, and ask Him to do those things in your life.

JUNE 23

WHERE YOUR TREASURE IS

Once upon a time there was a rich man who became very, very ill. The doctor said that he might die soon. While he was in hospital, his young daughter visited him every day. She sat at his bedside for hours on end. He was deeply moved by her commitment and love.

One afternoon some friends came to visit him. They brought him flowers and chocolates, but when they left, the little girl asked, "Are you going away from us, Daddy?" "Yes," her dad said, with tears in his eyes. "I don't think that I'll be around for much longer." The girl stood next to his bed and asked, "Will you have lots of friends and a beautiful house to live in, in the place that you are going to?" The girl's question made her dad think.

The next day the rich man asked their minister to come and visit him. "My daughter made me think," he said. "I know that I am a child of God, but I have done nothing to make sure that my friends will also go to heaven one day. And I'm not sure whether I have sent enough building material to heaven for a heavenly home! While I was healthy and strong, I just worked for myself and for my own family."

Then he and the minister prayed together and he decided to leave some of his money for the Bible Society. He wrote a letter that was read at his funeral. In it he said, "My dear friends, remember that earthly wealth cannot last. Only the things that we do for the Lord will be of eternal value." And these words were written on his tombstone: *Do not store up for yourselves treasures on earth, where moth and rust destroy ... But store up for yourselves treasures in heaven. For where your treasure is, there your heart will be also"* (Mt. 6:19-21).

In 2 Kings 5 you can read about another little girl who also helped a rich man to remember God.

THE POTATO, THE EGG, AND THE TEABAG

"You would never say that Aunt Nell and Aunt Yvonne are sisters!" Marina commented one day. "Why do you say that?" her mom asked. "Well, the one is gentle and kind and the other is unfriendly and harsh!" Marina's mom was busy cooking. "Come and see what I've got here," she said. Marina walked over to the stove, curious to see what she wanted to show her. "Look at this potato," her mom said. "When I put it in the water, it was hard. But when the water around it started to heat up and boil, it became soft. On the other hand," she continued while taking out an egg from another pot, "when I put this egg into hot water, it became hard." To prove her point, she broke the shell of the egg. The yellow and the white of the egg had hardened in the process of cooking. "Your aunts have both had a hard life and people react differently to suffering. Some become hard and bitter while others become more warm and sympathetic, like your aunt Yvonne."

"I hope I end up like the potato and not like the egg if I ever go through difficulties!" Marina said. She watched as her mom struggled on her crutches between the stove and the sink. "Can I make you some tea?" she asked. After a while, as she was pouring the fragrant tea, she suddenly said, "You know what, Mom? You are even better than a potato. You are like a teabag. A teabag flavors the hot water in which it is placed. You were in that terrible accident, but when you came home from hospital, you cheered us all up. Who would ever have dreamed that a wigglywaggly Mom like you could laugh and sing so much! Our home is twice as nice since you came home!"

And then the teabag mom and the potato daughter started dancing around the kitchen table as if there were no crutches between them!

**Read Isaiah 40:29-31 and find out
where Marina's mom got her strength.**

MICE CANNOT FLY

"Do you believe that we descended from apes?" Ron asked his dad. "No," his dad replied emphatically. "I do not believe the theory of evolution. The Bible says that God created everything after their kind. Although dogs and horses and butterflies can change a lot through breeding or circumstances, they still remain dogs and horses and butterflies."

"My teacher said that you only have to look at a bat to realize that evolution actually took place. The bat evolved from a small mouse-like creature whose front toes developed into wings by gradual steps until it could fly."

Ron's dad laughed. "You ask your teacher how this poor animal moved around while his front paws were gradually evolving into wings. With toes getting longer and skin starting to grow between them, it would certainly not have been capable of running! His limbs would have been too long to run with and too short to fly with. He would never have been able to survive. And apart from that, no fossils have been found to prove this theory!" his dad added.

"Our teacher says that we are virtually the same as apes." "I disagree!" his dad said. "We have the same Creator, and therefore our skulls and bones show similarities, but the Bible says that I was made in the image of God and was placed on earth to represent Him."

Ron's dad told him about an interesting event. "A zoo in Denmark once kept a human couple on show in one of the cages. With this exhibit, they wanted to show that man and beast are basically the same. But the behavior of the man and woman was so different from the apes in the cage next door, that their exhibition had the opposite effect: people had to admit that homo sapiens are, without a doubt, completely different from apes."

Why not read the story of creation in Genesis 1:26-28 and Genesis 2 once again?

So God created man in his own image, in the image of God he created him. Gen. 1:27

EMBARRASSED?

Jeremy wished that his dad had a different job. It sounded so cool to say, "My dad is at the office!" But Jeremy's dad sold plastic souvenirs to tourists from a street stall. When other kids asked him, "What does your dad do for a living?" he always said, "He is in business." Then he would quickly change the subject before anyone could ask details about the kind of business that his dad was involved in.

He was also upset that his dad had to work on Saturdays and many evenings. He was never free to watch Jeremy play in soccer matches. The other dads would stand on the sidelines, cheering and encouraging their sons, but his dad only said, "Enjoy the game, Jeremy! I wish I could be there to see you score the winning goal!" And in the final match of the final season, when he had been voted man of the match, his dad wasn't there to see it.

Jeremy dreamed of going to college one day, but he thought it was an impossible goal. Yet he prayed about it regularly. On his seventeenth birthday, his dad handed him a big envelope. *What could be inside?* he wondered. He hoped for money to buy new sneakers. But inside the envelope was a file of documents. "What's this?" he asked. "Those are application forms for college," his dad answered. "You can look through them and tell me which course you want to take." "But where will the money come from?" Jeremy asked, surprised. His dad smiled. "Ever since your sixth birthday, I have put Saturdays' earnings into a savings account for you. Now you can study at a college of your choice."

Jeremy felt a lump in his throat. "Thanks, Dad!" he said, as he eagerly sat down to study the information in the catalogs. "I'll work hard, Dad!" he promised. "I'll get a degree and a good job and then you won't have to stand on wet and windy street corners to sell your stuff any longer." His dad gave him a warm hug.

Read Ephesians 6:1-2

HOROSCOPES

As soon as the morning paper arrived, Jake grabbed the cartoons, his dad took the sports pages, and Vera, his sister, reached for the section with the horoscope. "Have you decided whether you are going to the Youth Camp this weekend?" her mom asked after a while. "It seems as if I shouldn't go!" Vera answered. "My horoscope says that if I do anything unusual this weekend it could be disastrous!"

Vera's mom looked sternly at her. "Vera, I've told you before that you shouldn't take astrology seriously! You told me that you only read it for fun." "I do," Vera said. "But often things happen exactly the way the horoscope predicted. Last week it said that I would have a big disappointment. And what happened? I lost my purse."

"How stupid!" Jake said. "I was born under a different star sign and I also had a disappointment!" "Shut up. You know nothing!" Vera said. Vera's dad spoke up. "The question we must consider is this: Is studying astrology good for us and is God pleased with it?" "Does the Bible talk about astrology?" asked Vera.

"Give me a few minutes and I'll show you what God's Word has to say about it," answered her dad as he walked into his office. After a while he came back with his Bible and said, "Listen to Isaiah 47:13-15: *'Let your astrologers come forward, those star-gazers who make predictions month by month, let them save you from what is coming over you. Surely they are like stubble; the fire will burn them up. They cannot even save themselves.'*" He turned a few pages and continued, "And in Romans 8:14 Paul writes, *'Those who are led by the Spirit of God are sons of God.'* So who is guiding you when you say that you won't go to Youth Camp?"

"Oh dear," Vera replied. "Maybe I'll have to think about the weekend again!"

Mark these verses in your Bible.

JUNE 28

THE FROG AND THE SNAKE

A frog made friends with a snake. The snake taught the frog to hiss and the frog taught the snake to croak. So Frog could hiss just like a snake and he had great fun scaring his friends while he sat hissing among the reeds. And Snake would lie croaking in the reeds next to the pond. When the other frogs heard this, they thought that it was their friend calling. But as soon as they got near enough, Snake would catch one and eat him.

This happened quite a few times. But after a while the frogs realized what was going on and they did not react when Snake started croaking. In the end Snake was so hungry that he caught Frog for supper. Just before Frog got swallowed, he said to himself, *How stupid I was! I became a friend of Snake and lost my true friends. And now I'm about to lose my life as well!*

You should also be wary of making friends with the wrong people. At first you may have fun being with a different crowd, but after a while you will discover that they do not really care about you.

David wrote about this type of friend in Psalm 55:12-14. His so-called friends seemed to be interested in the things that interested him, but eventually David discovered that they were bloodthirsty and deceitful (v. 23). Listen what he had to say about such a friend, *"My companion attacks his friends ... his speech is smooth as butter, yet war is in his heart"* (vv. 20-21).

Ask God to help you to make genuine friends and to get rid of those who have a bad influence on your life.

**Write down the names of five friends.
Underline the ones who mean a lot to you
and thank God for them. Pray for the others.**

JUNE 29

MIA'S SCARF

Once there was a little girl who was scared to go to bed at night. Her name was Mia and she always wanted her mom to stay with her until she fell asleep. But of course, her mom could not do that. So her mom came up with a good plan. She said, "Let me give you something that you can hold on to while you are in the dark: something that will remind you that Mom and Dad are not far from you. We are right here in the house, only a call away!" She took off her floral scarf and gave it to Mia. "This scarf will remind you that we are nearby and that we love you and that we will protect you with our lives."

Mia took the scarf and wrapped it around her. Then she turned over and fell into a peaceful sleep. The next morning at breakfast her dad read from Luke 22:14. He read how Jesus took bread on the night before He was crucified and gave it to His disciples. He also gave them a cup of wine from which they could drink. Then He told them to think of Him every time they ate bread or drank wine.

In this way they could remember Him. Suddenly Mia understood an important truth!

"It's like my scarf!" she said. "Jesus gave His friends something to remember Him by. Each time they were together and had bread and wine, they would be reminded that He was only a call away."

Mia now understood why they regularly had communion at church. It reminds God's children of Jesus' death and resurrection on their behalf. Eating bread and drinking wine or grape juice during communion helps them if they are scared or uncertain, just as Mia's scarf reassured her that her parents were near.

Does this story help you to understand why we should have communion at church?

June 30

SERIOUS ILLNESS

One afternoon when Jane got home from school, their neighbor, Mrs. Wiley, was waiting for her. "Your mom has been taken to hospital," she said. "Come over to our place." Jane was shocked "What's wrong with Mom?" she asked. "Your dad will tell you," Mrs. Wiley answered. She talked non-stop as she gave Jane some milk and cookies. *That's just to divert my attention*, Jane thought.

After what seemed like ages, her dad arrived. She ran to him and threw both arms around him. "Thanks, Lana!" her dad said as they said goodbye to their neighbor. When they were in their own home again, her dad explained, "Mom has cancer. Do you know what that means?" "Yes," Jane answered. "A boy in our class died of it." Her dad spoke softly. "We still don't know how serious it is. Mom will have to have surgery and radiation. The doctors are doing all they can to make sure she gets well again."

Millions of thoughts rushed through Jane's head. Who would help her with her homework? Who would clean the house and do the ironing? Would the doctors hurt her mom? "Do you want to go to the hospital tonight?" her dad asked. "Yes, please, " she replied eagerly. "Can I make Mom some fudge?" "Yes, you may! We will have to ask the doctor whether it's a good idea for her to eat it, though! You can also make a card that we can put with these flowers," her dad said.

Only then did Jane notice the lovely bunch of roses that her dad had bought. Jane paged through her mom's Bible, looking for a special verse to write on a card for her mom. She noticed that her mom had underlined Psalm 56:3-4: *"When I am afraid, I will trust in you. In God, whose word I praise, in God I trust."* As she copied the words, her heart was comforted.

Make a card with these words on it to
give to someone who must go to hospital.

July

July 1

Jealousy

One Sunday, Ethel heard about jealousy twice: her Sunday school teacher told the class that it is wrong to be jealous, but later, in church, the pastor read Exodus 20:5. *"I, the LORD your God, am a jealous God."* She couldn't understand that. "Why is it bad if people are jealous, but good if God is jealous?" she asked her brother. He was a college student and knew a lot about the Bible.

"When the Bible says that God is jealous, it means that He doesn't want us to worship other gods. He wants only what is best for us. And no other god can make us happy or take us to heaven."

"And you know, it's not always wrong for people to be jealous. There is also a good kind of jealousy for people."

"Like what?" Ethel asked. She knew she was jealous of Karen because Karen was prettier and smarter than she was. She also knew that it was a wrong kind of jealousy, because it really bothered her. What did her brother mean by a 'good' jealousy? He answered, "Say a man doesn't want his wife to flirt with other men, then it is a good kind of jealousy. God has said that a husband and wife should be faithful to one another. If the wife is unfaithful, then she is disobeying God. Then it is right for the man to be jealous. The Lord does not want us to envy someone who has more than we have. That shows that we are ungrateful."

Back in her room, Ethel thought about what her brother had said. She didn't want to be ungrateful. And she wanted to make the Lord glad. So she prayed, "Lord, help me to be friendly and caring toward Karen!"

Did these characters from the Bible have a good or bad kind of jealousy: Cain toward Abel, Saul toward David, Joseph's brothers toward Joseph?

THE LORD PROVIDES

You probably know the stories in the Bible that describe how the Lord looked after His hungry children. There were the Israelites who got manna and quails in the desert. And then there was Elijah for whom the ravens brought bread and meat each evening at the Kerith Ravine.

A similar miracle happened to a woman in the Philippines. There was a war in the country and bombs fell every day. Most people had taken refuge in the mountains and had built small houses for themselves so that they could stay there until the war was over. Among them was a Christian woman named Isabella. She had taken lots of food with her when she had left her home in the city, but the war dragged on and eventually she ran out of food. Then she started looking for plants and berries to eat. But she became very ill and she realized that she needed proper food. So she prayed to the Lord and asked Him to help her.

And guess how her prayer was answered! The next morning a big wood-pigeon came to sit in her window. It just sat there until she eventually took it. She believed that the Lord had sent her this meat and so she cooked it and ate it. The next morning the same thing happened. A pigeon was sitting and waiting for her on exactly the same spot. This continued for six weeks. By then she had become strong and healthy again. And then the pigeons stopped coming.

Do you think it was just a coincidence? No, it was the Lord who took care of His child!

Read how the Lord sent Elijah food when he needed it. (1 Kings 17:1-6)

God richly provides us with everything for our enjoyment. 1 Tim. 6:17

WHAT IS SUCCESS?

Lorna felt like a complete failure. First she heard that she didn't make the soccer team and then she got her marks for the math test. She got a big D-. The elections for class president were coming up and she knew no one would vote for her. "I wonder if anybody would even notice if I just disappeared into thin air!" she thought.

At choir that afternoon, she just pretended to sing. "See," she thought, "nobody even notices if I don't sing along!" But as the children were leaving, Miss Kramer called her back. "Lorna, why didn't you sing today? The choir sounded all unbalanced today because you were only moving your lips." Lorna was totally taken aback. It did matter after all whether she sang along or not.

Lorna walked home with Mandy. As they got to Mandy's house, she said, "You know – our friendship means a lot to me!"

Lorna sang happily as she walked the rest of the way home. "Oh well," she thought, "it doesn't matter if I don't excel in everything. As long as my life is making a difference."

When she got home, she asked her mother, "Mom, would you be very disappointed if I don't make a success of my life?" "It depends what you mean by success," her mother said. "If you're not rich or famous one day, I won't be disappointed. I'll think you're successful as long as you're happy. And I think you'll always be happy, because you love the Lord and other people." "Does that mean I don't have to do my homework?" she asked teasingly. "You little rascal!" her mom said. "If you love the Lord you will always do your best, not so?"

Read Ephesians 4:1. It says that we all have
a calling. If we are obedient to God,
then we are a success in His eyes.

BLUE DAYS

Christine and Amy were walking home from school. "What do you do when you feel down?" Amy asked. Christine thought a while and then said, "I go to bed or I go to the mall or I watch TV." "Oh no," Amy said. "That would make me feel even more depressed. I'd rather listen to beautiful music or go for a walk in the park."

"Why do you ask?" Christine wanted to know.

"Our Social Studies teacher wants us to talk about depression in class tomorrow. He says that more and more kids suffer from feelings of depression. I wonder why that is?" Amy exclaimed. "I don't find it strange," Christine said. And then she just started crying. She sagged down against an oak tree on the sidewalk and started sobbing uncontrollably. Amy sat down next to her friend. "Is there something that's bothering you?" she asked gently. Sobbing, Christine answered, "The last few weeks I haven't felt like doing anything! And my parents don't take notice of me anyway. They never have time for me. They rush from one thing to the next. I'm sure they sometimes forget that I even exist!"

"Hmm," Amy replied. "I know that feeling. But listen to this!" She dug into her pocket and produced a card. "My aunt gave this to me one day when I was feeling a bit blue. Isaiah 49:15: *Can a mother forget her baby at her breasts and have no compassion on the child she has borne? Though she may forget, I will not forget you!*"

"Do you think the Lord said that for people like us?" Christine asked. "I believe that with all my heart!" Amy said as she helped her friend to get up. She put the card in Christine's pocket and said, "Let's go down to the park when we've finished our homework and then we can chat some more."

Write the text on a card and keep it in your pocket so that you can think about it next time you feel a bit neglected.

The Lord is faithful, and he will strengthen and protect you. 2 Thes. 3:3

THE LINUS BLANKET

Nadine was reading the *Peanuts* comic strip. She liked the little character Linus who always took his blanket with him as a kind of comfort. She closed the magazine, lay down on her bed, and started crying. There were a lot of people in her life that were like a quilt of comfort to protect her against the storms in life, but the patch that was Grandma had been ripped out of that quilt.

Grandma had always had time for her. She always read her stories. And then suddenly she was taken to the hospital and never came back. Now there was a huge gap in her quilt and she felt cold and alone.

After a while her sobs quietened down and she thought of everything that had happened since Grandma's funeral. She looked at all the flowers, letters, and cards that people had sent her. Everybody knew how much she loved her grandmother. The boy next door even gave her one of his best marbles.

Nadine realized that the love and care of all these people also surrounded her and her family like a soft quilt. Many people had brought them flowers and food and some friends just came to sit with them. Sometimes they laughed through their tears as they talked about Grandma's quaint little mannerisms.

Nadine opened her Bible and read 1 Thessalonians 4:14 again, the verse that the pastor preached on at the funeral: *"We believe that Jesus died and rose again and so we believe that God will bring with Jesus those who have fallen asleep in Him."*

She took the photo of Grandma from her bedside table and pressed it against her heart. "Goodnight, sleep tight!" she said as Grandma always had when she tucked Nadine in for the night.

Pray for someone you know who is heartbroken.

The eternal God is your refuge, and underneath are the everlasting arms. Deut. 33:27

JULY 6

SEND ME

Have you ever heard about Jonathan Goforth? Probably not, because he was born in 1859 in Canada. But even though he lived a long time ago, we can learn many things from his life. He was 18 years old when he became a child of God and from then on he was always looking for ways to tell people about Jesus. One night a missionary came to speak in their church about his work in the Far East. He quoted the words from Isaiah 6:8 where the Lord asks, *"Whom shall I send? And who will go for us?"* In his heart, Jonathan answered the same way Isaiah did. He said, *"Here am I. Send me!"* From that moment on, Jonathan knew that he wanted to become a missionary.

With great excitement, he arrived at Knox College, where he wanted to prepare himself for the work to which the Lord had called him. But the other students thought he was a bit weird. Because he came from a very poor family, his mother had made all his clothes herself and everybody made fun of him because of that. Jonathan nearly quit on the first day. But that night on his knees he talked to the Lord for a long time and when he rose from his knees, he decided to go ahead with his plan, no matter what people said about him.

While he was studying, he often ministered to poor people about Jesus. His friends started to respect him for that. When he finished his studies, the other students chose to send him out as their missionary. They had grown to love him and many of his classmates talked about the good influence he had had on them.

He worked as a missionary in China for fifty years and led thousands of people to the Lord.

Would you like to give the Lord the same answer to His question that Isaiah and Jonathan did?

From No-Good to Man of God

George Mueller was a thief, a liar, and a drunkard. Before he was 10 years old, his parents suspected that he was stealing money from them, so they left money lying around on purpose. And indeed, he took the money and hid it in his shoe. His parents caught him red-handed and punished him severely.

But that wasn't the end of the matter. Time and again George was caught stealing. He even had to spend time in jail because of theft. Later in his life he started gambling and drinking. He did whatever he wanted to do, never thinking of any one else at all.

One night a friend invited him to a prayer meeting. "OK!" he said. "Tonight I'm going to pray instead of drink!" At the prayer meeting there were many children of God who made a lasting impression on George. That evening, when he got back to his room, he knelt down at his bed and gave his life to the Lord.

He was determined to do something for the Lord. One morning he prayed, "Lord, if you give me £20, I'll buy Bibles and hand them out to people who do not have your Word." Before the day had ended someone gave him £20 out of the blue.

This event encouraged George to keep trusting God for everything he needed. He did wonderful things for God in his lifetime.

We must never think that someone is too sinful or lost to get saved. Tomorrow we will read some more about this remarkable man.

Is there someone you care for who does
not know the Lord? Don't stop praying
for that person. See what Luke 19:10 says.

So that in me ... Christ Jesus might display his unlimited patience. 1 Tim. 1:16

July 8

A Father of Orphans

Ask your parents or grandparents if they have ever heard about George Mueller. I'm sure they have, because he was one of the most extraordinary people that ever lived. God used him to provide homes for thousands of orphans in England. He also provided them with three meals a day and clothes to wear. He saw to it that they grew up as children of the Lord. We could say that he was the father of ten thousand children!

But he didn't see it that way. He read in Psalm 68:6 that God is the Father and protector of orphans and that is why, from the day he first started the orphanage for thirty children, he trusted God for everything he needed.

He believed that because God was the Father of these poor children, all he needed to do was to tell Him what they needed. And the Lord always provided! If, for example, there wasn't enough food, he would call the staff together and pray with them. Often they had not even risen from their knees when a truck with vegetables, fruit, bread, or meat suddenly stopped in front of the kitchen door.

Mr. Mueller kept a record of every single time that the Lord answered their prayers. He published more than 50,000 such accounts in a book. His orphanages showed the world that God answers prayer.

The Lord also wants to answer your prayers. The most important prayer that you should pray is to ask God to forgive your sins and use you in His service. That is what George Mueller did when he was still a student and just look how God blessed him!

Read the second part of Philippians 4:16 in your Bible. It was George Mueller's favorite Bible text.

And my God will meet all your needs according to his glorious riches. Phil. 4:19

THE LORD WILL PROTECT YOU

"Mom, when is Dad coming back again?" Leanne asked for the umpteenth time. Cameron shut her up with, "How many more times must Mom tell you that it is never going to happen?" The three of them were sitting around the table where there used to be four places set. It had been a month since Leanne and Cameron's parents got divorced. "My love," her mom said as she gave Leanne a little hug, "Dad is not coming to live with us again, but you will still see him often. Especially on some holidays and maybe even on your birthdays."

Leanne started crying. "But who is going to look after us now? Who will protect us?" With this, her mother got up and bent down to give her a hug. "The Lord will look after us as He has promised," she said.

"Where has He promised that?" Cameron asked with sudden interest. "Go and fetch your Bible, then I'll show you," his mom said. When Cameron brought his Bible, his mom turned to Psalm 91. "Read a few verses aloud to us so that Leanne can also hear," she said to Cameron. He read the whole Psalm. He especially liked verses 14 and 15, and read them again: *"Because he loves Me, I will rescue him. I will protect him, for he acknowledges My name. He will call upon Me, and I will answer him; I will be with him in trouble, I will deliver him and honor him."*

"This psalm and many other promises in the Bible are meant for us," his mom said. "Because we trust in the Lord, we need never be anxious."

What a relief! Leanne thought. *Even if people disappoint us, our Heavenly Father will never do that.*

Thank the Lord if you belong to a happy family and pray for your friends whose parents are divorced. Think what you can do to make the tough times easier for them.

He is my refuge and my fortress, my God, in whom I trust." Ps. 91:2

JULY 10

ONE DAY

Richard's dad had taken him to a career expo. Each career option looked more exciting than the one before. "It will be hard to choose what I want to do one day!" Richard said afterwards. "I think I would like to become an electrical engineer. It looks as though the world is your oyster if you've got brains and are willing to work hard." His father listened with interest. "I could be a millionaire before I turn thirty!" Richard continued enthusiastically. "I'll drive a smart car and you will be proud of me!"

But then Richard noticed that his dad did not look as happy about his plans as he had thought he would. "Is something wrong?" he asked his dad. "Well, I think you know very well where your good brains come from. Do you think it's fair to use them only for your own advantage?" Richard frowned. "What about the two most important commandments?" his dad asked. Richard knew them. He heard them every Sunday in church. *"You should love the Lord your God with all your heart and all your mind and all your soul. And the second: Love your neighbor as you love yourself."*

Suddenly he realized that he had never thought about using his brains to honor God. He had also not thought about choosing a career that would make it possible for him to help other people. He had just thought of himself.

Then his dad said, "I will be proud of you when you're a good engineer one day, but I will be even more proud if you not only serve yourself, but the Lord and other people as well."

Look for a picture of someone who is doing
the work that you would like to do one day.
Put it above your desk and write Matthew
22:37-39 below that to remind yourself that the
Lord's children should not only work for themselves.

RUN AND HIDE!

Danny was all ears that morning in church. The sermon was about temptations and Danny was struggling with a big temptation in his life. He would love to have the victory over it! The preacher read Romans 6:13. *"Do not offer the parts of your body to sin, but rather ... offer the parts of your body to him as instruments of righteousness."* Danny's thoughts wandered off. He loved cars. Ever since he was a little boy, his dad had allowed him to hold the steering wheel when they were in the driveway. Now that he was twelve, he could drive quite well. Of course he knew he was only allowed to do it on his grandfather's farm. But he had also taken his mother's car a few times and gone for a drive when his parents weren't home.

He knew quite well that it was wrong and he realized what devastating consequences could come of it. But each time his parents went out, the devil came to him and said, "This is your chance, Danny!" It felt impossible for him to say NO on such occasions.

But then he heard what the pastor was reading from 1 Corinthians 10:13: *"No temptation has seized you except what is common to man. And God is faithful; he will not let you be tempted beyond what you can bear. But when you are tempted, he will also provide a way out so that you can stand up under it."* He explained, "All of us face temptations. James 4:7 says that we should resist the devil, then he will flee from us. Or do like Joseph did and run away from the temptation yourself."

"Help me, please Lord!" Danny prayed when there was time for silent prayer.

Is there a certain temptation that the devil often tempts you with? What advice would you give to someone who also struggles with the same thing? Ask the Lord to help you to follow this advice yourself.

"God is faithful; he will not let you be tempted beyond what you can bear." 1 Cor. 10:13

JULY 12

AND THEN?

Matt's parents had forbidden him to talk to strangers when he rode the train home from school. But when a friendly man sat down next to him one afternoon, he felt that he could make an exception. The man had a pleasant but serious face. In his hand was a tattered Bible. When he sat down next to Matt and chatted about school and family, Matt answered politely.

Eventually then the man asked, "What are you going to do when you finish school one day?" "I want to go to college," he replied. "Then I can start my own business." "And then?" "Then I'm going to get married, buy my own house and raise children!" He laughed out loud. "I haven't actually thought that far ahead, sir!" he said.

But the man with the serious eyes wanted to know more, "What are you going to do when your children are grown-up and out of the house?" "Probably retire and play golf and travel." "And when you're old?" came the next question. "Then I'll probably sit around and wait to die ... like everybody else does!"

He can't have any more questions now, Matt thought. But the man still had one more ace to play. "And what then?" he asked with a sense of urgency. Matt was a bit taken aback. "I have never thought about death," he admitted. "Can I read you something?" the friendly man asked. He opened his Bible to 1 John 5. He read verses 11 and 12: *"God has given us eternal life, and this life is in his Son. He who has the Son has life; he who does not have the Son of God does not have life."*

The train stopped and it was time for Matt to get off. He said goodbye to his companion, but their conversation kept running through his head. *Thank You that I am Your child, Lord, and that I will live with You eternally when I die one day*, he prayed.

Do you know Jesus as your personal Savior yet? Then you can pray the same payer that Matt did.

"God has given us eternal life, and this life is in his Son." Jn. 5:11

NO TO DRUGS! YES TO JESUS!

Patricia had to prepare a speech on drug abuse for the school debating competition. Over and above the information she got on the Internet and from books in the library, she also spoke to lots of children at her school. She was surprised to find out how many of them had already experimented with drugs.

"Why do you do it?" she asked each one. "It makes me feel good!" one of the boys said. "It's cool, that's all!" another answered with a laugh. "I do it to forget about all the hurt and terrible things in my life," one girl admitted. "But I must say, once it has worn off, I feel terrible all over again."

After she had read and heard how quickly drugs could get a hold on people and how many young people's lives were ruined by them, she decided: *No thanks to drugs for me!* In her talk, Patricia referred to articles written by doctors explaining the harm that drugs like ecstasy can do to the brain. And how your liver can get damaged from sniffing glue. And of the effect marijuana has on your lungs.

She ended her talk with these words, "I just want to say to all of my friends who think that drugs can help them to enjoy life: 'You're playing with fire!' There is a better way to handle stress: Say NO TO DRUGS AND SAY YES TO JESUS!" Then she read Jesus' words in Matthew 11:28 to the audience. *"Come to me, all you who are weary and burdened, and I will give you rest."*

Although Patricia didn't win the competition, she was very glad that she participated. She had learned important things and also had a chance to be a witness for Jesus. And it had given her the opportunity to warn her friends against the terrible dangers of drugs.

Read 2 Corinthians 6:16-18.

JULY 14

DO YOU BELIEVE IT?

Lorraine and her cousins were at the seaside for the holidays. Every evening the whole family went walking along the beach, but one night the children were lagging behind. It was so great walking on the sand in the twilight! They didn't feel like going home at all. "OK," Lorraine's mom said. "Stay a bit longer, but make sure that you're back home by ten o'clock."

The children played games on the sand until they were exhausted. They flopped down and started chatting. The evening sunset was enchanting. The waves were breaking on the shores forming shimmering silver stripes. The mountains lay dark and secretive in the distance. "To think that God made all of this out of nothing!" Lorraine said with wonder.

Her cousin Claude burst out laughing. "Do you still believe that?" he asked with surprise. "Most people today know that the story in Genesis is only a fairytale!" "Do you want to argue against things that people have been believing for centuries?" "Oh well, back then, before people knew any better, that was just the way people went about explaining things," Claude said with conviction. For the rest of the evening he expanded on what he believed about the Bible. "You can only believe certain parts of the Bible," were his last words as they reached the beach house.

Lorraine was really quite confused. She asked her mother for a note pad and then sat down cross-legged on her bed. She made a list of all the things she wanted to ask her Sunday school teacher once they got back home. After that, she prayed. "Lord, help me not to doubt that the Bible is the truth. And help me to say the right things when I talk to people who do not believe You."

Do you also sometimes wonder if the Bible is true? Why don't you make a list of the things you have questions about. Then you can ask someone you trust about it. Read John 3:18 to see why it is important that we believe.

Thus the heavens and the earth were completed in all their vast array. Gen. 2:1

A SLY ENEMY

Rob the Seal lived in the Arctic. He would have been without a care in the world if it hadn't been for the devious plans of Ursa the Polar Bear. No other predator was so sly when it came to hunting down his prey! Usually, when Ursa saw a seal, he swam under water, only coming up for air every now and then. He looked exactly like a small iceberg drifting closer. As soon as he was close enough to his prey, he would suddenly rise up from the water and attack it!

At other times he would crawl on his stomach close to the seals' playground, so that no one could see him. Or he would hide behind the heaps of snow close to Rob and the other seals' hideout so that he could catch them when they came out. Rob had to be on his guard against Ursa all the time. But that didn't stop Rob from being a happy seal! As long as he was alert and kept close to the other seals, who could warn him, he could enjoy the snow and have fun on the ice.

We also have an enemy who disguises himself and tries to lure us to do things that are against God's will. The Bible says that he pretends to be an angel of light. This means, for example, that some kinds of entertainment could appear to be quite innocent, but could cause us to drift away from God, our safe haven.

That is why we shouldn't just watch any movie or video. If there are things happening on the screen that are supposedly good and nice, but you know in your heart that it is wrong and ugly, you should know who is behind that story. Satan wants to lure you away from the Lord and you have to be careful. Your whole life does not need to be spoilt by the devil. 1 John 4:4 says that He who is in us is greater than the devil, who is in the world.

Read 1 Peter 5:8-9.

A BAD NAME

"I'm going to have a bad name forever!" Zaida sobbed. She was lying on her bed and crying into the pillow. "And what's even worse," she continued, "is that I've also damaged the family name!"

Her mother stood looking out of the window while listening to her. She said nothing. She was still very shocked about what had happened. Zaida had been caught together with a group of friends, smoking marijuana. Her mother knew that it would be a long time before Zaida's name would be cleared. She could also not help thinking what their friends would say when they heard the news. Gossip travels fast in a small town like theirs.

Eventually she spoke, "That your name and the family name have been blackened is not the most important issue here. The sad thing is that we've done a great dishonor to the Lord's name. Everybody knows you're a Christian and people who are not believers will now be quick to say, 'Just look at what the Christians do. Then they have the nerve to preach to us!' Let's first take this matter to the Lord and then we can ask Him to restore our name again."

Together Zaida and her mom read Psalm 51. This is the Psalm David wrote after he had sinned greatly and had dragged his own name through the mud.

Then Zaida prayed, "Lord, I'm sorry that I was stupid enough to do wrong things with my friends. I don't mind if the principal and my parents punish me, Lord! I deserve it! But please forgive me and help me to restore my good name again. I want to be a shining star for You! Amen."

When her mother put her arms around her, it felt to Zaida as if God's grace enfolded her.

Read Luke 7:36-50 and find out how a sinful woman started to improve her reputation.

A good name is more desirable than great riches. Prov. 22:1

Your word is a lamp to my feet and a light for my path. Ps. 119:105

WHY DO WE NEED TO READ THE BIBLE?

The Sunday school class was eager to participate in Miss Hall's competition. She had promised a prize to the person who could come up with the best reason why we should read the Bible. However, some of the reasons didn't make the grade! "It helps you learn new words" and "It could help you win a general knowledge quiz" just didn't make it.

But the children gave lots of good reasons and one Sunday morning they all shared their ideas in class. Some children said that the Bible is like a letter the Lord has written to us and that is why we should read it. Others said that it is a weapon with which to fight against Satan. Heather said that the Bible comforted her when she was sad and her twin sister Suzy said exactly the same. "Did you copy each other's ideas?" Miss Hall asked. "No!" Susan said. "Grandpa died last week and Mom read us some comforting verses from the Bible."

"The Bible tells us what is going to happen when we die!" Olivia read her answer out. "And why is that a good thing?" Miss Hill asked. "Then you can prepare yourself," Olivia answered. "That's why I said that we should read the Bible so that we know how we can be saved," Gerald, the pastor's son, said. "I also said that the Bible shows us what our purpose in life is." "And what is that?" Mario asked. "To do good deeds. That's what it says in Ephesians 2:10." "I'm sure your dad helped you!" Jeanette piped in.

"I read my Bible because I learn from it how much God loves me," Cathy said. Miss Hall liked all these answers. "You all gave good answers," she said and gave each one a chocolate bar to which she had attached a card with a Bible verse on it. As they were leaving, she said, "Now go and use your Bible: it's a real treasure chest."

**Read 2 Timothy 3:16, the verse
that Miss Hall wrote on the cards.**

July 18

Who Pulled the Trigger?

Three teachers lived all alone in a house on a mission station in Zimbabwe. They lived there and taught the children from the village, even though there were many terrorists in the area. Two of the women slept in the house at night and the third one had a room on the enclosed porch. One night, while they were all sleeping, some terrorists came into the house. They dragged the two women who were in the house outside, but didn't know about the woman in the porch room. She peeped through the window and saw that her friends were taken into the bushes. She fell on her knees and asked God to protect her friends.

In the meantime the terrorists forced the two women through the bushes toward a nearby mountain. The women were also praying as they walked along. "O Lord, please help us!" they asked. Suddenly the group stood still. A shot had been fired from somewhere! The terrorists dropped everything and ran. They left their captives just there. In the pitch-dark night the two women walked back to the mission station.

Back in the village, people had started looking for them. They were immensely relieved when they returned safely! But nobody could determine who had fired the shot that made the terrorists flee. Neither the woman who stayed behind nor the people from the town had done it. The Lord must have caused a sound like gunshot when His children cried to Him for help!

That evening one of the women read Job 42:5 with tears of gratitude: *"My ears had heard of you but now my eyes have seen you!"*

Do you find this story hard to believe?
Read what Mark 10:27 says.

AT THE GRAVE

Phil. 1:21

For to me, to live is Christ and to die is gain.

Kylie and her mother had gone to put flowers on her grandfather's grave. It was quiet and peaceful in the graveyard. All that could be heard were the pigeons in the cypress trees and the bees that buzzed from flower to flower.

"Mom, I'm afraid to die!" Kylie suddenly exclaimed. She looked at the hard granite stones on the graves and all the small pebbles that now covered the place where Grandpa's coffin had been lowered into the earth. She shuddered as she thought about the dark hole in the ground.

Mom put her arms around Kylie's shoulders. "It's natural that you would feel that way," she said. "Right at the beginning people weren't made to die. The Lord made Adam and Eve to live with Him forever in Paradise. But then they sinned, and death came into the world. That is why death still feels wrong and unnatural for us."

"But you can now look at death in a different way," her mom continued. She took a small twig and let one of the bees climb onto it. "Do you see this bee? Do you see its sting?" Kylie stepped backwards. She wasn't keen to be stung by a bee. "If I take out the sting, would you still be afraid of the bee?" her mother asked. "No ways!" she laughed.

"Paul said that he wasn't afraid of death, because its sting had been removed. When Jesus rose from the dead, everything changed. God's children now know that they will live even though they die physically. We all tend to be afraid of the unknown. But at the other side of the grave is Someone whom we know well. He is waiting for us with open arms. That is why Grandpa's gravestone reads, *"For to me, to live is Christ and to die is gain"* Philippians 1:21.

**Draw a bee and write 1 Corinthians 15:55
next to it. Keep it in your Bible.**

JuLy 20

LEARNING AS YOU PLAY

Dale came home from youth with a big smile on his face. "To-day Shaun let us play a game until we were tired out!" he said. "Didn't you have a lesson at all?" his sister asked, surprised. Shaun was the youth leader and he wouldn't let a meeting pass without sharing something about Jesus. "Yes, we did learn a few things, but through the game." "Tell us more!" said his younger brother, Fred.

"We played 'Simon says'. Shaun stood in front of us and he gave all kinds of instructions. But we only had to do the ones when he said 'Simon says.' If Shaun said, 'Put your hands on your head' and you did, then you were out." "Why?" his brother asked. "Because Shaun didn't add 'Simon says'. But if he said, 'Simon says, sit down' and you didn't sit down, then you were also out. The last person still in was the winner." "Stupid game!" his sister said. "Is not!" Dale retorted. "We learned three things from it: We have to listen carefully, we have to distinguish clearly and we have to obey! Exactly what the Lord expects from us as well!"

"Where do you find that in the Bible?" his sister asked. Dale felt quite proud that he could answer that question himself. "In John 10. There it says we should listen to our Shepherd, we should distinguish between His voice and the voice of strangers, and that we should obey and follow Him."

"What does that mean?" Fred asked. "That means that if Mom reads from the Bible, you should listen and not kick the cat, and when naughty Nick wants you to do something bad, then you must say NO. It also means that you must go and do your homework now, because if you listen to Mom and Dad, then you're also doing what the Lord says." Fred went to his room thinking, *I can't wait to join Youth group next year.*

Read John 10:1-5.

JuLy 21

DISCONTENT

Dina was at boarding school because her parents were missionaries in Madagascar. The school on the mission station where they lived only went up to the fourth grade. Each Sunday afternoon after lunch, the children at the boarding school had to write a letter to their parents. On Friday, when they received their mail at lunchtime, there was usually a letter from Dina's parents.

One Sunday Dina decided to pour out her heart and tell her parents all the things that were bothering her. She wrote:

Dear Mom and Dad, I miss you and am also unhappy because I don't have nice clothes like the other children have. I hate living with three other girls in a small room and the food is horrible. Please write soon. Love, Dina.

Dina knew that she wouldn't get an answer as soon as the Friday of that week, but when she opened her weekly letter from her parents, she found a picture of some of the children at the mission station with it. Dina looked at their tattered clothes and blushed. They were standing in front of their hut made from mud and Dina remembered that a whole family including the grandparents and an aunt lived there. She also knew that they only had porridge to eat every day. She wished she hadn't complained about her old clothes, the bad food, and small room in Sunday's letter!

The following Sunday she wrote:

*Mom and Dad, you don't need to reply to my complaints of last week. I found an answer in the Bible myself. In Hebrew 13:5 the Lord says, **"Be content with what you have."** And I now also say, like Paul did in Philippians 4:11, "I have learned to be content, whatever the circumstances." I've made a list of everything I can be thankful for and the paper had too few lines! Love you! Dina.*

**Why don't you also make a list of
all the things you can thank God for?**

July 22

WHAT IS GOD LIKE?

The Top Teens had an all-night social at the church. They first made sandwiches and played games in the church hall. Then they sang songs until almost midnight. After that, the youth leader showed them a video about the amazing wonders of creation. The kids had brought pillows and blankets and some of them fell asleep while the video was running. But after that, when everybody fried marshmallows over candles, they were wide awake again.

After a mug of hot chocolate, everybody was ready for a serious discussion about Biblical matters. "What is God like?" William, the youth leader, asked. "Strict!" said one of the boys. "Why do you say that?" a girl asked. "He doesn't let sin go unpunished. That's what the Bible say. He is like your father who punishes you if you've done something wrong." "That's only half the truth," William replied. "He doesn't leave sin unpunished. That is why He punished Jesus for our sins. But if we accept the grace Jesus earned for us, we don't get punished!"

"God is not like my dad!" Dinky said. "My dad gives me everything I want, but God doesn't." "He is better than any dad," said one of the girls whose parents were divorced. Theo started playing softly on his guitar and the kids joined in singing. *"Father, we love You, we worship and adore You!"*

Then William handed out pieces of paper on which Scripture verses were written. Each child got the opportunity to read a verse from his or her Bible. As the birds started singing their morning chorus, the children were still busy underlining the verses in their Bible that describe how wonderful our God is.

**Look up these verses about God: Genesis 16:13;
2 Chronicles 30:9; 1 John 1:5; Revelation 4:8.**

INNOVATORS FOR GOD

Roger and Margie Upson were missionaries in Nigeria. Not only did they tell people about the Lord, but they also helped them in many different ways. They had a clever way to show the people who lived there that they really cared.

They saw that the women who live there used a lot of wood to make fires to cook their food. They had to walk long distances every day to gather all the wood they needed to cook rice and sweet potatoes. But eventually there were fewer and fewer trees in the area, and it started raining less and less. When it did rain, there was a lot of water erosion because there weren't tree roots to anchor the soil anymore.

What could the Upsons do to protect the environment and help the people? There wasn't enough money to buy gas or paraffin for stoves. Then they prayed for a solution – and guess what a clever plan the Lord gave them!

They took a calabash (a dried hollow pumpkin) and covered the inside with tin foil so that the inside of the calabash would be shiny and reflect the sun. Then they painted the calabash black on the outside and took a piece of glass big enough to cover the opening. A pot of food could be put inside the calabash in the morning, covered with glass, and placed outside in the sun. By lunchtime the cooked food was ready to eat. Now nobody needed to go and look for wood and cut down trees to cook their meals anymore.

The women were thrilled with their solar energy cookers. Suddenly they were also more interested in Roger and Margie's message from God.

Don't you think that God is very happy when we help other people and make plans to protect nature, like the Upsons did?

**Read Joel 2:21-27 to find out
how God feels about nature.**

JULY 24

LONELY?

Laura went straight to her room when she came home. She lay down on her bed feeling terribly lonely. Before she had decided to follow Jesus, she had had many more friends than she did now! Today was especially bad. They had to present speeches about different cultures in their social studies class, and Irene, a new girl whose family had emigrated from Greece, wore her country's traditional clothes. Irene looked beautiful but the kids made fun of her. She went home after the first lesson. Laura was very upset. "Shame on you!" she exploded. "I didn't think you would stoop this low and hurt someone's feelings like that!"

Then everybody was even more horrible to her. "Shame, we didn't know there was someone here from the SPCA!" they mocked. "Seems like there's someone here to defend the poor lame puppies!" Although she knew that she had done the right thing, Laura felt very lonely. Almost like Elijah, she thought. She remembered the lesson they had read about Elijah and the broom tree a few weeks ago in Sunday school. She took her Bible and turned to the story in 1 Kings 19. Elijah also thought that he was all alone, but then the Lord showed him that He Himself was with him and that there were many other people who also served God in Israel.

Then Laura remembered that there were some children who hadn't mocked Irene. One of the girls even squeezed her arm supportively when the others were so mean. It was probably her way of showing that she thought she had done the right thing.

"I must make more of an effort to make friends with the kids in class who aren't mean," she thought. "And I also need to spend more time with Irene. Just think how lonely she must feel today."

Think of something you can do to support someone who is always alone.

Turn to me and be gracious to me, for I am lonely and afflicted. Ps. 25:16

AFRAID?

Harold once belonged to a gang that used drugs and sometimes even robbed shops. But then he attended a tent meeting in their neighborhood and gave his heart to Jesus. He knew from the start that it wouldn't be easy to break with the gang, but he had no idea how they would harass him. They threatened him saying that they would chase him and beat him up because he had quit. Every day he went to school with fear in his heart.

Cathy lived in a neighborhood where it was dangerous to be out on the streets in the evenings. There was so much crime and violence that the whole family had to stay indoors after dark. But some nights her mother had to work late shifts. Then Cathy would be riveted by fear: what if her mother was attacked along the way?

Henry's father was a fisherman. He went out early in the mornings and only got home very late. One day a storm was brewing and the waves of the sea were as big as houses. Everybody wondered how the fisherman's boat would get home safe in such bad weather. Henry waited anxiously with his mother on the shore.

Maybe you don't know anxiety like that which gripped Harold, Cathy, and Henry. But there probably are things that scare you and make you feel afraid. What do you do then: do you panic or pray?

Let's look at Psalm 71 to see what one man did when he was anxious. He called to God in his moment of fear and praised God for the times when He had helped him in the past. He also made a resolution to tell others every time God helped him. In the end he could say, *"You have done great things, O God!"*

**Which words from Psalm 71 do you
like best? Go and learn them by heart.**

JULY 26

HOW GOD USED A DOG

There was a program on TV about a psychologist who worked on a hospital ward with children who had cancer. The medicine and treatment that these children received often made them feel nauseous and weak. Sometimes the treatment would make them lose all their hair. What made things even worse was the fact that they often had to watch how their little friends in the same ward did not recover. Of course, this was very distressing to them. Jenny did all she could to make their stay in hospital as pleasant as possible.

Because Jenny loved animals, she went to the SPCA and chose a puppy that had been abandoned by its owners. Terry was a lovable little dog with big brown eyes. Jenny started taking him with on her hospital rounds. Right from the start, Terry's visits delighted the little patients, and they loved him more and more each day. They cuddled him, played with him, and sometimes even dressed him up in their own clothes. Even when a child was feeling very ill, he or she could still manage to smile when Terry pranced into the room.

But then something terrible happened! Terry became seriously ill and the vet said he had ... cancer! Can you believe it! The dog that meant so much to the little sick children was now sick himself! Jenny cared for him. She had him operated on and also took him for radiation therapy. Eventually the day arrived when Terry could once again walk into the children's ward at the hospital. What joy! The kids looked at the dog with new eyes. Because Terry had had the same sickness as they had, he could mean even more to them. He gave them hope that they could perhaps also recover from cancer.

It is so often the case that people who have themselves suffered, can give hope to others who are in trouble.

There is a verse in the Bible that says the very same thing. Read it for yourself: 2 Corinthians 1:3-4.

My mouth would encourage you; comfort from my lips would bring you relief. Job 16:5

WHY IS GOD SO GOOD TO US?

Esther and Rona listened to the sounds of the night outside their tent. They were thinking about all the things that they had seen over the last few days. Some college students had wanted to go on a mission outreach, and had asked the girls' parents to be the team leaders. That is why they had also made the journey from Pretoria in South Africa to Morgenster in Zimbabwe.

On this mission station, they had seen things that they had previously only heard about. They saw people so thin and weak from lack of food that they could hardly stand upright; children who were so hungry that they ate scraps of food and bark off trees; twelve-year-olds who had to look after their younger brothers and sisters because both their parents had died; AIDS-patients lying hopelessly in bed, waiting to die. And there were thousands who knew nothing about God!

"Why do you think God is so good to us?" Esther asked. "We have parents who care for us, we have never been really hungry, and we have heard about the Living God from the time we were babies." "That's true," Rona said. "I feel like falling down on my knees and praising God for all our privileges."

Esther replied, "Well, this team of students has shown us one very practical way in which we can say thank You to God. Today one of them in the soup kitchen said something that really made me think. He said, 'We are blessed so that we can be a blessing!'" "It's such a shame that so many people do nothing to show their gratitude toward God, who has invested so much in their lives!" Rona responded. "From now on I'll make sure that I'm not one of those." "Hit me if I ever complain again!" Esther said seriously before she turned over in her sleeping bag to doze off into a restless sleep.

Read Psalm 65 and make a list of everything for which you can thank God. Think of ways in which you can show your gratitude.

WORSHIP IN THE OUTDOORS

Henry deeply admired his grandfather. Grandpa was one of those people who made it easier for others to believe in God. He went to church every Sunday and Henry often wondered whether that was the secret of his meaningful life. He remembered how his grandpa had looked for a church even when they were on holiday in a strange place. He loved gathering together with other members of God's family. When Henry gave his heart to the Lord, he decided that he would follow his grandfather's example and never miss a service on Sundays.

But one weekend Henry and some of friends went hiking in the Porterville Mountains. There wasn't a building in sight, let alone a church! But when Henry woke up on Sunday morning he really wanted to worship God. He found a rock a little way away from the campsite and waited with his Bible as the dawn broke.

Soon the sky above the mountains became purple and orange with morning light. He opened his Bible and began to read. He stopped at Psalm 5:3 and read, *"In the morning, O Lord, you hear my voice; in the morning I lay my requests before you and wait in expectation."*

Birds began to sing all around him and an eagle flew gracefully from a high cliff. Henry felt as if he could sing a hymn of praise together with the birds and, in his mind's eye, climb up to the throne of God high above the earth. He continued to read the rest of the psalm and then thanked God for the worship service that he could attend outdoors. The steep mountainsides were the church walls, the birds' song was the choir and the rock on which he sat, was the pew in this magnificent cathedral. The Holy Spirit brought the message straight from the Bible to his heart.

If you happen to be far from a church one Sunday, try to meet up with God outdoors, like Henry did.

All you have made will praise you, O Lord; your saints will extol you. Ps. 145:10

BUILD ON THE ROCK

Every Christmas, Mrs. Dorian put a beautiful wreath on her front door. One year she made a wreath of raffia and red ribbons. Early one morning, she heard a strange noise at the front door. She opened the door, but no one was there. But later that day she discovered who the visitor had been: a tiny bird had started to build a nest in her Christmas wreath!

All her neighbors regularly came by to see how the little bird was getting on with building its nest. And when the bird laid her eggs in the nest, everyone in town was very excited. People came from far and wide to see this amazing sight: a neat little nest in the curve of the Christmas wreath with the red ribbon weaved through it. And on a bed of soft down were four little eggs.

Mrs. Dorian was concerned that something would happen to disturb the nest, so she put up a sign: PLEASE USE THE BACK ENTRANCE A few days before Christmas the birds were born. What a joy! The local newspaper took a color photo of this unique Christmas decoration and used it on the cover of their Christmas edition. This wonderful picture caused a warm glow in many people's hearts.

The little mommy bird had chosen a good place to build her nest. It was sheltered from the wind and the weather and her landlady guarded her as if she herself was the grandmother of the little birds.

The Bible teaches us to build our house on a rock and not on sand. That means that we must be careful how we organize our lives. We must stay within the boundaries of God's loving commandments. Then He can protect us from danger and evil and people will be attracted by our lifestyle. In that way, we can bring glory to the Lord.

**Read Jesus' advice on the selection
of a building site in Matthew 7:24-26.**

HALLELUJA!

You have probably heard the Hallelujah chorus from *The Messiah* by Handel. Maybe your church choir has sung it or your parents might have it on CD. Here is the story behind this famous piece of choral music.

George Frederick Handel was a composer who lived in Germany many years ago. Even as a child he loved music, and all his toys were musical instruments like trumpets flutes and drums. One day his father went into his room and was furious. "Why are there only musical instruments in this room?" he shouted. "Where are the books? I want my son to be a learned man one day, not a musician!" And with these words he threw all the musical toys into the fireplace.

The young George was very sad. He missed his music. The only delight in his week was on Sundays when his aunt took him to church. There he could listen to the beautiful sounds of the organ and the singing. He often looked at the organist and thought: *One day I'll sit there and then I'll make music for God.*

After his father's death, Handel went to Hamburg to study music. He became the conductor of a big orchestra and he also became famous as a composer. But he never lost sight of his dream to make music for the Lord. One day he began to compose music about the life of Jesus. He called the work *The Messiah.* He worked on the piece of music for 24 days, hardly taking any breaks at all. His candle burned right through the night and he ate very little. One morning he called his servant to his study. Tears were running down his cheeks when he said, "I've seen the open gates of heaven, and have heard the angels sing Hallelujah in a choir!"

When you hear that chorus again, listen with your whole heart, and think about the little boy whose dreams came true all because he wanted to use his talent for the glory of God.

Read Psalm 150.

Let everything that has breath praise the Lord. Praise the Lord. Ps. 150:6

SCARED TO DIE

Pastor Wong Ming admitted that he had always been scared of dying. Even as a child he often couldn't sleep at night because he was sacred to die. Finally, he decided to ask his uncle, for whom he had great respect, whether there was a way in which he could escape death.

His uncle gave him some discouraging news. "If you could get away from the hustle and bustle of everyday life and go and live in the mountains in a cave, there is a chance you could live forever. But you will have to forfeit all earthly pleasure and friendships. You will have to drink the dew on the grass and eat mushrooms from the soil. Then you might become immortal."

"Take me to the mountains! I want to try it!" Wong Ming pleaded. But his uncle always had a reason why he could not take him there. Later, when he was a student, Wong Ming read about two kings, Chin-Shih and Han-Wu, who spent their whole lives searching for a way to escape death. They had tried everything, but in the end they had died and were buried, just like everybody else.

What hope is there for me, an ordinary man? he wondered. But then somebody told him about Jesus, who said, "I am the resurrection and the life. He who believes in me, will live, even though he dies" (Jn. 11:25).

Wong Ming received the Lord Jesus as his personal Savior and he became a pastor. He wanted to tell the good news about Jesus and everlasting life to as many people as possible.

**This verse is worth learning
by heart, don't you think so?**

August

MOTH-EATEN

Wanda's aunt had given her a beautiful blue jersey. When summer came, she put it in a suitcase under her bed. As soon as the first chilly winds of winter blew, she opened the suitcase. But oh dear! When she put on the jersey, she saw that it had tiny holes all over it. "The fish moths must have done that," her mom said. She tried to mend the jersey, but it didn't help! The jersey would never be the same again. Wanda felt like crying, even though her mom promised to buy her a new jersey in its place.

That afternoon Wanda tuned in to a Christian Radio broadcast while she was packing away her summer clothes. A woman was talking about bad habits. "Swearing and being nasty and telling lies can become bad habits," she said. "We must fight against them, otherwise our character will become moth-eaten." Wanda thought about her moth-eaten jersey, and tried to picture the same thing happening to her. She shuddered to think that a hole could appear in her character every time she used bad language or told a lie.

Lately she had been acquiring quite a few bad habits. She listened carefully while the woman gave advice on the matter. "We can ask Jesus to forgive us and we can ask Him to help us to cultivate better habits," she said. The lady then read Colossians 3:8-9: *"But now you must rid yourselves of all such things as these: anger, rage, malice, slander, and filthy language from your lips. Do not lie to each other, since you have taken off your old self with its practices."*

"Lord Jesus," Wanda prayed. "Help me to live like a new person. I know that it would stop Satan from vandalizing my character." And she put some extra mothballs in between her clothing.

Read Colossians 3:8-17.

AuGuSt 2

UNWELCOME VISITOR

Two sisters, Nazimango and Anesi, lived in a mud house with a thatched roof in Malawi. They had a goat and a few chickens, which they took with them into the hut at night, to protect them from the lions and leopards that lurked in the bushes nearby. They had no other relatives and even though they did not know anything about Jesus, their lives were fairly peaceful.

But then one night a hungry lion came prowling around their hut. He could smell that there were people and animals inside. He could not find a way to get into the hut, though. You see, the door of the hut was securely locked and their house had no windows. The two women could hear how the lion growled in the dark outside. They were very scared. Then the lion retreated. But it was only so that he could have enough space to gather speed so that he could jump onto the hut. He landed on the roof with a thud and started to dig a hole in the dried grass with his huge paws. With a loud thump, he fell into the room, covered with sticks and mud and dry grass. The women screamed, the chickens cackled and the goat ran about wildly.

One of the neighbors heard the noise and came to their rescue. He chased the lion away, but Nazimango had been hurt. Their friends made a stretcher out of two poles and they took her to the mission hospital at Nkoma. Anesi went with them to help.

All the doctors and nurses at the hospital were Christians. They told the two sisters about God and how Jesus came to save us. Before Nazimango was well enough to go home, she accepted Jesus as her Savior. When they were on their way back to their home, Anesi said, "It was a good thing that the lion visited our home that night. Otherwise we would never have heard the good news about Jesus!"

Pray for the doctors and nurses at mission hospitals. Pray that the patients who are treated there will all learn to love and obey God. Read Psalm 22:27-28.

DEAR DIARY

Dear Diary, when Karl took that balloon today and blew it until it burst, I thought: *that's exactly how I feel!* There's so much stress in my life that I feel like I'm going to burst. I can't keep up with my schoolwork, but that's not what's upsetting me so much. The thing that worries me most is Mom and Dad's fighting. They are forever at each other and it hurts me so much. There's a knotted-up feeling in my tummy that never goes away. Because of that, I lose my temper with Karl all the time and I'm also unkind to everyone. Even Snoopy suffers because of my grumpiness. Maybe my parents would fight less if we had more money. But there never seems to be enough money for all the bills that keep streaming in.

Sometimes I feel like running away and hanging out with the bad guys at school. But I realize that I'll regret that sort of thing afterwards. It helps to write down these feelings, but I wish I had somebody to talk to!

This is what Hannah wrote in her diary one night. Have you ever felt like this? Maybe you also have to cope with circumstances that make you feel like a balloon that's about to burst. It was a good idea for Hannah to write down her feelings in a diary. Maybe you can try the same. But sometimes it's best to talk to someone when you are very tense. Is there a friend or a grownup with whom you could share your thoughts?

But remember, your best Friend in any situation is Jesus. Talk to Him each day. It's not only a good habit, but it will help you to handle heavy and stressful burdens. Listen to what the Bible says in 1 Peter 5:7: *"Cast all your anxiety on him, because he cares for you."*

When you are feeling stressed, remember this verse, and do what it says. Perhaps you could give this verse to someone else who is feeling stressed out.

IMPOSSIBLE?

"This is impossible!" Phil said when he got home and started unpacking his books. He stared at the pile of new books he had been given that day. "I will never be able to catch up on all this!" Phil and his family had moved to a new school district, and his new school seemed to be doing completely different work from what he had been doing. His mom was busy preparing supper. She felt sorry for him. She was also finding it hard to adjust to their new neighborhood. She had started a part-time job, but everything at work was strange and different.

She looked through a pile of recipe books. "Somewhere among these books there is something from Grandma that we both need now," she said. Phil was hoping it was a pancake recipe.

"Aha, here it is!" his mom said. "This is a bit of information that Granny once wrote down for me when I was going through difficulties that seemed insurmountable." His mom read:

"It is a well-known fact that the bumblebee cannot fly. This can be proven on paper and in a wind tunnel. Its wings are too short for its body. Experts have come to this conclusion after careful, intricate calculations: an insect with the proportions of the bumblebee will never be able to fly. It is an impossibility. But of course, the bumblebee knows nothing about all these experiments and research. So it just carries on with its work. In spite of all the projections of educated scientists, and to everybody's amazement, it is flying about with glee!"

"Is that true?" Phil asked. "Yes!" his mom said. "And you must remember that, although things might look impossible, with God's help the most improbable thing can come to pass!" "You mean that I can even get through seventh grade this year?" Phil asked. "Of course you can!" his mom replied, and gave him a high five.

**Read Luke 1:26-38 to see what
improbable thing an angel once told Mary.**

Jesus looked at them and said, ... "All things are possible with God." Mk. 10:27

THE PIT

The following story was told at the funeral of a well-known preacher from Cape Town. The Lord used him during his lifetime to bring the message of God's love to thousands of people throughout South Africa. He recorded the following incident in his diary: "Last week I was preaching in a small building near the outskirts of Cape Town. In my sermon, I mentioned the consequences of bad habits and I said that sin could be like a deep pit into which one could easily fall.

"It was when I mentioned the pit that a little five-year old girl jumped up and started walking toward me. She held out her hand and I could see it was wrapped in a huge bandage. 'Look, Sir,' she said. 'Look what happened when I fell into a pit!' I was standing at a little table and for a second I thought of sending her back to her mom, who was rather embarrassed by her bold performance. But suddenly I got an idea, most probably from Above! I picked her up and sat her on the table next to me. Then we entered into a conversation.

'Where was this pit?' 'Near the dam on the farm.' 'Didn't Mommy tell you not to play there?' 'Yes, she did!' 'Now, how did the accident happen?' 'I wanted to see what the pit looked like.' 'And then?' 'Then my foot slipped and I fell inside.' 'And then?' 'Then I called for help!' 'And who helped you?' 'My mom ran to me and made a plan to get me out of the pit.' 'Why did she do it?' 'Because she loves me!'

Then the preacher turned to the congregation and asked, "Can anyone give a better illustration of God's saving grace than that."

If you ever get into trouble through your own sinful habits, call on God and He will rescue you because He loves you.

Read what Acts 2:21 says about this.

THE FOX AND THE CAT

A fox and a cat once went for a walk. They realized that there could be some danger lurking along the path they were following. Fox started bragging, "Oh, if any danger crops up, I won't stress about it! I have quite a few plans for dealing with trouble." Cat replied, "I have only one plan, and that is good enough for me!"

Just then they heard the barking of an approaching pack of dogs. The cat jumped into a tree and hid amongst the leaves. "This is my plan," Cat shouted to Fox. "What's yours?" Fox could not decide which of his plans would suit the situation best. While he was still considering what to do, the dogs reached him. The hunters soon came up and killed the fox.

This is an old fable with a clear message for us. We must decide beforehand what we will do in dangerous situations. We should never think that we have lots of options when it comes to sin. There is only one plan of action needed for a Christian: FLEE! We are not strong enough to conquer Satan on our own. We must get alone with Jesus and stay there until the enemy has gone.

Remember this when you are tempted. Write down a code of conduct for yourself. It could say things like: *I will not use swear words. I will not surf the Internet for porn. I won't watch R-rated videos. I will not copy someone else's homework. I will not say mean things about others. I won't smoke, drink, or take drugs.* And if you meet any of these dangers along the way, go for the escape route: start praying!

That is what 2 Timothy 2:22 advises us to do. It says, *"Flee the evil desires of youth, and pursue righteousness, faith, love and peace, along with those who call on the Lord with a pure heart."*

Read the rest of this chapter in 2 Timothy.
It contains some valuable advice.

THE PRECIOUS VASE

When Jacques was in a bad mood, everybody had to stay out of his way. He was furious when his dad said that he would not be allowed to keep a canary in his room. With arms waving wildly, he stormed to his room, and on his way he pushed one of his mother's valuable vases off the Welsh Dresser. She had inherited this beautiful vase from her grandma. Jacques got a fright when it shattered at his feet, but he still rushed to his room and slammed the door.

His dad immediately went to work to try to put the pieces back together again. His mom sat at the kitchen table and cried. After a while she got up, washed her face and went to Jacques' room. "Who's there?" he asked when she knocked. "Its me: Mom!" He seemed relieved when she entered the room. He wanted this episode to pass as soon as possible. His mom spoke softly, "Tell me how you feel when you carry on like you've just done." "I feel like swearing, or breaking something, or hurting somebody." "That's exactly how I felt when you broke my precious vase," his mom confided. "But that's not acceptable behavior. Let's make a list of responses that will be acceptable when we feel furious." She took a pen and paper and started writing while Jacques made suggestions. "We can hit the punching bag, or throw darts at the dart-board, run around the house as fast as we can for as long as we can, or tear up an old newspaper into tiny bits!"

"There's something else we can do," his mom prodded. "Oh, yes," he said. He knew what his mom was going to suggest. "We can pray about it!" he added. His mom nodded and suited the action to the word: "Dear Lord, please forgive us our sins of rage and help Jacques and me to handle our tempers in a way that is pleasing to You. Then we will have no regrets afterwards!"

"Thanks, Mom. And I'm really sorry, Mom!" he said while giving her a hug.

Read Psalm 4:4.

THE MEN IN SHINING GARMENTS

Do you believe in angels? The Bible mentions angels more than 300 times. And there are people even today who say that they have had encounters with angels. We shouldn't say that we do not believe in angels just because we ourselves have never seen any. There are many things that we cannot observe with our eyes, but that doesn't mean that they don't exist!

John Paton was a missionary who worked in the South Sea Islands. One night a gang of unbelievers ambushed the mission station. They threatened to burn down all the buildings. John and his wife were very scared, but they prayed to God for help. And then, suddenly, the shouting mob turned and left the area.

John and the rest of the people on the station sang songs of praise to thank God for their deliverance. But nobody knew why the attackers had changed their minds so suddenly.

A year later many of these people came to John and told him that they wanted to become Christians. Their chief was one of the new converts. While John was asking them about their past experiences, the leader asked John, "Who were the people with the shining garments who protected you on the night when we wanted to burn down the mission station?" Then John knew that God had sent angels to watch over them that night.

So you see, God not only used angels ages ago when he protected Daniel against the lions and helped Peter to get out of prison. He still assigns angels to go out and protect His children. That's why Hebrews 1:14 says, *"Are not all angels ministering spirits sent to serve those who inherit salvation?"*

You can read more about angels in Psalm 91:11.

For he will command his angels ... to guard you in all your ways. Ps. 91:11

DO YOU BREAK OR BUILD?

Something was wrong at Radikids. At first, the group had consisted of children from the church who really wanted to serve God flat-out. But after a while they began to lose their enthusiasm for the projects they were involved in. Jim, their leader, decided to do something about it. One night, when the kids arrived at their den, he handed each one a sheet of paper. He asked them to pin the paper onto each other's shirts. He gave them some markers and told them to write words of appreciation on their friends' backs. They could write down anything that they liked about the person involved. Then they unpinned the pieces of paper and read what their friends had said.

A lot of kids were surprised to find how much the others really liked them. Jim encouraged the group to build into each other's lives instead of criticizing one another. He then gave the kids a chance to thank God for all the good characteristics that He had built into their characters.

Many years later, the Radikids decided to have a reunion. After a delicious barbecue they shared some memories of the days when they had attended Radikids meetings. One guy took a tattered piece of paper from his jeans pocket. It was the sheet of paper that had been pinned onto his shirt on the night when Jim talked to them about the importance of encouragement. "My friends, there was a time in my life when I felt like a total failure," he said. "Then you guys wrote kind words on my back." He read off the sheet in his hands: "You are a hard worker." "You are honest." "You know your Bible." Those words meant so much to me that I decided that I would not disappoint you. It has been an inspiration ever since." Then many of the others joined in and said how much that evening had meant to them.

Are you building into your friends' lives?

**Read what Proverbs 12:18 has
to say about encouraging words.**

AUGUST 10

TONGSTON

Do you like Bible stories? Did you know that some children never hear Bible stories? What kind of stories do their parents tell them? Here is one story that is told to children who grow up in Buddhist homes.

Once upon a time there was a shoemaker. His name was Tongston. He was very lonely because his wife and son had both died. A monk, who had come to have his sandal fixed, asked him why he looked so sad. Tongston told the monk what had happened. "Now I have nothing to live for!" he said. "You need to strive to reach Nirvana," the monk said. "Do not think about your own sorrow or happiness any longer. Then you will one day reach the state of Nirvana where you won't feel anything at all."

From then on Tongston tried to put aside his feelings. He was hoping that he would one day vanish into the nothingness that is Nirvana.

What would we as Christians have told Tongston? We could tell him, "Tongston, there's nothing wrong with being sad. But there is a God in heaven who wants to help you in your grief. He sent His Son Jesus to earth so that people who are heartbroken can be comforted. He died on a cross because He wanted to take people's grief on His shoulders. If you believe that He died for your sins, you will one day live with Him in heaven. There will be no more tears, only lots of joy!"

That would have been good news for Tongston, don't you think? Then we could have given him a Bible so that he could read about the Lord. He could ask God to forgive his sins and to make him into a new person. Then he would have had something to live for: he would have wanted to tell everybody about heaven and about how to get there.

Read Revelation 21:1-26. It tells us
what heaven will be like one day.

THE SANDWICHES

When Sandy got home, Maureen saw that she had been crying. Maureen knew that her sister would go outside to practice basketball until she began to feel better. *What could be the matter?* Maureen wondered. Two hours earlier, her sister had left the house in such a good mood. One of her friends had been selected for the district basketball team and their coach had organized a surprise party. Each of the team members had to take a plate of eats, and Sandy had made some scrumptious rainbow sandwiches. She bought everything she needed with her own money, and made them herself. She arranged them on a platter with small tomatoes and lettuce. It really looked delicious!

Maureen went outside to where Sandy was bashing the ball against the garage door. "How was the party?" "Fine," Sandy muttered. Silence followed. They both knew that it was a lie. Maureen waited, Sandy would soon tell the real story.

"There was so much cream cake and other delicacies that no one even glanced at my sandwiches!" she said after a while, and came to sit next to Maureen. "And then Dorothy's mom threw them in the trash can," she said with tears in her eyes. "I know how you feel," Maureen said. "Have you ever made something that someone threw away?" Sandy asked curiously. "No, but last week I worked every lunchtime on a project for my boss, and she thinks it was successful because of what someone else did. She just ignored my contribution." Sandy moved closer to Maureen and put her head on her sister's shoulder. Maureen said, "The Lord said that whatever we do, we should work at it with all our heart, as working for the Lord, not for men. So if we have done something and He thinks it's excellent, then it is excellent!"

She grabbed the ball and aimed at the ring against the wall. It went through perfectly. "Well done!" Sandy shouted and jumped up to join in the fun.

Read Colossians 3:23-24.

DRAMA IN THE LOCKER ROOM

Freddie gave his heart to Jesus at a youth rally at church. He bought himself a What-Would-Jesus-Do wristband and started reading the Bible seriously, trying to obey all the things Jesus said we should do.

One afternoon he discovered that somebody had broken into his locker. He was distraught because his wallet was missing. His mom had asked him to pay a bill on his way home and now the money was gone! His family couldn't afford to lose so much money. He felt like bashing open all the lockers.

Suddenly his eyes fell on the WWJD-wristband on his arm. *What would Jesus have done in these circumstances?* he wondered. He wrote the following words on a sheet of paper:

To the guy who broke into my locker: Jesus loves you!

He then pasted it on the door of his locker.

That afternoon his mom asked, "Did you pay the account at the grocery store?" "Not yet," he said. That night he prayed fervently, "Lord, please let the person who took the money bring it back again." The next day he went to the locker room after each class, but nothing changed.

What on earth would Jesus have done? he thought again when it was time to go home. But then, just when he went into a toilet cubicle, somebody pushed an envelope through the opening underneath the door: it was his wallet with the money in it! Freddie was so glad that tears ran down his cheeks.

Years later he discovered who had responded to the letter on his locker. A classmate, who had since moved, wrote him a letter: "Dear Freddie, I was the one who stole your money that day. Your message on your locker really touched my heart, and I have become a Christian too. I wanted to let you know this before I take my first communion at church. Your friend, Claude."

Read Jesus' words in Matthew 5:13-16.

THE SABBATH

"Granny says that if we do needlework on a Sunday, it's like poking the needle in God's eye," Anne said as her mom quickly stitched a button onto her brother's shirt. "And what do you think about that?" her mom asked. "I think it's nonsense," she answered. Her mom walked to her desk. She picked up the notebook that she always used during her quiet time. She gave it to Anne. "On page 10 I've written down a few verses from Scripture that talk about the Sabbath," she said. "Read it when you have a chance." That afternoon Anne made herself comfortable in the hammock in the garden and read her mom's notes on *THE SABBATH*.

The verse that struck her most, was Isaiah 58:13: *"If you call the Sabbath a delight and the holy day of the Lord honorable, and if you honor it by not going your own way and not doing as you please ... then you will find joy in the Lord..."* What about Uncle Danny who must work on a Sunday? she wondered. Then her eye caught sight of Jesus' words in her mom's handwriting: *"Luke 14:5: "If one of you has a son or an ox that falls into a well on the Sabbath day, will you not immediately pull him out?"* Maybe the ox is in the well for Uncle Danny, she thought. *He sure needs the job!*

When she discussed the matter with her parents later on, her dad said, "Well, if you have to work on a Sunday, you should put apart some other time especially for the Lord. Remember that He loves us and that He wants us to have a special date with Him regularly." "Yes," added her mom. "When I cannot go and have tea with Grandma on a Wednesday afternoon, I go on another day. I do not put our appointment off completely!"

"Because you don't want to stick a needle in Granny's heart, do you?" Anne said laughingly.

Read Matthew 12:1-8 for more info on this important subject.

AUGUST 14

MURDER!

Liana sat down at the kitchen table and asked, "Mom, what is abortion?" "It is when a mother has her baby removed from her womb before it is born." "Why would anybody do that?" Liana asked. "Some women do not want a baby, or they think that it is not the right time to have one. But what made you think of that?" her mom asked. "I saw a crowd of people marching in the street with posters. They had written ABORTION IS MURDER! Do you agree with them?"

"I believe that a baby is a gift from God and I don't believe that people have the right to decide whether such a baby should live or not. The people who do abortions say that an unborn child is not a person yet. But I don't agree. In Psalm 139 David said that God knew him even before he was born. And babies are perfectly formed long before they are born! God has a plan with each life and people who kill unborn babies will one day have to account for it before God," her mom said with conviction.

"But what about over-population? Our teacher said that soon there won't be enough food or water of fresh air for everybody on this planet." "Of course we should make plans to solve such problems," Liana's mom agreed. "But killing babies is not the answer." "Abortion is not against the law, though," Liana added. "It doesn't matter," said her mom. "We must obey God rather than men. Although we are supposed to obey the people who govern us, if they say that something is right, it doesn't mean that God is pleased with it." Her mom continued, "You were born eleven months after your brother and I'm glad that we didn't discard you. We would have missed a real treasure!" Liana smiled and kissed her mom on both cheeks.

Read Psalm 139:13-16.

WISEGUY PETER

There's an interesting story about an imagined conversation between Peter and the Lord. According to this legend, Peter once made a suggestion to the Lord about improving life on earth. *If people could know beforehand what would happen to them, things would work out so much better,* he thought. *Then they could plan ahead and they would be able to handle crises in a much better way.*

So he told the Lord, "As things are, the poor folks on earth never know what lies ahead of them! You could have given them foreknowledge so that they could be better prepared." "Instead of that, I've given them hope!" The Lord answered. "Hope doesn't help," Peter replied. "Precaution is what they need."

So they planned an experiment. The Lord gave Peter the gift of foreknowledge. Peter was able to see everything that would happen to him one day ahead. He could see exactly what experiences lay in wait for him. And what did Peter see? He saw how he knocked on the door of an inn at night and how a dog rushed out and bit him on the ankle.

All that day, Peter tried to be calm and collected as he strolled along. But he could hardly see the flowers and trees and stones of rare beauty along the way. The whole day had been spoilt for him. Later on he started counting with dread the steps that took him closer and closer to the inn. He was terrified thinking of the vicious dog with the sharp teeth that was going to bite him.

"Lord," he eventually said, "I admit that I was stupid. Please take away the foreknowledge that You've given me, and give me hope instead."

Then the Lord touched his eyes and he walked along happily in the direction of the inn with the song of hope in his heart.

Look up 1 Corinthians 13:13. What three things did Paul count as essential for Christian living? Think about the middle one.

TURN IT OFF!

Donald and Eliza's mom printed out three Bible verses and placed them on top of the television set:

- *"Above all else, guard your heart, for it is the wellspring of life"* Proverbs 4:23
- *"Do not conform any longer to the pattern of this world, but be transformed by the renewing of your mind"* Romans 12:2.
- *"If your right eye causes you to sin, gouge it out and throw it away"* Matthew 5:29.

"Why did you do that?" asked Eliza. Her mom replied, "It is to remind all of us that TV programs can be very harmful." The two kids looked at their mom with questioning eyes. She answered seriously, "Everything that we see or hear fixes itself in our minds. All those things form the basis for who we are and how we conduct ourselves. If we continually watch TV programs where people have no regard for God's laws, then wrong things can start looking right and good things can start looking out of date and boring. And that's exactly what the devil wants."

"What should we do, then?" Eliza wanted to know. "I think the Lord expects us to show which side we're on when offensive programs are broadcast. If you keep watching wrong programs, you vote for the enemy. But if you put off the TV, you show that Jesus is more precious to you than half-an-hour of entertainment that can contaminate your thoughts."

"Don't worry, Mom!" Donald said. "We'll check on each other. And, anyway, I have already made a resolution that I will not watch TV if I have not also spent time studying the Bible. That should help my thought life, don't you think?" " It certainly will!" his mom agreed.

Why don't you make a neat sign to put up near your TV? You can write something like VOTE FOR A HEALTHY MIND on it.

I will set before my eyes no vile thing. Ps. 101:3

GOALS

Pete was scared. His dad had opened his school report, but hadn't said a word. *Tonight after supper I'll hear all about it!* he thought. He knew that he hadn't done well in Math. Once the dishes had been stacked in the dishwasher, his dad called him. He was just about to watch his favorite TV program, but he turned around straight away and went to his dad. His dad opened the report and said, "I see that you did well in Social Studies and English." "Yes, thanks dad," he said. "And your other subjects are OK," his dad continued. "But what went wrong with Math?" "I knew you would be furious!" Pete said. But his father looked at him kindly and gently. "It seems as if you struggle with arithmetic. We will have to make a plan." Pete was relieved that his dad wasn't cross with him. "I'll work much harder next term," he offered. "How are you going to do it?" his dad asked with interest. "I'll do my homework regularly and I'll ask whenever I don't understand something!"

"That sounds like a good plan," his dad said. "It's a good idea to set goals for yourself. Let's write them down, so you will remember them better!" They made a list of all Pete's subjects and wrote his grades next to them. Then they made another column and Pete wrote down the grades he wanted to aim for. He aimed at higher marks in all subjects. "Paste this above your desk, then you will see it whenever you sit down to do your homework," his dad suggested.

Pete's dad then wrote a note to his teacher at the bottom of his report card: "Pete has set some goals for himself and he will have better results in Math next term." "How do you know that?" Pete asked. "Someone who knows the goals he is working toward and who trusts the Lord as his Helper, can be sure of success!" his dad answered with confidence.

Do you think that Pete did better after that?

Read Philippians 3:14 to see how Paul describes his goal.

AUGUST 18

A MILLION YEARS FROM NOW

Ken and three of his friends were joining the youth group for a hike. The night before the hike they all slept at his house because his parents had volunteered to take them to the starting point before sunrise. The four boys had also planned a secret midnight feast for that night! After bedtime they set out all treats they had smuggled into Ken's bedroom, lit a candle, and feasted as they sat on their sleeping bags on the floor. William took out some jellybeans. "I brought along some pills!" he said. "What sort of pills?" Derrick asked suspiciously. They were all thinking about what they had heard about drugs at school. "Futuristic pills!" William said. "When you swallow one of these, you can see what will happen to you in the future." The others were thrilled with this game and each one took a "pill". When Derrick swallowed his jellybean with a gulp of soda, he said, "My pill says that in ten year's time I will be a doctor with my own practice." Jerry had trouble washing down his "capsule". "My pill says that twenty years from now I'll be a rich and famous business executive. I'll be driving around in a red Lamborghini!" Ken chewed his future pill and said, "Forty years from now my son will be as old as I am now and I'll be a golf champion."

Then it was William's turn. He swallowed his jellybean and said dramatically, "A trillion million years from now I'm going to be in heaven with God!" His friends looked amazed. "How can you be so sure about that?" Ken asked. "Look in your Bible!" William replied. " John 3:16 says that those who believe in Jesus will have everlasting life. And I believe in Him!"

Just then Ken's mom appeared in the doorway. She smiled. Pretending to be really cross, she said, "I predict that if you don't get into bed immediately, you four will lag behind tomorrow!"

Are you one of those who will one day live with God forever and ever? If you're not sure, talk to your Sunday school teacher about it.

BEHIND BARS

Matthew 25:43 says, *"I was sick and in prison and you did not look after me."* These words that Jesus spoke so long ago haunted Elizabeth Fry. She lived in London at a time when the conditions in prisons were very bad. She was a busy mother, but her heart was also filled with compassion for people who were suffering. When she heard about the dreadful circumstances in which women had to live in the London prison, she asked permission to go and see them.

The governor was surprised. "Not even I go in there!" he said. "Those women are like wild animals." But Elizabeth kept on asking until she was eventually granted permission. On the day of her first visit, a terrible sight awaited her. Three hundred women lived in that place without lighting, bedding or washing facilities. Little children played on the floor, naked and hungry. Some of the women had been locked up because they had stolen money. Others were there because they could not pay their debts.

The women stared at her. She picked up a dirty, crying toddler and started soothing him. The women came closer to hear what she said. She spoke to them about God's love and she said, "Let's try to make this prison a better place to stay in. God will help us!" And then she prayed. Some of the women began to cry. They all promised to help her with her ideas. After that Elizabeth visited the prison every day. Some of her friends joined her. After a few weeks the place was clean and the terrible smell had vanished. Eventually she arranged for the women to get better facilities, better food, and better clothing. She also organized needlework classes for the women and schooling for the children. Many women later testified that their lives had been changed by her efforts, and, through her example, many other prisons in England and around the world were upgraded.

**Pray that people who are in prison will get
to know Christians who can lead them to Christ.**

AUGUST 20

ARE YOU TRUSTWORTHY?

Bart's parents received a letter from his teacher. "Please would you make an appointment to see me," he asked. They wandered what could have gone wrong at school. When they walked into Mr. Wall's classroom, he started talking immediately. "I have a problem and I wonder whether you can help me. We are considering submitting Bart's essay for a nationwide competition. But I want to make sure that he did not copy it from somewhere else. It is difficult to believe that someone in the eighth grade could write an essay like that. I want to know whether you helped him with it, or if you perhaps know where he got it from."

Mr. and Mrs. Swan looked at each other. Then they started talking at the same time, "It is his own work!" "He did not copy it from anybody!" they said with confidence. "Wouldn't you like to look at the essay first?" asked Mr. Wall. "How can you be so sure that it is all his own work?"

Bart's father answered, "Sir, we know Bart. He would never do a thing like that. He is painstakingly honest in everything he does. From his earliest childhood he would rather be punished than tell a lie." "And I know that he can write beautiful essays," his mom said. "I would love to read this one as well!"

Bart's teacher gave his notebook to his parents. They sat and read the essay in silence. Mrs. Swan wiped away a tear. "Thank you, Lord," she said softly, "that You have given Bart this talent, and that we can always trust him."

"Congratulations!" Mr. Wall said. "There are not many parents who can trust their children so completely. And, of course, congratulations on a fine piece of writing."

They talked about the matter with Bart when they got home. "Thanks for trusting me!" Bart said. "Thanks for being trustworthy!" his dad added.

Can your parents trust you completely?
Read what the Bible says in 2 Corinthians 8:21.

ROOM TO LET

On the Turner's front gate there was a poster that said: ROOM TO LET. Their eldest son had gone overseas and now they had an empty room in the garden. They got many applications from unmarried couples that wanted to stay there. "We are sorry," they said. "We cannot prescribe to you how you must live, but we are Christians and we believe that a couple must be married before they can live and sleep together."

Wendy heard what her dad said when he turned one of the couples away. "But, Dad, everybody does that nowadays," she said. "That doesn't mean that it's right!" her dad replied. "But isn't it better to live together for a while to get to know each other?" she asked. Her dad answered with conviction, "The Lord expects His children to wait until marriage before they live together. He is the one who has the final say, because we belong to Him."

Wendy's mom spoke up, "Remember, my dear: God's laws are there to protect us. He knows that we can be badly hurt if we live intimately together with somebody and the relationship suddenly breaks off. Living together and sleeping together ties people together in a special way and it's best if it's reserved for marriage, which is more permanent."

Wendy thought about one of her favorite series on TV. It was about a couple that had lived together for a while, but then the guy left the girl for someone else. In one of the episodes the girl said that she felt as if she had lost part of herself. *Maybe she did!* Wendy thought. *I think I'd rather stick to God's laws.* "Where in the Bible does it say that sleeping together before marriage is wrong?" she asked. She wanted to go and underline those verses in her Bible.

**Do you also want to see what the
Bible says on this matter? Turn to
1 Thessalonians 4:3-8 and Hebrews 12:16.**

ISLAM

"My sister is going to marry a Muslim," Heidi told her friend Celia. "Wow! And what will their children one day be: Christians or Muslims?" "They will be Muslims, because my sister is going to convert to Islam." "What do your parents say about that?" "Oh, they say it's all right. As long as she has some kind of religion, they're happy. Muslims are very strict in their faith. They pray five times a day and they don't drink alcohol. And they're very generous to the poor."

"But do they believe the Bible?" Celia asked. "Not all of it. They have another book, the Qur'an. They believe that an angel gave it to Mohammed, their great prophet. But there are some things in which they agree with us Christians." "For instance?" Celia wanted to know. "Like us, they believe that there is one Almighty God. They call Him Allah. And they believe in angels and in the devil and in a day of judgment, when some people will go to hell and others to heaven," Heidi explained.

"But how can your sister just forget about Jesus?" Celia asked with concern in her voice. "She won't! Muslims do believe that Jesus lived on earth and that He ascended into heaven. But they see Him as a great prophet, not as the Son of God. And they don't believe that Jesus died on the cross as punishment for our sins. They say that each one of us will have to pay for our own sin."

"Thank goodness that we don't believe that!" Celia said. "Well, half a billion people in the world are Muslims, and they believe it," Heidi said. "We'll have to pray for them!" Celia said seriously. "And I suggest you ask your sister when last she read about what Jesus did on the cross for us."

That night Heidi herself read John 19 and she fell asleep with great concern for her sister.

Pray that missionaries who work amongst Muslims will continue to convey the true Message about Jesus.

Jesus answered, "No one comes to the Father except through me." Jn. 14:6

THE GIFT

Cedric was badly disabled. He could not walk, talk, or eat by himself. His whole body was deformed and his arms and legs often jerked out of control. And yet the people who looked after him in the home where he stayed loved him dearly. There was a peace about him that affected everyone around him. All the nurses who washed, dressed, and fed him, said that he meant a lot to them. "He is never moody or impatient," said one of the caregivers. "He is full of love and always grateful for what we do for him. His smile can lighten up my whole day," another agreed. "When I feel stressed out, I just go and sit with Cedric for a while. Within a few minutes I feel better."

Every Sunday afternoon Cedric's family came for a visit. "When I see how contented Cedric is with the little that he has, I can't help but feel grateful for my own health," his brother said during one of their visits. "We take too many things for granted. I think that people like Cedric are put on earth to stop us from grumbling about nonsense."

"Yes," his dad replied. "Each person is put on earth with a purpose. Maybe Cedric was given to our family to make us realize what is really important in life."

"He also taught us that nobody's life is worthless," his mom added. She remembered how upset she had been when Cedric was born. *What will happen to this child?* she thought. But God looked after him in a special way and she would never have wanted to be without her precious little boy. Before they went home that Sunday, each family member gave Cedric a warm hug. He smiled at them, and that smile meant just as much to them as the pastor's blessing at church that morning.

**Read in John 14:27 about the gift that
God wants to give to all of His children.**

WE CAN ALSO HELP

Alicia was very disappointed because she could not go with the youth group on a missions trip to Malawi during the winter holidays. They were planning to go and help at a home for AIDS-orphans. But each volunteer had to raise $1,400. Alicia simply could not gather so much money. "I prayed so much about it," she said sadly. "I really can't understand why God didn't supply me with the money."

The first Tuesday during the holidays, her mom took her to Esperanza, a home for the elderly where her aunt stayed. It was a big place and many elderly people lived there. What Alicia saw broke her heart. There were so many weak and frail old people who needed care, and the place was so short staffed that the caregivers had no time to spend talking to the elderly. She started talking to some of the old people, and they held her hand tightly, not wanting to let go when she got up to leave.

"Please bring me a drink of water!" one old, toothless gentleman asked her. He gulped down the water and said, "Look at this!" He eagerly took a gold watch from his pocket. "It belonged to my dad," he said. His tired old eyes began to glow as he told her about his childhood on a farm. Alicia was fascinated as she listened to his stories from long ago. "Do come again!" he urged her when her mom came to fetch her. Her new friend offered her a peppermint from a crumpled packet. "I'll come again soon!" she promised him, and she really meant it. She slowly realized that the Lord had another mission for her while her friends were in Malawi.

Are there elderly people in your neighborhood to whom you could reach out? Remember Jesus' words in Matthew 5:7.

TREASURES IN HEAVEN

Judy was fascinated by what she saw on the back porch. Rex was in the front garden, and two squirrels had discovered his food bowl. They were very cute as they took the dog pellets and held them in their front paws while nibbling with glee.

But suddenly the peace was disturbed. A black crow chased the squirrels away and started feasting on the pellets himself. He threw the pellets on the cement and then pecked up the pieces that broke off. When he had eaten enough, he took the pieces one by one and put them in the branches of the blackberry bush in the garden. He flew back and forth, pushing the dog food underneath the bark in a fork of the tree. He wanted to store these for later.

But the little drama had not yet ended. When the crow flew away, the squirrels gathered all the bits from his pantry and took them to their own nest! Judy filled up Rex's bowl again.

She couldn't wait to tell the rest of her family about what she had witnessed that day. Her dad said, "It makes me think of the rich fool who gathered grain until he had no more space for storing it. And then he suddenly died. If he had given some of his harvest to poor people who had nothing to eat, then he would have been rich with God, as the Bible says." " It makes me think about the parable of the talents," her mom said. "Remember, one fellow hid his talent instead of using it. His master wasn't happy about that!"

"Yes, perhaps Rex and the squirrels and the crow could all have been fed if they were prepared to share the abundance," Judy added thoughtfully.

Read these two parables. The one is in Luke 12:13-21 and the other in Matthew 25:14-28.

LEARNING FROM A BEE STING

A little boy could not understand how Jesus' death on the cross had any meaning for his own life. Every year at Easter, the message about the cross simply went over his head. But then something happened that explained the whole matter to him.

One afternoon he was playing in the backyard while his mom was ironing in front of the open kitchen door. He saw a bee and started teasing the little insect with a stick. Suddenly the bee came straight at him! He tried to chase it away by swinging his arms, but it buzzed furiously around him.

Eventually he became quite scared. He jumped up and ran to his mom. He grabbed her around her waist with both arms and hid his face in her apron.

When his mom saw that the bee had followed him, she realized that he was in trouble. She put her arms protectively around him. And then the bee stung her on her arm! She was in pain, and began to remove the sting. But she comforted her little boy, saying, "Now, now! You needn't be scared any longer. The bee will not bother you any more. He stung me instead."

The boy looked at the red mark on her arm. He felt sorry that his mom had been hurt because of him. His mom realized she could use this opportunity to illustrate what Jesus did on the cross. "That is how Jesus took our punishment upon Him when He died on the cross," she said. "God had to punish the people who disobeyed Him. But Jesus came between God and man and took the punishment on Himself. Now He puts His arms around all of His children, so that they needn't be afraid of anything."

The boy often thought about this incident. And one day when a preacher read Isaiah 53:5 at church, he understood it immediately.

You can read the rest of this verse in your own Bible.

WHAT IS IMPORTANT?

"Mom, please don't drop me at the front of the school!" Frankie begged. "Why ever not?" his mom asked, surprised. "I don't want the other kids to see our wreck of a car!" Frankie grumbled. "My friends don't care what car we have," said Leah, who was in the twelfth grade. "It's not important what car we drive!" "Friends? You still have friends?" Frankie asked. "I have none left. They all look right through me without noticing me at all!" He got out of the car at the corner.

"Don't worry, Mom," Leah said. "I also went through a stage like that. I didn't bring rich friends to our house because I didn't want them to know where we lived. But at "Camp Together" I learned a lot about priorities. I learned that fashionable clothes and skin color and the size of your wallet are not important when it came to friendship. Anyway, none of those things will matter in heaven!"

"Clever girl!" her mom said as she dropped her at the school gate. "I hope that's true when I write that Math test today!" she laughed as she kissed her mom before the old, yellow Volkswagen moved off.

When Frankie got home that afternoon, he saw that his mom had put up a poster behind the bathroom door:

The Lord never asks what car you drive: only how many people you gave a lift to when they had no transport. He never asks how big your home is: only whether you were hospitable. He never notices in which neighborhood you live: only whether you were a good neighbor. And He is not interested in how many friends you have. He wants to know how many people you were a friend to.

Frankie fetched a notebook and copied these words. "It's something to think about!" he said.

Read the parable of the Good Samaritan in Luke 10:25-37.

He answered: " ... Love your neighbor as yourself." Lk. 10:27

AUGUST 28

AUGUSTINE

On August 28, many people remember a famous man who lived long ago. His name was Augustine and he was a great leader and teacher in the church. That is why people still honor his memory on St. Augustine's day.

But Augustine hadn't always been a good person. His mother, Monica, prayed for forty years for his salvation. In a book that he wrote about his life, he described how naughty he had been at school and how sinful his life was at university.

He told of an incident where he and his friends raided a pear orchard. They picked pears that weren't even ripe and threw them away afterwards. It was such an unnecessary act of willfulness and waste, as were many of the horrid things that he did as a young man.

Augustine became a professor at the University of Milan. There he met Ambrosius, a man who really loved and served the Lord. Augustine admired him, but he still lived recklessly. But his mother never stopped praying for him.

One day, while he was sitting on a bench in a park, two words came distinctly into his mind. *Tolle lege.* They meant: Take and read. *What am I supposed to take and read?* he wondered. Then, on the bench next to him, he saw a scroll. It was a section of the New Testament! He started to read it slowly.

Suddenly he realized that what he was reading was the truth. He committed his life to Christ and he became one of the greatest leaders in the church.

Monica prayed for Augustine for forty years. Read what the Bible says about persevering prayer in Luke 18:1-8.

And pray in the spirit in all occasions. Eph. 6:18

THE REAL GOD

Would you like to live in a strange country far away from home? That is what happened to Joshua and Amy. Their dad had to go and work in Thailand for a while, and they had to attend an English school in Bangkok. Everything was very different from what they had been used to back home.

One afternoon their parents took them to see the city. First, they went to where they could ride an elephant. Josh and Amy enjoyed this very much. They had to climb onto the elephant's back with a stepladder and then they sat on his back in a colorful saddle with silky tassels. A small man sat on the elephant's neck, tickling him with a stick to make him move forward.

Then they went to look at one of the big temples in Bangkok. People came from all over the city and the country to bring flowers and incense and leave them in front of a big statue of Buddha. Some of the tourists knelt in front of the statue, but Amy and Josh's parents did not want them to bend their knees to this idol. "We only bow before God!" they said. Everywhere they saw young men with shaved heads and wearing bright orange robes. They were monks and they were only allowed to own an umbrella and a bowl with which they begged for rice to eat.

"Wow! They must really love Buddha!" Josh said. "I wouldn't easily shave my hair and live in a temple for two whole years." He felt ashamed that he had often complained about long church services and Sunday school lessons back home.

A lady suddenly stood before Amy with a baby in her arms. She muttered something in her native language. "What did she say?" Amy asked their guide. "She said that she wanted her baby to be just like you," the tour leader answered. That night Amy prayed, "Lord, please let that baby also believe in the One true God and let her serve You with all her heart."

**Read the story about Daniel's
friends and the idol in Daniel 3:1-30.**

AUGUST 30

TO SWIM AGAINST THE TIDE

"In all the years that I have been a teacher, I have seen enough to convince me that smoking is bad for everyone, but especially for children," Mr. Drummond addressed his class. "Apart from the damage that it does to one's health, children who start smoking before they are sixteen never get far in life."

After class, the kids talked about what their teacher had said. "He's just trying to scare us!" Dean said. "But it's a fact that smoking can cause lung cancer and that it's bad for your heart," Eric said. His dad was a doctor who specialized in lung diseases. "That's the reason why cigarette companies aren't allowed to advertise their products freely. They have to put a warning on cigarette packets."

"But a few puffs can't do any harm!" Neil said. "Probably not, but it's habit-forming! I won't ever take a risk like that. Grownups pay lots of money just to try to stop smoking." Eric persisted. "Why don't you go and play with your little friends in the crèche? We *men* are about to light up!" Dean mocked. The other boys laughed as they went for a smoke.

Neil wasn't sure what he should do. *Should he go along or should he stay with Eric?* Then he remembered the gift his uncle had brought him from Japan. It was a big balloon in the shape of a carp. Dads in Japan gave these to their sons. A carp can swim upstream with ease. "If you want to get anywhere in life," parents tell their children when they hang these balloons in their rooms, "you will have to learn to swim upstream. Anyone can drift downstream: even dead fish! But it takes guts to stick to your principles when the crowd wants you to do something wrong."

"Count me out," Neil said at long last. He was relieved and in his heart, he thanked Jesus for helping him to make the right choice. His swimming flippers had grown much because of it!

Draw a fish and write Ephesians 6:10 on it. Put it up in your room.

Be strong and very courageous. Be careful to obey all the law. Jos. 1:7

WHERE DO WE COME FROM?

Harold was frowning. "What's wrong?" his dad asked. "Our teacher acts as if there is no God. Today we had a quiz in class and he asked, 'How did the earth come into being?' When I said, 'God made it', he said that that wasn't the answer that he was looking for."

"Maybe Mr. Walters is not a believer," his dad said. "People who don't want to believe in God say that the universe came into being by chance and that bird and animal life started by chance. They believe that we came out of nothing, that we live for nothing, and that after death we will be nothing again. I'd like to have a word with your teacher!"

"Are you going to argue with him?" Harold asked. " No, but I would like to hear how he explains creation. The Bible and science aren't enemies. The more research is done, the closer scientists get to the truth of the Bible. Quite recently it was still believed that the universe had no beginning. Then, in 1960, scientists announced that everything started with a big bang! A little more research, and they'll discover that Genesis 1:3 is the truth." "What does it say?" Harold asked. *"'And God said: 'Let there be light' and there was light."*

Harold's father continued, "Scientists will one day have to confess that God designed everything to the tiniest detail. If you picked up a watch on the beach, would you think that the sea and the sand manufactured it? Of course not! Similarly, I believe that a big Designer created our Universe. It is easier to believe that than to believe that it is all coincidence." The frown on Harold's face disappeared as he looked at his own wristwatch.

**Make a poster of beautiful scenes
in nature and write Psalm 19:1 on it.**

"By your will they were created and have their being." Rev. 4:11

September

SEPTEMBER 1

NEVER AGAIN!

Aurelia's mom urged her to join the youth group at their church. "Just pop in there one night," she said. Eventually she did go, but she decided she would never set foot in there again. She felt completely out of place. Most of the children simply ignored her. Others looked her up and down and whispered to each other. One of the boys kept teasing her and nobody talked to her. When the meeting started, nobody welcomed her. *I could just as well not have been there!* she thought as she walked home after the meeting.

That summer her family moved to another town. One of the girls at her new school invited her to their Christian Club, which got together on Sunday nights. She remembered her previous experience with a Christian youth group, and at first did not want to go. But Veronica kept on asking her, so she finally agreed.

What a surprise awaited her! Many kids came to tell her how glad they were that she had come. The girls all wanted her to sit with them. During the Bible study, Keith, the leader, asked her what she thought about the passage of Scripture that they were looking at. He also offered to take her home after the meeting, together with some other kids who lived far away.

"Will you come again, Aurelia?" Keith asked when he dropped her at home. "For sure!" Aurelia said. "And you can put my name down for making posters and helping at the jumble sale on Saturday! I'm keen to help with your missionary project!"

Do you attend youth meetings at your church? Do you make newcomers feel welcome at the church and at Sunday school? Read Acts 2:42-47 and see how the first Christians behaved toward one other.

SEPTEMBER 2

RESPECT ONE ANOTHER

An elephant and a monkey became great friends. One day Elephant told Monkey, "See how big and strong I am!" "Yes, and watch how agile and cute I am!" replied Monkey. "Strong is better than agile!" Elephant said. "Oh, no, it isn't" Monkey replied. "Agility is more important than strength!" "Is not!" "Is!" "Is not!" "Is!" they argued, back and forth. Finally they decided to go and ask the Wise Owl who he thought was the most important: the big, strong elephant or the small, agile monkey.

Owl opened and closed his eyes slowly. "Do what I tell you to do and then I will give you my answer!" he said. "We will do anything you say!" they agreed. "Go to the big river that flows through the meadows and bring me some of the mangoes that grow on the other side," Owl said.

Elephant and Monkey went on their way. When they got to the river, Monkey stood still. He could not swim across the river on his own! Elephant picked him up and carried him to the other side. Now they stood under the big mango tree full of ripe, yellow fruit. Elephant stuck out his trunk, but he could not reach the mangoes. Monkey climbed into the tree and started throwing mangoes onto the ground. Then they both picked up the fruit. Monkey carried some in his arms and Elephant carried some in his mouth, and they went back across the river.

When they arrived at Owl's home, they placed the mangoes in a neat row on the ground. "And who has been the most important on this venture?" Owl asked. Elephant and Monkey looked at each other. "We were both important!" they said. "We really needed each other!"

This fable is told to children in India to teach them that we are all different and that each of us has a task to do. We should help and respect each other.

The Bible teaches the same truth.
Read what Paul said in 1 Corinthians 12:4-11.

THE DREAM

One night a teacher had a dream that Jesus came to their town. What a hustle and bustle ensued! The principal asked her to organize all the children. She had to seat them on the seats of the stadium where Jesus would make His appearance. She arranged them in neat rows: first all the black children, then all the brown children, and in the back rows, all the white children.

But this didn't seem right. So she changed everything and told the boys to sit in front and the girls to sit at the back. But before she could finish this arrangement, the trumpets sounded, the orchestra started playing, and Jesus stepped into the arena.

She wanted to vanish into thin air from sheer embarrassment. She so badly wanted everything to be nice and orderly when Jesus arrived! But the children were all mixed-up now. But when she looked up to see how Jesus mingled with the children, she noticed that they all looked alike in His presence. Each child was equally important to Him.

There will always be people who think that one group is better than another. In Acts 10:9-16 you will find the story of how Peter's attitude toward non-Jewish people changed dramatically. Before that event, he felt hatred and fear towards the Romans, but afterwards he looked at them with new eyes. He now realized that Jesus, the Messiah, did not come only for the Jews. God wants to adopt people from every nation into His family.

God gave Peter a dream that convinced him that God cares equally for Jewish people and people of other races. He loves all nations and He paid for their salvation with His precious blood.

Do you think that you are better than other people? Read this story in Acts and ask God's forgiveness for your wrong attitude.

You are all sons of God through faith in Christ Jesus. Gal. 3:26

KEEPING A GOOD HEART

Natalie du Toit won a medal for South Africa in the Olympic Games in 2000. She is friendly, enthusiastic, and kind. Those are extra special characteristics in this nineteen-year-old. On February 26, 2001, while she was riding her motorcycle, she was knocked down by a car. The accident left her with only one leg!

Did she get angry with God for letting this happen? Was she sorry for herself because her leg had to be amputated? Not at all! She decided that she would not give up her goals. As soon as she could, she returned to the swimming pool where she did most of her training.

After she had received an artificial leg, she had to learn to walk again. And she started practicing her swimming again, training for twenty hours a week. She wants to represent her country in the next Olympic Games and to bring home some more medals!

"I am still the same person I was before the accident," she says. "Only the challenge to succeed is much bigger now!" What is the secret of Natalie's perseverance? "It is God!" she says. "He helped me to get over the shock and the disappointment after the accident and He is the One that inspires me to go on with my life."

When she was asked what message she would like to give to other people who are disabled, she said, "Believe in yourself. Fight till the end. Trust God."

Her story makes me think of Paul's words in 1 Corinthians 9:26-27, "*I do not run like a man running aimlessly ... No, I beat my body and make it my slave.*"

Find a picture of a disabled sportsman or woman and let it inspire you to set positive goals and to persevere, no matter what difficulties you face.

We know that suffering produces perseverance. Rom. 5:3

JESUS WILL COME AGAIN

The local newspaper ran an article about a group of people who believed that the world would soon come to an end. They gathered in their church building and waited for the coming of Judgment Day. One person, who called himself a prophet, even predicted on which date all this would happen. He said that Jesus would come and take His children on that specific day, and that the rest of the world would go up in flames. But that date came and went, and nothing happened.

When Felix read this article, he became curious. "When will Jesus come?" he asked his dad. "Nobody knows. But we do know that He is coming again!" his dad answered. "People who think that they can predict the day on which He will return, do not know their Bibles. Jesus said that only His Father knows when that will happen."

"Tell me more!" Felix encouraged his dad. He knew so little about Jesus' Second Coming. "We should read Mark 13 together," his dad said. "There you will find a lot of information about the last days. The Bible teaches that Jesus will come with glory and power. All His angels will be with Him. And everybody on earth will see Him. People who did not want to believe in Jesus will be very scared, because they will be punished. But God's children needn't be afraid, because Jesus has paid for all our sins. We will be very glad on that day, because Jesus will be coming to fetch us."

"What would you like to be doing when Jesus comes so suddenly?" his dad asked. "That's a difficult question!" Felix answered. "But one thing I know: I wouldn't like to be busy with something that would make me ashamed to meet Jesus!" "Then we better never do things that make us ashamed!" his dad said with a laugh.

Read Mark 13:24-33.

SEPTEMBER 6

GOD WILL SUPPLY

A minister once told his congregation that the Lord would never ask anything from them if they did not have it to give. This was how he explained it.

One Sunday morning, before the service, he gave a hundred dollars to one of the elders. "You must bring it up to the pulpit as soon as I ask for it!" he said. When the minister started preaching, he said, "Brothers and Sisters, I need a hundred dollars today and I know that somebody in this church building is going to give it to me!" The people in the pews did not look their preacher in the eyes. *What if he expects me to give him the money?* everyone thought. Then he said, "I now ask the man who wants to give me the money to come forward." The elder came to the front and with a broad smile gave the money to the preacher. The people were amazed! The man did not think twice before he handed the cash to the preacher. And what's more, he didn't seem to mind at all! "Are you wondering how this brother could give away the money so easily?" asked the minister. "It is because I gave him that money. In the same way, God asks us to do certain things for Him, but He supplies everything we need so that we can obey Him. If, for instance, He wants you to go to the mission field, He will see to it that you have enough money, support, and health to be able to go! And if He wants you to be a joyous witness for Him, then He will give you the ability to encourage the people around you!"

"What would have happened if the elder did not bring me the money I had given him? Then I would have called in the police!" the preacher concluded. "In the same way we will be punished if we get gifts from God that He wants to use for His Kingdom, but we just keep them to ourselves!"

Read the parable about the talents in Matthew 25:14-30.

READING WITH HIS TONGUE

Ps. 34:8

Taste and see that the Lord is good.

A man in Kansas City lost both his hands in an accident. His face was badly burnt in the same accident. The doctors did what they could for him, but they could not save his eyes. He became completely blind. Now, this man was a child of God and he loved his Bible very much. It made him sad to think that he could not read it any longer. Other blind people could still read the Bible in Braille with the tips of their fingers, but this was not possible for him. And in those days there were no tapes or CDs so he couldn't listen to a recording of the Bible.

Then this unfortunate man heard that there were people who could read Braille with their lips! They felt the knobs in the Braille Bible with their lips and in that way they could read the letters. He ordered a Braille Bible immediately and tried to use his lips to read the writing. But the nerves on his lips had been damaged in the accident and they weren't sensitive enough to feel anything. When the man realized this, he put his head on the Bible and started to cry: he was bitterly disappointed! After a while, he licked away his tears and his tongue touched the Bible with the little knobs on it. He became very excited, because he could actually feel them! He found somebody to teach him Braille and soon he could read the Bible by licking the pages! During the rest of his life, he read the Bible four times from cover to cover – with his tongue!

There are three questions you can ask yourself: Do you love the Word of God enough to go to such lengths to be able to read it? Would you have had enough perseverance to keep on trying? Do you praise God for the wonderful way in which He made us – with a tongue so sensitive it can even read His Word!

**Read Psalm 119:103 and think
about the meaning of these words.**

WE MUST STAND TOGETHER!

"The people at your church are all a lot of lazybones!" Kenneth said to Jerome. "And you are a bunch of hypocrites!" Jerome said. Ugly words were flung between them and they ended up in a fistfight.

Later that day they were both summoned to the principal's office. "Boys," he said sternly, "I'm going to tell you a story that should make you think: Two boys once went for a walk through the woods. Suddenly they saw the footprints of a lion. The next moment they heard the lion roaring!"

Kenneth looked at Jerome. Why was the principal telling them this story? He went on, "They turned around and started running. But suddenly the one boy stopped and took off his shoes. 'Are you crazy?' asked his friend. But the barefoot runner rushed past him. 'I can run much faster than you!' he bragged.

It was quiet in the principal's office. The two boys were thinking about the foolish boy who wanted to compete even though his life was in danger. Then the principal spoke again. "We live in troubled times," he said. "The Bible says that Satan is prowling around like a roaring lion. It is totally unacceptable for God's children to fight and compete with each other."

The principal took a newspaper clipping from one of his drawers. "I cut this from a Christian newspaper," he said. The boys looked at the sentences that were highlighted. "In Romania, after the communists destroyed all the church buildings, there was no strife amongst the Christians. People from all denominations learned to respect each other and to stand together against their common enemy."

Both boys blushed when they realized how silly they had been. When the principal asked them to shake hands, they did so eagerly.

Read 1 Peter 5:8-9 and pay special attention to the second part of the warning.

TRUE BELIEF

Blondin was a famous tightrope walker. He was completely comfortable on a rope high up in the air, as casual about his movements up there as we are on firm ground. Once he had a steel cable placed over the Niagara Falls and many people came to see him cross over the Falls on a thin steel cable.

The spectators bit their nails, and yelled as they watched him make the long trip across the Falls. *What would happen if he lost his balance? Or if his foot slipped?* But he moved confidently along the wire, even though there was no security net underneath.

When he got to the other side, he asked the cheering crowds, "Do you believe that I am as comfortable on this rope as I am on the ground?" "Yes!" they all shouted. "Do you believe that I can push someone across the Falls in my wheelbarrow?" The crowds were a little hesitant now. Far fewer answered, "Yes." "Who is willing to be that person?" he asked.

But everybody was quiet. It was one thing to believe that Blondin was an excellent tightrope walker, but it was something else to trust him with your life! Nobody was willing to do that.

In the same way, many people say that they believe in God and they even believe that Jesus died on the cross for the sins of the world. But they do not trust Him with their lives. If you really believe that Jesus saved you from hell, you will trust your whole life into His care.

Are you prepared to give up your just-looking-after-myself lifestyle to follow Jesus? He will teach you how to follow Him and how to serve other people. Then you will show by your actions that you really have faith in Him.

Look up James 2:14-20. It has something to say about people who have the wrong kind of faith.

THE GOOD SHEPHERD

Jewish rabbis have a lot of legends about Bible characters that are not necessarily true, but they show us something important about the way God deals with His people. One such story is about Moses. When he lived in Midian, he looked after his father-in-law's sheep and goats. One day one of the young goats ran away from the herd. Moses followed him until he came to a little brook. The goat had knelt down and was drinking from the clear running water.

"You poor thing!" Moses said. "You must have been very thirsty! Come, drink enough water and then I will carry you back to the flock. I can see that you are exhausted from running so far." Then Moses picked up the little goat, placed it on his shoulders, and carried him home. Shortly after this incident, God said to Moses, "You know how to lead a flock with love and patience. I want to use you to lead my people to the Promised Land."

The Bible has lots of stories about shepherds who lovingly cared for their sheep. Each of these stories is a reference to the Lord, who is our Shepherd. Many people will tell you that their Bible falls open at Psalm 23 all by itself, just because they read that psalm so often. It is very comforting to know that we belong to God's flock and that He cares for all our needs.

John 10:11 tells us that Jesus said that He is the Good Shepherd who was willing to lay down His life for his sheep. *"I know my sheep and my sheep know me,"* He said. Jesus also told the parable of the Lost Sheep. You can read it in Luke 15:1-10. In this parable He showed us that He will go after one sheep that has lost his way, and He will save that sheep and carry it safely home.

Doesn't it make your heart sing with joy to know that our Good Shepherd will never allow one of us to be lost?

**Read Isaiah 40:9-11 to see how the
Lord, our Shepherd, looks after us.**

SCARED OF FLYING?

The Kramer's grandpa sent his grandchildren three plane tickets so that they could and visit him in Durban. The two girls were very excited, but Dan was scared. "Why can't we go by train?" he asked. He had had a fear of heights ever since he was a toddler. "I'm not scared of dying," he said. "But I wouldn't want to die in a plane crash. Flying is OK, but falling..." he shuddered.

That night his dad called them all to his study. "I found a few interesting facts on the Internet," he said. "Researchers have discovered that most children and young people who die, die in car accidents." Judy smiled. Dan's room was full of posters of racing cars! Her dad continued, "That's followed by burning, drowning, and poisoning. Even to choke on your food is more common than being involved in a plane crash," he said and winked at Lana, who always had to be warned because she ate so fast.

"We are God's children and we do not need to be scared of death," their dad said. "When we die we will live with the Lord forever. Do you remember Psalm 23?" He took his Bible from the shelf and read verse 4 in a brand new way. "Even though I fly high up in the clouds in an airplane, I will fear no evil, for You are with me." The children smiled at the way in which he changed the words. "Besides, we will not die before it is our time to go," he said comfortingly.

"Thanks, Dad!" Dan said. Luckily he still had a week in which to work up the courage he needed before they got onto the plane. *Maybe it's a good idea to learn those words by heart,* he thought.

**Read what Paul had to say about
death in 1 Corinthians 15:54-55.**

A BRIGHT FUTURE

Have you heard the following joke? Three men were passengers in a small twin-engine plane: an elderly gentleman, a younger man, and a schoolboy. Suddenly both engines of the plane stopped working. The pilot grabbed a parachute and jumped from the plane. "Sorry, folks," he shouted. "I have a wife and kids at home who need me. I hope you will be OK!"

To their dismay, the three passengers discovered that there were only two parachutes left. "I have to live," the boy said as he grabbed a parachute. "I have a scholarship to study medicine, and I believe I'm going to discover the cure for cancer. Ahead of me lies a bright future! Good-bye, oldies!" he shouted as he jumped from the plane. The other two men looked at each other. Who should get the one remaining parachute? The old man spoke fast as the plane started to plummet. "Young man, you can have it! My case with God is settled. I know where I will spend eternity if I die today. Go, and make the best of the remaining part of your life!" The young man laughed. "Don't worry, Sir!" he said. "There's a parachute for each one of us! The brilliant future doctor took my backpack when he jumped!"

This type of joke is called "gallows humor" and we usually feel guilty when we laugh at such macabre stories. But there are some things that children and young people do that sometimes make us smile, but deep down they cause much sorrow.

When young people think that wealth and fame and popularity will bring them happiness in life, then we should be worried about their attitude. How many wealthy people die every day without ever thinking seriously about eternity? Make sure that you grab the right parachute when you plan for a bright future!

**Read the good advice that Solomon
gave his son in Proverbs 13:20.**

"For I know the plans I have for you," declares the LORD. Jer. 29:11

SEPTEMBER 13

WORK AND PRAY

Martin Luther was mightily used by God to rectify serious errors in the church of his day. He was a bold and courageous man, and you might learn more about him at church or in school. He had a friend, Myconius, who often told him, "The work that you are doing is wonderful. I will pray for you!"

Myconius kept his promise. Every day he prayed for his friend and for the work that he was doing. But the more he prayed, the more uneasy he felt. Then one night, he had a dream. He saw Jesus with pierced hands, beckoning him to follow Him. They walked to the top of a hill and Jesus showed him a large herd of sheep in the valley below: there were thousands of sheep! One man was trying to shepherd them all.

After a while Myconius saw that the shepherd was his friend Martin Luther. Then Jesus asked him to turn around. On the other side of the hill there was a cornfield. One man was trying to bring in the whole harvest. The lonely reaper was his friend Martin. When Myconius woke up, he said, "It is not enough to pray for my friend. I must go and help him!" He packed his bags and went to assist Luther in the great work that he was doing.

Is there somebody for whom you are praying regularly? That's good! But perhaps God wants you to go and help that person. Are you praying for a sick friend? Why not visit him or her? Are you praying for people in faraway countries who do not know Jesus? Maybe God wants to send you there one day.

John 4:35 says, *"Open your eyes and look at the fields. They are ripe for harvest!"* Often we pray and God uses our prayers to do mighty things. But sometimes He wants us to get up and go and do the very thing that we are asking Him to do.

Think of something that you can do for someone for whom you are praying regularly.

"Ask the Lord of the harvest, therefore, to send out workers into his harvest field." Mt. 9:38

LOST AND FOUND!

Jesus replied, "What is impossible with men is possible with God." Lk. 18:27

There's a painting hanging in an apartment in Somerset West that needs some explaining: An ant seems to be pushing a glass bowl that is glittering in the sun. When people ask about it, the owner eagerly tells the story. Friends of hers once went mountain climbing. A rope ladder had been hung against a huge rock face to help the climbers reach the top. When one of the women reached the grassy ledge at the top, she wiped the perspiration from her eyes, knocking one of her contact lenses out. It fell all the way down the cliff they had just climbed. *Where did it land and how will I ever find it again?* she thought.

This was a serious situation, because she could not see properly without the lenses, and she would not be able to move around freely without the missing lens. "Please God," she prayed, "we came on this outing to worship You in the beauty of nature. And now everything had been spoiled! Please help us!" Some of the other hikers started searching amongst the rocks and bushes and stones for the tiny piece of glass, but everyone thought that it was impossible to find.

Suddenly a stranger joined the group. "Has anyone lost a contact lens?" he asked. They turned to him with astonished faces. He took the tiny piece of glass from his hanky. "I saw something glistening in the sun," he said. "And I was about to move on, but then I saw that this thing was moving. When I looked closer, I saw that an ant was pushing the lens to who-knows-where!" The whole group started to talk at once. "If God can help someone find a lost contact lens in the vastness of the Drakensberg mountains, He can do anything!" one said.

The artist who drew the picture of this incident wrote a caption underneath it, which says: "Lord, I don't know why I must push this thing, but since You told me to do it, I will gladly comply!"

Read Luke 8:22-25 to see how Jesus once intervened in nature in order to help His friends.

THE TWO MICE

Field Mouse invited his friend Town Mouse for a visit. While they were looking for tidbits in the meadows, Town Mouse said, "You live here in poverty! Come with me to the city and I will treat you to the most delicious food!"

Field Mouse agreed and so the two mice traveled to the city where Town Mouse lived. When they arrived, Town Mouse took Field Mouse to a pantry where dried beans, dried figs, nuts, raisins, and even cheese were stored. Field Mouse enjoyed himself thoroughly and he was just wondering how he could ever have been satisfied with so little for so long, when the door of the pantry swung open! The two friends had to run for their lives. They ran into a hole in the pantry cupboard and sat there trembling. Then someone else opened the door of the cupboard and they had to look for another place to hide. They had to stay in their new hidey-hole till late that night, because the big gray cat was sleeping on a chair in the kitchen.

The next morning Field Mouse said to Town Mouse, "Thank you very much for inviting me to come and stay with you. But I'd rather go home. Enjoy all the food that you have here. It's far too dangerous here for me. I prefer to look for simple food in the cornfields, because there I can feel safe." Then he went back to his little home in the meadows.

This fable teaches us that peace in the heart is worth more than all the riches in the world. Some people might invite you to live dangerously and extravagantly. But if the things they ask you to do bring no peace to your heart, then Jesus would not approve of those activities.

In Proverbs 15:16 we read, *"Better a little with the fear of the LORD than great wealth with turmoil."*

**Also read Proverbs 23:4 and ask
your parents to explain it to you if
you do not understand what it means.**

THE TWO DOGS

Peter was an evangelist and he drove from farm to farm telling farm workers about Jesus. Some of them took his messages seriously and asked Jesus into their hearts. Sammy was one of them. One day when Peter visited Orange Farm again, Sammy asked, "Peter, why do I still sin every so often? I sometimes wonder whether I really became a Christian. I do not want to sin, but before I know it, I've lost my temper or I've used the Lord's name in vain or had filthy thoughts. I'm ashamed of my own behavior!"

"Then you are exactly like Paul!" Peter said. "Look what he wrote." He took out his Bible and read Romans 7:19, "*The evil I do not want to do – this I keep on doing.*" "Did the great apostle Paul say that?" Sammy asked with surprise. "So how did he manage to live a good life after all?"

Pete was wondering how he could explain this to Sammy. Then he saw two dogs fighting in a field nearby and remembered an illustration his pastor had used a few weeks back. "Sammy, it works like this," he said. "Deep inside us we all have the urge to sin. It's like a bad dog that encourages us to do the wrong things. But when Jesus comes into our hearts, He gave us some new desires. They are like a good dog that leads us on to do good things. The bad dog and the good dog inside each of us are forever fighting with each other. But if you feed only the good dog, the bad one won't have a chance to win."

"How can I feed the good dog?" Sammy wanted to know. "Read your Bible, pray, go to church, and spend time with friends who know the Lord," Peter said.

Sammy walked home and went straight to his backyard where he had been brewing a large amount of beer. He tipped the canister over and let the beer run out. "From now on, I'm going to starve the bad dog!" he muttered to himself.

Decide today how you will encourage good desires and snuff out bad desires in your life.

Those controlled by the sinful nature cannot please God. Rom 8:8

THE BOOMERANG

Do you know what a boomerang is? It is a curved weapon used for hunting. The Aborigines in Australia used to use boomerangs to hunt animals. Because of its curved design, no matter which direction you throw it in, it will come back to you – unless it hits something first!

Did you know that bad events can sometimes be like a boomerang? The Lord can turn things that are heading for disaster around and make good come out of them.

Here is a true story that illustrates this: A Jewish physician, Dr. Felix Ruh lived in Paris. One day his granddaughter fell seriously ill. The doctors said she had diphtheria. In those days there was no cure for this terrible disease. Her grandfather could do nothing to help her and she died. Because he loved her so much, he mourned her death for a very long time. But then the boomerang started to turn. This doctor decided that he was going to find out what causes diphtheria and how it could be cured. He wanted to prevent other people from going through the same trauma he had experienced.

The doctor joined Dr. Louis Pasteur's team, who had been researching the spread of various illnesses. Dr. Ruh eventually discovered that a few diphtheria germs could be used to strengthen the body against this disease. If these germs were put into your body, it would start fighting against them. In the process you would become so strong, that when a whole army of these germs attacked you, they would be wiped out completely.

Soon children could be inoculated against diphtheria and very few people get this disease today.

The Lord caused Dr. Ruh's sad experience to boomerang so that something really good could come out of it.

**Read about another good thing that can
come out of suffering in 2 Corinthians 1:3-4.**

ARE THERE PEOPLE ON MARS?

"What nonsense!" Grandpa said as he read the newspaper. Harold and John were playing on the floor. "What are you talking about, Grandpa?" they asked. "Listen to what this newspaper reporter says," Grandpa answered. "The most important thing that science has taught us about our place in the universe is that we are not special at all." Grandpa snorted as he read these words. "But maybe we aren't so special!" Harold said. "Maybe there are more important people on other planets." Just the previous day they had been discussing the exciting idea that there could be people on Mars.

"Children at school say that Martians will be hairy because it's always cold there. Their legs will be long, because there's less gravity. But they will have huge torsos and lungs because the air there is thinner than on earth," John said. "Yes, and they will have enormous ears and long noses because sounds and smells move slowly in thin air!" Harold added.

Grandpa laughed at their wild speculations. "In fact, as far back as 1949, astronomers proved that the only living things that could ever have lived on Mars were primitive plants. Humans, animals, and even trees could not survive in those conditions."

"But what about life on other planets?" Harold asked. "It's highly improbable," Grandpa said. "In order for life to exist on other planets, they would have to have very specific conditions, such as an orbit similar to ours and a specific circumference and atmosphere. And even if another planet had such specific conditions, it still wouldn't take away anything of the wonder of planet earth. The Bible tells the story of God's unique plan for the earth and, according to His Word, we are very special indeed. So special that God even calls us to be His children!"

"And He even sent His Son to save us!" John added with wonder.

Read Psalm 148.

MAKING A HAPPY BOX

Jolene sat down at the breakfast table and said, "I feel like drinking some poison!" Her mom was shocked. She could see that Jolene had been very depressed lately. "What's wrong?" she asked. "Oh, Mom, don't worry! I'd never really do something like that, but some days the world does seem such a dreary place." Her mom wanted to say something more to her, but Jolene jumped to her feet and grabbed her books. "I'm late for school," she said, and ran outside through the backdoor. That morning, as her mom went about her work, every now and then, she prayed, "Dear Lord, how can I help my child?"

When Jolene got home that afternoon, her mom was reading a book. "This book was written by a woman who also felt very depressed at times," she said. "She devised all kinds of schemes to make sure that negative thoughts could not settle in her mind." Jolene came to sit next to her mom. "She said that she had discovered that laughing makes you relax and it sets free certain chemicals that keep your body healthy. She says that doctors should prescribe a dose of 'laugherine' to all their patients."

Then Jolene's mom took a shoebox from her cupboard. It was covered in bright-colored paper. "I decided to make a happy box. Would you like to help me with it?" she asked. "What do we put into it?" Jolene asked, interested. "Anything that can make us laugh or smile!" her mom said and took out some clippings that she had cut out from the newspaper that morning. She had included some of Jolene's favorite cartoon strips. Her mom had also put a comical figurine that she had bought in Venice in the box. On the lid of the box she wrote, "A cheerful heart is good medicine" (Proverbs 17:22). For the first time in weeks, Jolene smiled.

Why don't you make a Happy Box, for yourself or for a friend who is depressed?

September 20

Becoming a Winner

Do you like the cartoon character Charlie Brown, who usually struggles to get his kite to fly, and seems to be a born loser? At one stage cartoons about him were regularly published in 1,800 newspapers worldwide. The man who created him was Charles Monroe Schultz and the Charlie Brown and Snoopy cartoons were so popular that he became a billionaire because of them.

But everything hadn't always been so good for Charles Schultz! He had a hard time when he was a kid. His parents were poor, he did not do very well at school, and he had no friends. But he did have a hobby that gave him a lot of pleasure: he could draw cartoons. But at first nobody appreciated his efforts. His work wasn't even accepted by the school magazine.

And yet Sparky, as he was known, kept on drawing. After he graduated, he applied for a job at the Walt Disney Studios, but was turned down. He decided to start drawing cartoons about all the disappointments in his own life. Charlie Brown became a little boy who, like him, always seemed to be on the losing end.

He called his stories *Peanuts*, and a New York newspaper was the first to publish it. People quickly came to love this little character who never seemed to manage to succeed in anything. It didn't take long for Charles Schultz's life to turn around though. He soon became very successful, and Hollywood even made a film about Charlie Brown. When Charles Schultz died in his sleep in February 2000, millions of people who knew him through his cartoons mourned his passing. For fifty years he had entertained people who came home from a hard day's work to read *Peanuts* in the newspaper. The escapades of Charles, Linus, Marcie, and Snoopy will always make people smile tenderly.

God has given us all certain talents. Do not neglect yours and do not give up if things do not work out successfully at first.

In John 6:9 you can read what Jesus did with the offerings of a small boy.

COMPUTER MADNESS

Henry threw his satchel on the kitchen floor and greeted his grandma hastily. Then he ran to his room and parked himself in front of the computer. Grandma brought him some cookies and a glass of milk. *He must have a lot of assignments to complete for school!* she thought. *Today's kids are so privileged to have things like computers to help them do their work.*

But after Granny had spent a week with the Mitchell family, she started to worry about Henry. Her grandchild never played outside, never read books, and never had time to talk to her. One night she decided to mention this to his mom. "Do you know how much time Henry spends in front of the computer?" she asked. "No," said his mom. "But aren't you glad that he is so clever? Children nowadays have to be computer literate." " That might be the case," said Grandma, "but I'm concerned that in the process other important things are being neglected." "What do you think he misses while he is sitting in front of the computer?" his mom asked. "Well, he hasn't got time to fight with his sister, or time to laugh with the family, to mention only two things!"

Henry's mom thought about what Grandma had said. She had noticed that Henry seemed to get bored very easily lately. Maybe he was addicted to the thrill that he got from computer games. What's more, he no longer went surfing or cycling.

She decided to talk to his schoolteacher about it. Mr. Small was glad that she had come. "I have also been worried about him," he said. "I miss him at tennis, and he is grumpy with his friends. I suggest that you limit his time at the computer."

And that was exactly what his mom did. They both agreed on a reasonable amount of time for him to spend at the computer and Grandma, his fox terrier and the rest of the family were very glad that Henry once again joined in the family fun times.

Read the warning in 2 Peter 2:19.

GOOD MANNERS

Franz had come to spend the holidays with the Jordans so that he could learn English. But he was taught more than a new language during those holidays. He learned good manners.

On the night he arrived, Mrs. Jordan asked him not to sit down before the ladies had taken their seats. She also asked him not to stuff so much food into his mouth at one time and not to chew with his mouth open. When he started picking at his teeth with his fingers, she offered him a toothpick, but when he used his fork to scratch his head, she was really shocked.

After supper, Mrs. Jordan talked to all the children about good manners. "Good manners are the way we show respect for other people. It simply means that we are considerate toward others," she said. "If you are courteous to other people, then they will also treat you with respect," she continued. Then she gave the girls a chance to say what kind of behavior they most appreciated from boys. "I admire a guy who gives his seat to older people in the bus," Mary said. "And I like someone who keeps his word and who's not always late," said her sister. "Oh, and the words *please, thank you* and *excuse me* sound like music in my ears when used at the right time!"

Then the boys had a turn to speak. They described the kind of behavior they didn't like. "Swearing and dirty jokes are out!" Mr. Jordan said. "Sneezing while sending missiles out left, right and center is terrible!" John said. Franz spoke in his broken English. "I not like people say things behind my back. You OK. You help me do right thing."

"I can see that we can live together in harmony," Mrs. Jordan said. "They say that it takes seven years to drop a bad habit, but we can try and crash a few records during this holiday!"

Read James 3:17-18.

Who is wise and understanding ... Let him show it by his good life. Jas 3:13

PRESS ON TO THE VERY END!

William was bitterly disappointed when he kicked the soccer ball toward the goal posts, and missed. That kick could have given his team the victory of the season. The score was 2 all. If he had succeeded, they would have won! When the ball had been passed to him, the spectators had cheered and whistled, but then he kicked and the ball sailed past the right goal post. The spectators booed, and the final whistle blew.

As he rode home on his bike, he thought, *It didn't matter that I missed by only half an inch. All that counted was that I didn't make it! And it will be printed in black and white in all the local newspapers for all the world to see: Hatfield lost to Fairview!*

That Sunday night a visiting preacher spoke at William's church. He knew nothing about the sporting events of the weekend, but quite coincidentally, he talked about life as being like a tough game. William felt as if the preacher were talking directly to him. "In the game of life, we all want to score goals," he said, "but we fail time and again." Then he read Romans 3:23, *"All have sinned and fall short of the glory of God."* "These words mean that we have missed the goalposts," he said. "We cannot escape the consequences, even though we try very hard. Only Christ can change the final score of our lives. He can free us from sin and from the guilt and sorrow that it causes."

But how? William wondered. As if the preacher had read his thoughts, he said, "Christ changed the scoreboard when He died on the cross. Where we had once lost to sin, we can now be winners in Christ!"

When he gave the congregation the opportunity to rededicate their lives to Christ, William bowed his head. A deep peace settled in his heart. "Thank You, Jesus!" he said softly.

Underline Romans 6:23 in your Bible.

The gift of God is eternal life in Christ Jesus our Lord. Rom. 6:23

SEPTEMBER 24

YOU MUST CHOOSE

Each person must choose for himself whether he wants to serve the Lord or not. That's what Jesus said. In Luke 16:13 He said that it is impossible to serve God and something else, like Money. He wants to guide you and He wants you to worship Him. But if you choose not to follow Him, you will never fully become the person He created you to be. Trying to serve two masters brings conflict into your life.

An incident that occurred on January 23 1944 will illustrate how important it can sometimes be to make a choice. On that day, there was a terrible train crash in Spain. Hundreds of people died in the disaster.

A long, heavy passenger train had to go through the El Toro Tunnel. There was an engine in front that pulled the coaches and an engine at the back that had to help by pushing the train up the steep railway track. Suddenly the front engine came to a halt in the tunnel. The driver of the engine at the back went into reverse gear to try to pull the train out of the tunnel.

Unfortunately, there was no communication between the two drivers, and the front driver began to try to get the train to move forward again. Each driver was trying to build up enough steam to move the train in his direction. But the train stood still! More than 500 people suffocated because there wasn't enough fresh air in the tunnel. And all because the coaches of the train were pulling in different directions!

Satan wants us to listen to him and God pulls us towards Himself. Who will you listen to? We must make a choice, like Joshua did in Joshua 24:14-15. Are you FOR the Lord or AGAINST Him?

If you make the same choice that Joshua did, then write today's date next to this verse in your Bible.

CHOOSE GOD

Idah Peterside from Nigeria made an important decision to choose God over man. He was the goalkeeper of a famous soccer club. Before important matches, his teammates used to take muti – a concoction brewed by the sangomas and traditional healers that was supposed to make them better players. But Idah never took any. "I am a Christian," he said. "I believe in the Bible, and it says that we should not have any gods apart from the one true God. If I put my trust in the muti of the sangomas, God will be jealous. He Himself said so in His Word." One day the team captain insisted that he participate in certain rituals that were supposed to help the team win the match. But he refused, saying, "I must obey God rather than men!"

Over the next few weeks the team lost some very important matches. "It's all your fault," the others said. "You brought us bad luck by not taking the muti!" But Idah still believed that he had done the right thing by obeying the Bible. Soon after that he lost his place in the team. But God had prepared another job for him. Today he is a pastor and a commentator for soccer matches.

We must be careful not to put our trust in good luck charms or mascots that are supposed to bring us good fortune. Do you have a teddy bear or a charm or an armband that you believe can bring you good luck? The Lord doesn't want us to trust in things like that. If you are his child, you do not need a good luck fairy. And even if you wear a cross or fish as a symbol of faith, be careful not to put your trust in that object. Place your trust in the Lord only.

Read the story of the Israelites and the golden cow in Exodus 32. Verse 35 tells us what happened to them!

Trust in the LORD with all your heart. Prov. 3:5

DON'T SKIP THE PIT STOP!

Roland worked on a fruit farm, packing plums, during the school holidays. It was hard work, but he enjoyed doing it. He liked competing with himself. Each day he tried to pack more than he had the previous day. And the more he packed, the more money he got at the end of the week!

Everything went well for the first week and by the end of the week he was known as the champion packer! The second week he really had to exert himself to stay ahead of the rest of the packers. He decided to keep on working when the others had their tea break, and eventually he skipped the lunch break too. But he just couldn't seem to keep up with the others. He couldn't understand it! He started before the others in the morning and kept on going till the shed closed at night and he really did his very best! When they were paid on the Friday evening, he struggled to hide his disappointment. "I don't know why I don't do better!" he said to the farmer. The man looked at him kindly and said, "Maybe you shouldn't skip the pit stop, Roland!"

Roland's mistake was that he forgot to recharge his batteries for the hard work that had to be done. If he had relaxed when the others did and had enjoyed some refreshments, he would have performed better.

We must make sure that we are not so busy that we have no time to recharge our spiritual batteries. We need to set aside time for our pit stops, when we can be quiet before God, speak to Him, and read His Word. Then we will stay spiritually fit.

The Lord wants us to be alert, energetic and to serve Him wholeheartedly. We need enough energy so that we can be friendly, helpful, and caring to others. We also need to be strong so that we can be a witness for Him, and resist the devil when he comes to tempt us. We need enough spiritual fuel to keep going. That's why our quiet time is so important!

Read Isaiah 40:29-31

A DROP IN THE OCEAN

Pat frowned as she read the letter on the church notice board. A children's home had asked for donations of used toys, sports equipment, clothes, toiletries, and canned food. She had things at home that she could give them, but 500 children lived in that home.

Later, in Sunday school, Miss Peterson read Micah 6:8 to them. The theme of her lesson was charity. "How can we obey the command to show mercy?" she asked. "We can take things to the children's home!" Pat said. "We could all bring something next week," Miss Peterson suggested. They were all enthusiastic, except Eric. "What we bring will only be a drop in the ocean!" he said. "But something is better that nothing!" Miss Peterson replied.

Eric's mother was the secretary for the women's group at church and she put the needs of the home on the agenda for their next meeting. Many of the women promised to gather all kinds of things to send to the Sunshine Home. One of these women worked at a big department store in town. She told one of her friends how she had searched for things to send to the children's home. Her manager overheard her. "Mrs. Wilson," he said, "come with me to the storeroom. There are some items there that you can send to this home."

Later that month, when one of the elders came to fetch everything that had been collected for the home, he whistled in surprise. They would need a truck to transport all the stuff. Pat and her friends came to help when the truck was loaded. They made a big banner, which they placed on top of everything. **"From Devon United Church, to the children at Sunshine Home, with love!"**

Pat winked at Eric and said, "The drop in the ocean caused some huge waves!"

Keep your eyes open for opportunities like these!

THE NEST

Mattie watched the finches building nests in the pepper tree in their backyard. One of them had been busy since dawn. He brought some long reeds and weaved them neatly into the nest. Late that afternoon he had finished his job! He settled on top of the nest, threw back his little head, and sang triumphantly. After a while his mate came to inspect the nest. She looked at the new home for a while and then started to tear it apart. She scattered reeds and twigs all over the place, and scolded at the top of her voice. The house was not to her liking at all. The male finch's hard work lay in ruins on the grass.

Slowly, the finch started all over again, with new building material. A few times he tried to use the reeds that had been discarded, but his mate was very fussy. She tore these out and threw them away. She knew exactly what she wanted. Eventually the nest was good enough for her, and she moved in while he perched happily on top of their new home.

She's a real snob! Mattie thought. *Wants the very best and doesn't care about someone else's feelings!* Suddenly she remembered something. Wasn't that exactly what she had done the previous day when her mom had made her a new denim jacket? She had simply ignored the love and care her mom had put into making the jacket. She realized that, even though she had the right to give her opinion, she needn't have been vicious and cruel about it.

Mattie suddenly felt a surge of gratitude toward her mom. Her mom was just like the male finch – she unpicked everything and started again to make the jacket exactly how she wanted it. *I'd like to be as obliging as that!* Mattie thought and began to write a thank you note to her mother.

Read Philippians 4:5.

But the fruit of the Spirit is love, ... gentleness and self-control. Gal. 5:22-23

SHE'S GONE

The headlines in the morning paper read: GRUESOME ACCIDENT DESTROYS FAMILY. All the girls came to school with eyes red from crying. Jolene Rathbone, a sixth grade pupil, had died in that accident. The school choir began practicing the hymn that they would sing at her funeral, and all Jolene's classmates were going to attend the service.

Nobody paid much attention to what was being taught at school that day: their thoughts were somewhere else.

She will never win a race again. She won't have her birthday party next week. We will never again hear her joyful giggle. This was the kind of thing that raced through the minds of all the school children that day.

"I can't get used to it!" said Hannah, her best friend. "It makes me scared!" said Peggy. "We never really think that anyone can die when they are still so young!" "I've never felt so miserable in my whole life," said Val, who was Jolene's neighbor.

The boys all wanted to know how the accident occurred. "Her dad was driving too fast!" Pierre said. "The other driver was drunk!" Hugo insisted. "There's going to be a court case," said Jolene's cousin. "But it won't bring her back!"

At the funeral, the minister, speaking quietly, said, "We are all sad because Jolene is gone. And there's nothing wrong with mourning. Even Jesus cried when his friend Lazarus died. But remember, today she is in a better place than we are. She is with Jesus. She knew Jesus as her Savior and the Bible tells us that she is now in heaven where there is no pain or tears or sadness." Then he read Revelation 21:1-4. Jolene's friends and family were greatly comforted by these words.

Make a card with these words on it and save it for a day when someone you know is sad because of a loved one that has passed away.

He who was seated on the throne said, "I am making everything new!" Rev. 21:5

SEPTEMBER 30

NO SECRETS

Do you feel uncomfortable when you remember that God knows everything about you? Are you hiding certain things from people, hoping that they never find out?

John had a secret like that. He kept a lot of magazines under his mattress that he read whenever nobody else was around. The only other person who knew about these magazines, was Jeff, who had given them to John.

But then John read a pamphlet that had been distributed at church. It warned people about the dangers of pornography. *If you look at pictures and videos that arouse unclean thoughts in your mind, you can get addicted to it. You will begin to feel far away from God, and your conscience will be completely silenced. You will not be able to hear God's voice at all.*

The writer then quoted some verses from the Bible that stated that sinful thoughts were just as bad as sinful deeds. John looked them all up. Matthew 15:19-20 really made an impression on him. Jesus said that bad thoughts can contaminate your whole being.

John had to admit that he felt dirty every time he had looked at those magazines. The tract closed with the words of Jeremiah 4:14, *"Wash the evil from your heart and be saved. How long will you harbor wicked thoughts?"*

John knew what he had to do with those magazines. One day when his parents weren't home, he took them to the backyard and burned the whole lot. "Heavenly Father," he prayed, "forgive me for polluting my mind with this stuff. Let me remember that I cannot hide anything from You. And help me never to do anything of which I ought to be ashamed. For Jesus' sake, Amen."

The next day he put the tract in Jeff's suitcase.

Read Proverbs 4:23.

If anything is excellent or praiseworthy - think about such things. Phil. 4:8

October

WHAT DO HINDUS BELIEVE?

The Daltons rented the movie *City of Joy* to watch one Friday night. It is a gripping film about the lives of people who lived in the streets of Calcutta, one of the biggest cities in India. They were born on the streets and they died there, without ever having lived in a house.

After they had seen the video Elaine and Ben were very curious about these people. "What do they believe?" Elaine asked her parents. "Most people in India are Hindu," her dad said. They serve three main gods, Brahman, Vishnu and Shiva, and 330 000 other gods.

"Wow! Do they have to obey all those gods?" Ben wanted to know. "To a certain extent," his dad replied. "They believe that honoring the gods can assure good karma for them." "What's that?" Elaine asked. "Hindus believe in reincarnation: that when you die your soul comes back to live in another body on earth. The good or bad things you do in one life are linked to the kind of life you will live in the next life. This cause and effect is summed up in the word karma."

"The poor people in last night's film must have had really bad karma!" Ben said. "I'm glad that there are people in India that tell the Hindus about Jesus!" "Yes," their mom said. "There are more than 40 000 Christian missionaries working in India. We must pray for them. Many Hindus have become Christians and now believe that there is only one God who loves them. They believe that because they have accepted Jesus Christ as their Savior, they will go to heaven and live with Him forever when they die."

"Then they will discover what a real City of Joy looks like!" Ben said.

Read Hebrews 9:27 to find out why Christians know that people are not reincarnated. Isaiah 44:6 teaches us that there are no gods apart from our God Almighty.

"I am the first and I am the last; apart from me there is no God." Is. 44:6

EARTHQUAKES

Jeanne couldn't sleep. They had been learning about earthquakes at school. Mr. Jameson had told them what had happened in San Francisco at 16:56 on October 17, 1989. The earthquake lasting only fifteen seconds had rocked the city, causing severe damage. Sixty-seven people died, about four thousand were injured, and the Red Cross had to find accommodation for more than 64 000 people! Homes, businesses, and other buildings were destroyed, and over a million households were left without electricity.

Jeanne thought what it would be like if everything around you started to shake and walls tumbled down. She went to the kitchen. "Are you still awake?" her mom asked. Jeanne said, "I've been thinking about the enormous amount of energy simmering beneath the earth's surface that can erupt at any second." Her mom made Jeanne a cup of hot chocolate, and said, "I understand what you feel, but remember that God is even more awesome. The power of an earthquake can cause a lot of damage, but God's power brings about good things on earth."

"What are you talking about?" Jeanne asked, very interested. "Well, think about the day when God held back the waters of the Red Sea so that the Israelites could pass through. And I have often faced enormous problems and difficulties in my life, but God's power has always ensured that everything has turned out for my best. For example, my friends tried to convince me that following the Lord wasn't worthwhile. It felt if I was being sucked away from my faith by a mighty vacuum cleaner. But God kept me safe."

Jeanne and her mom talked about the awesome power of God and when Jeanne got into bed, she prayed, "Thank You, Lord, that You are omnipotent and that You will always protect me."

**You can read Exodus 14:19-31 to refresh
your memory about God's intervention
when the Israelites faced what seemed impossible.**

OCTOBER 3

DON'T TALK ABOUT IT!

"Be careful not to do your acts of righteousness before men, to be seen by them ... when you give to the needy, do not announce it ... to be honored by men ... do not let your left hand know what your right hand is doing. Then your Father, who sees what is done in secret, will reward you." David read these words from Matthew 6:1-4 one morning before Sunday school.

"I'm going to try that today," he said to himself. "It should be fun!" But he soon found that it wasn't that easy to keep quiet about your good deeds. He started by emptying all the wastepaper baskets in the house, but nobody even noticed it! So when he picked up the one in his dad's study, he dropped it on purpose. His mom heard the noise, saw what he was doing, and said, "Thanks for helping me before I even asked, David." It was very rewarding to get such a warm smile of approval from his mom. But he immediately realized that he had done his good deeds before men! He would have to try again.

This time he decided to put $20 of his own money into the children's thank offering at Sunday school. He would tell nobody how much he had put into the envelope. But when his friend Robbie collected the offerings, he held David's envelope against the light and said, "Wow, you must have put a whole $10 in here!" And before he could stop himself, David retorted, "Not so! It's $20!" His classmates were very impressed, but David was disappointed. He had once again let people know of something that should have been kept a secret.

"This time I'm not going to fail the test again!" he said as he sat down that afternoon to write a thank you note to his Sunday school teacher. He would not write his name at the bottom, he decided. He would just write: **From a secret admirer.**

See how many kind things you can do this week without telling others about it.

"Then your Father, who sees what is done in secret, will reward you." Mt. 6:4

OCTOBER 4

FRANCIS OF ASSISI

More than 800 years ago a man lived in the little Italian town of Assisi and he is still known all across the world today. His name was Francis and he was the son of a very rich merchant. He had been a happy, carefree child, but then he fell ill and had to stay in bed for a long, long time. He spent much of that time thinking about life. When he was finally well again, he had a different outlook on life.

One day he met a leper in the street. At first he turned away from the man in disgust, but then he remembered how much Jesus cared for people like this. He walked up to the man and gave him everything that he had with him that day. Then he bent over the sick man and kissed his deformed hands.

Soon after that he went to live among the poor people in the slums of the town. His father was very upset because he wanted Francis to carry on with the family business. But Francis gave up the luxuries of his home to help people in need. He persuaded a few of his friends to join him in committing their lives to serving God through ministering to poor people, and to living a simple lifestyle. Together they built a little church on the outskirts of the town.

Francis of Assisi did many things, and many legends grew up around him. He loved all animals, and one legend says that he used to preach to them. When he had finished his sermon, the birds would sing their most glorious songs to praise their Creator – or so the legend says!

On October 4 people in Italy hold all kinds of festivities to commemorate the little monk who dedicated his life to the service of the poor and who inspired many others to live simple lives in honor of God.

Read Matthew 5:3-12. This was Francis of Assisi's favorite Scripture passage!

"Blessed are the pure in heart, for they will see God." Mt. 5:8

OcToBeR 5

SURPRISE!

Nick was nervous. His parents weren't believers, and he had often invited them to go to church with him, but they had always said no. But tonight they had agreed to attend the service with him. Nick had joined the church youth group when his friends had invited him, and one Friday night he had given his life to the Lord. After that he started going to Sunday school and church. Now he was wondering what his parents would think of the church service. He prayed, "Lord, please let them like it so that they will want to come again!"

While the pastor was preaching, Nick kept glancing at his parents from the corner of his eye. He tried to see how they were reacting to everything, but they didn't show what they were thinking. When the congregation sang, his parents stood up but they did not join in the singing. Nick wondered what they would say after the sermon.

What a great surprise awaited him! When they got home, his dad said, "Tonight's service brought back some memories of my childhood, when I attended church regularly. Maybe I'll go with you more often." And his mom said, "I never went to church when I was a child, but tonight did me a world of good. Maybe I'll also go again." Nick couldn't hide his joy. "That will be great!" he exclaimed. "Then you can see me in the Youth Play next week!"

Before he climbed into bed that night, he knelt next to his bed. "Lord, thank You so much for working in Mom and Dad's lives. I know that there's a verse in the Bible that says that You never leave any work incomplete. Please let there be a day when my parents accept You as their Lord and Savior!"

**Look up the verse Nick referred to in your Bible.
You will find it in Philippians 1:6. And never
forget that grownups can be led to Christ by a child.**

OCTOBER 6

HOW GOD PROVIDED

Mrs. Fisch and her husband were missionaries to China and lived in the town of Kuyuan. They didn't mind that there were no conveniences like running water or electricity because they were excited about being able to share the gospel message with the people of that region.

One day Mr. Fisch became seriously ill. His wife gave him some medicine, but he did not get better. They did not consult the village doctor because his medicines were made from traditional ingredients like powdered snake. She couldn't get him to a hospital either, because the nearest one was a week's journey by horse and cart. What could she do to help him get better? Mrs. Fisch prayed fervently and asked the Lord to heal her husband.

One night, when he was at his worst, there was a knock at the door. When Mrs. Fisch opened the door she saw twelve men in uniform standing there. "Have you perhaps got place for us to sleep tonight?" one of the men asked in English. "Please come in!" she said. "My husband is very sick, but I will find a space for each of you."

"Well," replied the officer, "one of my men is a doctor and he has a whole bag full of medicine. Maybe he can help." The doctor examined Mr. Fisch and had just the right medicine for him.

Why did those soldiers come to Kunyuan that night? They were on an expedition to the interior of China and we believe that God had sent them to that particular house that night. The story had some even more startling results. When the people of Kuyuan heard how the prayers of the Christians had been answered, they were eager to learn more about the God of love who cares so miraculously for His children.

Read Psalm 34:17. Why not learn the words by heart?

WHO ARE YOU?

A little, barefoot, scantily dressed boy was standing in front of a shop window, shivering in the cold. A smartly dressed woman walked past. When she saw the little fellow with his nose pressed against the window, she stopped and asked kindly, "What are you looking at?" "At the shoes!" he answered, a bit embarrassed. She noticed his dirty little feet and felt sorry for him. "Come with me!" she said and took him into the shop. The assistant looked surprised when the rich lady walked in with the neglected child at her side. He wrinkled his nose in disgust when he looked at the boy's dirty feet.

"Do you have a basin with hot water and soap, and a towel for us?" the lady asked. The man brought what she needed. The lady sat the boy down on one of the smart seats, took off her gloves, and went on her knees to wash and dry his feet. After that she asked for socks and shoes for the little fellow. He tried on different pairs until they found a pair that suited him. She paid the assistant, gave the little boy a hug, and said goodbye at the door of the shop. As she walked away, she felt a tug at her coat. "Lady," the child asked in awe, "are you God's wife?"

This story reminds us of the passage in the Bible where Jesus washed the feet of His disciples. You can read it in John 13:1-15. It also helps us remember that we are God's representatives on earth. He wants to use us to help people who are in need.

Jesus was always on the lookout for people He could serve and help, and we should also have our antennas alert to see where we can show people Jesus' love and compassion. Then people will want to know Him and become His children.

Be on the lookout for someone who needs some help, and do what you can to show them God's love.

"I have set you an example that you should do as I have done for you." Jn. 13:15

FREE OF CHARGE

Sandra woke up. *Where am I?* she wondered. *This looks like a hospital room!* And then she remembered. She had gone to a movie with some of her friends and afterwards they had driven around for a while. She had deliberately ignored her promise to her mom that she would be home as soon as the movie ended. School was out and the summer holidays stretched ahead with lots of plans for fun times. Who wanted to go home so early? And who cared that Andrew was driving without a license?

She tried to remember what had happened, but her head hurt so badly that it was best just to lie still. She noticed a huge flower arrangement next to her bed. She picked up the card that lay next to it. It read, "We love you! From Dad and Mom." Sandra felt so ashamed! Her parents hadn't been all that happy for her to go out the previous night. She had told them all kinds of lies about who was driving and what film they were going to see. Slowly she remembered the details of what had happened. There had been shrieking brakes, screams, a loud crash, pieces of shattered glass, flashing lights, and then everything went black …

Somebody looked around the door of her room. It was her parents. Her mom kissed her softly on the forehead. Her dad took her hands in his. Sandra started to cry. "I behaved disgustingly and you are so kind!" she sobbed. "Don't cry," her mom said soothingly. "Everything's going to be OK." They told her that her friends had all got off with slight injuries, but the car was a write-off. She had been given stitches in her head, but she would be able to go home in a few days. Before her parents left her that morning, her dad prayed, "Thank You, Lord, that You protected Sandra and her friends and that You love us, even when we are disobedient!" For the first time Sandra understood the meaning of the words unconditional love.

**Read 1 John 4:16. God loves us
unconditionally because He is love.**

OCTOBER 9

YOU HAVE THREE SECONDS!

Chris shoved his last T-shirt into his backpack. In a few minutes his parents would arrive to take him home from the clinic where he had lived for the last six months. He thought about the day when he first got here: hopelessly hooked on drugs and with morbid suicidal thoughts: a total failure!

Ever since he had first smoked marijuana, his life had slowly deteriorated. At first the pleasant sensation had helped him escape from the stress of everyday life. But soon he had to use more and more of it to get the same effect. Eventually he started using stronger drugs until he completely lost control over his life. The only thing that mattered to him then was where and how he could get his next fix.

He began lying and stealing to get hold of it. Life had lost all meaning for him. When his parents found out what was going on, it was too late for simple solutions. The only hope they had was booking him into this clinic.

One night he confessed to one of the counselors that he had lost the battle against addiction. He realized that the Lord was the only One who could help him. After he had confessed his sins and asked God's forgiveness, he could start walking the difficult road of withdrawal. And now he was ready to face the outside world again. He knew that without God by his side, he would not succeed.

When he left with his parents, the principal greeted him with these words, "Remember you have three seconds!" "What does that mean?" his mom asked as they drove away. "It's the three seconds after my friends have asked me to drink with them again!" he said. "In that short time I must decide what I am going to do. With God's help I'll say NO!"

Read the Bible verse that Chris put up in his room as soon as he got home that day: 2 Timothy 1:7.

Do not think about how to gratify the desires of the sinful nature. Rom. 13:14

WHAT THE KING LEARNED

A cruel king once was riding his horse in the meadows. When he got to a little hill, he rested for a while and looked at the fields around him. As he looked, he saw a fox creeping up on a lamb that was innocently grazing on the green grass. He caught the lamb by the throat, but before he could eat it, a dog appeared on the scene. He grabbed the fox's back leg between his sharp teeth, and the fox ran away limping.

While the dog was guarding the injured lamb the farmer came and used his whip to chase him away. At this point the owner of the dog rode up on his horse, and punched the farmer because he had hurt his dog. The horse bolted in fright and threw his master to the ground.

"Well, well!" said the king. "This has been an interesting little scene. How clearly it has shown me that cruel deeds lead to bad results."

When he arrived back at his castle, he told his counselors, "From today onwards I am going to rule over my people with kindness. I know now that one act of aggression can cause a whole chain of cruel events. It must therefore also be true that one deed of kindness can bring about a whole chain of good results."

Since that day the cruel king thought twice before he did anything in anger.

Read about these two chains in Ephesians 4:31-32 and ask the Lord to make you a link in the chain of kindness.

BLESSED ASSURANCE

Fanny Crosby became blind when she was six years old. But she was a remarkable little girl. She memorized large portions of Scripture when she was still very young. She knew the first five books of the Bible, most of the Psalms, and many books from the New Testament by heart!

She loved nature and, because she was blind, she used her other senses to appreciate its beauties. She listened to the sounds of nature with sensitivity: birdsong, running water, rustling leaves. And she was able to identify most plants by their fragrance. She also enjoyed touching flowers, leaves, and the bark of trees. She wrote songs and poems about her experiences. She had decided that she would not allow blindness to spoil her life. She brought sunshine wherever she went.

Fanny loved the Lord passionately and she wrote many songs of praise for Him. By the end of her life she had written more than eight thousand hymns to the glory of God. Many of these hymns are still sung in churches all over the world today.

She was often invited to talk at meetings or church services to tell people about the special challenges that she, as a blind person, had to face. She did this gladly, and many people heard her testimony of God's faithfulness in her life.

One night, when she was ninety-four years old, she wrote a letter and a poem before she went to bed, and that night she passed away in her sleep.

When you next sing or hear the hymn *Blessed Assurance*, think about the courageous woman who wrote that song more than a hundred years ago and who lived a life of victory in spite of her severe disability.

**Would you agree that 1 Corinthians 4:16-17
could also be applied to someone like Fanny?**

He will remind you of my way of life in Christ Jesus. 1 Cor. 4:17

WHO WAS REBECCA'S ANGEL?

Eph. 2:10   For we are ... created in Christ Jesus to do good works.

"Are there really angels who look after each believer?" Jo wanted to know at Youth Club. "Oh yes!" Leah, the youth leader said. "You can read about it in Hebrews 1:14. But I think we can also be angels for one another." "How?" one of the girls asked. "We can do good things for each other in secret!" Leah answered. Each month we can do something special for someone else without letting them know who has done it."

Now everybody started talking. Ideas came tumbling out. Leah then wrote the names of each of the youth club kid on strips of papers and put them in a basket. One by one, they pulled names out of the basket. "For the rest of the year you must do kind, little things for that person in secret!" she said.

David frowned when he looked at the name he had drawn. When the rest of the children had gone home, he stayed behind. "I got Rebecca's name," he muttered. "I really do not like her!" Leah was surprised and spoke seriously to David. "You know that Jesus said that we should love our enemies," she reminded him. "Yes, but He didn't say that we should like them!" "We need to treat everyone with kindness," Leah explained. "I'm not taking part in this game, and that's final!" David said.

A few months later, the kids had the opportunity to tell each other what their angel had done for them. When Rebecca shared, everyone agreed that her angel had really taken the most trouble of all. "One morning there were flowers on my desk. One afternoon I found some information for the project I was struggling with. And one morning when I went to fetch my bike, it had been washed and polished." Leah glanced at David, who was playing with his pencil as if he had nothing to do with all this. *I know of an angel that has made God very proud*, she thought with gratitude.

**Why don't you try being an angel to
somebody that you do not particularly like?**

OCTOBER 13

SUFFERING

Ina had never thought that so many sad things could happen to one person in such a short while! Within one year her brother had died in an accident, her dad had lost his job and her mom had contracted cancer and was now staying in a frail care center. Ina had to help with all the chores in the house, cook meals, and still cope with her schoolwork. And she and her dad were both struggling to cope with their grief.

What carried her through those difficult times? Her Christian friends and members of her church helped her in many different ways. Her heart was so broken that she struggled to pray on her own, but people from the congregation came to pray with them often.

Even though she was weepy a lot of the time, her friends did not avoid her. Neighbors brought round cards and notes of encouragement, little gifts, and cooked meals to show how much they cared. One Saturday the Smiths invited her to spend the day on their yacht. And one of the elders arranged for people to come and help with the ironing and cleaning windows.

Ina's mom died after some months in the frail care center. But at her funeral the pastor read something that gave her some hope. *"These in white robes – who are they, and where did they come from? … These are they who have come out of the great tribulation … He who sits on the throne will spread his tent over them. Never again will they hunger; never again will they thirst. …. For the Lamb at the center of the throne will be their shepherd. … And God will wipe away every tear from their eyes"* (Rev. 7:13-15).

She held onto these words as a promise that things would eventually be better for her.

**Think how you can help
someone who is suffering now.**

THE TASTE BERRY

Her is an old story that gives us something to think about. One morning the sun did not appear in the sky. There was no dawn, no daylight, and no birds sang. At twelve noon, it was still pitch dark outside. There were only bats and owls and other night creatures in the sky. People had to work by candlelight, and the streetlights had to be given extra gas. People did not go to sleep that night, but wept and cried out and prayed that the sun would shine again.

Early the next morning everyone gathered outside and looked expectantly toward the east. When the sky began to shine with the glorious colors that heralded the rising of the sun, they cheered and laughed with joy. And as the rays of the sun tipped the mountaintops, people fell to their knees and praised God. Never again did any of them take the rising of the sun for granted.

Too often we only learn to be grateful for something when we have almost lost it. It often takes a severe illness for people to appreciate good health. We should learn to thank God for all the good things that He gives us. When we regularly count our blessings, we will be happy and grateful people.

There is a legend about a berry that is said to grow in Central Africa. It is called a Taste Berry because after you have eaten one, everything else that you eat tastes very sweet. People who live where it grows are very glad when they find one of these berries because it can make other bland and tasteless food taste delicious.

Gratitude is like a taste berry for our hearts. If we are grateful for the things that we have, the things we face that are not so pleasant will be easier to handle. If we are thankful for the daylight, the night will not seem so dark after all.

**Read Psalm 145 as a hymn of
praise and thanksgiving to the Lord.**

YOUR OWN 1 CORINTHIANS 13

Miss Hardy gave the sixth grade class some Sunday school home-work. She asked them to read 1 Corinthians 13 and then rewrite it in words that were relevant to their own lives. She explained that this chapter is, apart from Psalm 23, probably the best-known passage of Scripture. Because we hear it so often, we don't think about what the words really mean. She gave each one of them a strip of paper and asked each of them to paraphrase one verse. "Next Sunday we will put together our very own chapter on love."

It was wonderful to hear how the kids had understood Paul's love message to the Corinthians. Miss Hardy was so thrilled with the answers they brought the following Sunday that she had it printed in the church newsletter. Many members of the congregation thanked the children for once again opening their eyes to the beauty of this passage.

This is what they wrote:

> If you love someone, you do not mind waiting for that person. You regard that person as your friend and you want the very best for him or her. You shouldn't boast about yourself to your friend, or be nasty to him. Always try to encourage your friend. Never lie to your friend and be prepared to make sacrifices when your friend needs you to. If your friend has done something wrong, don't keep reminding him of it. Give him another chance. You should cry with your friend when he is sad and laugh with your friend when he is glad. Notice all the good things your friend does, and trust him. Stand by him at all times because the greatest gift you can give him is your love.

Try to write your own paraphrase of 1 Corinthians 13.

THE STORY CIRCLE

The Thompsons had a special family tradition. Whenever they go on vacation, they set aside one night to have a story circle. Dad, Mom, and all four boys gather around the campfire or lie on the grass in the moonlight and tell each other stories.

One night they all gathered on the big sofa bed in their uncle's cabin in the mountains. Dad started with a story about when he had gone hunting. Danny told the story of Marco Polo, which he had learned in history. John gave the others the beginning of a well-known tale and told the rest of them to create their own story: "There was a granny and a wolf and an axe ..." The family laughed at his clever way round the tradition! James had just started reading *The Three Musketeers*, and he started telling the others all about it so enthusiastically and in so much detail that Dad had to cut him off! Then André told a story that he heard at kindergarten. "A donkey had to take a basketful of bread to town and the baker sent his dog with him to look after him. On the way there the dog got hungry and asked the donkey for some bread. But Donkey said, 'You can eat grass like I do!' Just then a lion came running out of the forest to attack the donkey. Donkey shouted, 'Dog, Dog, please chase the lion away!' But Dog replied, 'You didn't help me, so I won't help you!' Then Lion ate the donkey and the bread."

"What can we learn from this story?" Dad asked. "My teacher said that we must be good to other people and then they will be good to us!" André replied. Finally Mom told a Bible story about Jesus who went around helping poor people. "He helped people because He cared for them and not because He wanted something from them," she said. "We must be like Jesus."

"Who will pray for us tonight?" Dad asked. Danny prayed, "Lord, help us to be kind to people who have nothing to offer us. And thanks for tonight's story circle. Amen."

Read Matthew 5:43-48.

OCTOBER 17

THE MUSIC BOX

You have probably seen some of the delightful musical boxes that girls often keep their jewelry in. When the lid is raised, they play cheerful tunes. Some of these boxes must be wound up before the music can be heard, and others have tiny ballerinas inside that dance when the music plays.

There is a story of a woman who had an amazing experience with such a music box. God uses all kinds of things in all kinds of wonderful ways in people's lives.

But one night, as Jean was about to get into bed, she suddenly heard the tune from her music box begin to play. Now Jean lived alone, the music box was in a back room she did not often go into. *That's odd!* she thought. *It's been such a long time since I last wound up my box and there is nobody in the house to lift the lid.* She went to investigate but when she entered the room the music stopped. As she was turning back to her bedroom, she smelled something strange. She investigated further and discovered an electric wire that was beginning to burn through.

Immediately she switched off the electricity and phoned the fire brigade. When the firefighters arrived, they found that the wiring in that back room was faulty. "If you had not let us know, there would have been a serious fire in your house tonight!" they said.

When the firefighters had left, she fell on her knees and praised God for warning her about the threat of fire. She was overwhelmed by His love for her, and was convinced that He had caused the music box to play a tune to attract her attention to the impending danger.

**Proverbs 14:26 reminds us of
how God protects His children.**

He who fears the LORD has a secure fortress. Prov. 14:26

OCTOBER 18

BECAUSE OF LOVE

"My parents don't love me," Donny said to the school psychologist. "Why do you think that?" she asked. "They punish me unfairly!" "For example?" she asked. "If I don't do my homework, or if I come home late," he pouted. "Are you a Christian?" Miss Palmer asked. "Yes," Donny answered. "Then I'm going to read you something," she said and took a Bible from her drawer. She turned to Hebrews 12:6: *"The Lord disciplines those he loves, and he punishes everyone he accepts as his son."*

"What does this verse say about why God punishes His children?" she asked. "Because He loves them," said Donny softly. "Your parents discipline you for the same reason. If they didn't care about you and love you, they would let you run wild and do anything you wanted to. And what would happen to you if that were so?"

Miss Palmer then read verse 11, *"No discipline seems pleasant at the time, but painful. Later on, however, it produces a harvest of righteousness and peace for those who have been trained by it."*

"What does that mean?" Donny wanted to know. "It means that your parents are trying to help you to form good habits, because these will help you make a success of your life. If you do not learn to do your work diligently and be on time for your appointments you will not do very well when you are grown up and have to make your own way in life."

Later that afternoon Donny took his dog for a walk. Shadow was still very young and restless. He kept pulling on the leash. "If you don't listen to me now, you won't do well in the dog show next month!" he said in sternly. The puppy whimpered. Donny knelt beside him and gave him a hug. "Remember, I train you because I love you!" he said.

Read Hebrews 12:5-11.

WHY?

Marsha was helping her grandmother to make bread. "Grand-ma," she said, "Ivan said that it's not fair that God should punish him so severely. He only went round the block on his brother's motorbike and then he was in an accident. Now he has lost his leg and he will have to cope without it for the rest of his life. Do you think that it was God's way of punishing him?"

Grandma answered, "How my heart goes out to Ivan! It is true that God sometimes punishes people through the conse-quences of the choices they make. But not all tragedies are a pun-ishment from God. Sometimes they are simply the result of our own bad choices. Ivan knew that he was not experienced enough to drive a motorbike in a busy street. He risked his life and this terrible accident happened." Grandma continued, "I know that God loves Ivan very much, and I know that He will help Ivan in a special way with the loss of his leg. I believe that if Ivan stays close to God, he can become a spiritually strong person because of the things he is going through."

After a few minutes Grandma spoke again. "In Bible days people also thought that illnesses or disabilities were God's pun-ishment. But Jesus showed that this is not so. He once said that a certain man was not blind because of his sins or those of his parents, but because God could be glorified through him." "But how can God be glorified if Ivan has to hop around on one leg?" Marsha wanted to know. They were forming the dough into balls that could fit into the bread pans. "Ivan will learn to trust God for everything because of his disability. And when you put your trust in God and not in yourself, wonderful things can happen," Grandma said as she put the pans into the oven. "God forms us into vessels for His glory and sometimes we have to spend some time in the fiery furnace before He can use us!"

Read what Paul had to say on this subject in 2 Corinthians 12:9-10.

For when I am weak, then I am strong. 2 Cor. 12:10

OCTOBER 20

STOP THE FIGHTING!

As soon as Hugo's mom walked through the door, she sensed that something was wrong. The boys had been in a fight, she realized. "What happened?" she asked. "Some bullies wanted to hurt Billy, but I fixed them," Lawrence said. "They took his lunchbox and when he tried to take it back, they punched him!" Lawrence tried to clean up the bloodstains on his shirt. Only then did mom notice that his jacket was also torn. "I didn't want to fight, but they wouldn't listen. I couldn't let them hurt my brother!" he said fiercely. Then Billy spoke up, "Lawrence really let them have it! They won't bother me again," he said proudly.

Mom had taught the boys from the time that they were little that God wanted them to be peacemakers. But she also realized that there would be times when her sons would have to defend themselves. She took out some band-aid and started cleaning their wounds. Then she took the torn jacket and walked to her sewing machine. She smiled. The previous week Lawrence and Billy had been fighting like cat and dog and she had taught them how to solve their differences in a peaceful way. But today, when they were up against enemies, they could stand together.

"Why are you smiling?" Billy asked. "I was thinking about something that I read this morning. The Bible says that there will come a day when all fighting and wars will come to an end. Won't that be great!" she exclaimed. Lawrence asked, "Where did you read that?" He was nursing his bleeding knuckles and such a possibility sounded very good to him. "In Isaiah 2. But it also said that these things will only happen after everybody had confessed that our God is Lord of all!"

That night before bedtime, Billy and Lawrence both prayed for peace in their home, at school, and in the whole world. "Yes, Lord! Let your Kingdom come!" their mom added.

Read Isaiah 2:1-5.

OCTOBER 21

WE SHOULD WARN PEOPLE

Betty sometimes worried about Sheila, her best friend. One day she asked her dad, "Will Sheila go to hell if she doesn't follow Jesus?" "Yes," her dad said. Betty was shocked. Sheila had often teased her because she went to church and because she prayed, but she had never been nasty about it. "Are you sure there's actually a place like hell?" she wanted to know. "Oh yes," her dad said. "The Bible mentions it in a few places." "And who will go there?" she asked. "People who choose to live without God. If they keep on telling God that He must leave them alone, He eventually does just that. When they die they will find themselves in a place where God never goes. And that is hell," her dad said with a shiver.

Betty thought about her friend. Once Sheila had said, "Nobody, not even God, will tell me how to lead my life. I will decide for myself!" Betty realized that she would have to warn Sheila. But how?

Then her dad started talking again, "Some people do not know that they are on a road that takes them further and further from God. They also do not know where that road is leading. You can start by praying for Sheila," he added. "Only God can change her heart. Ask Him to show you how best to talk to her about these things. Remember that He cares even more about her than you do. He doesn't want her to go to hell. He sent His only Son into the world to die on a cross, so that people needn't go to hell. He wants them to live with Him in heaven for ever and ever!"

That night Betty prayed, "Lord, help me to make Shirley understand how much You love her so that she can start walking on the path that leads to heaven! Amen. "

Read what 2 Thessalonians 1:8-9 says about hell.

THE TENTH COMMANDMENT

Jeremy threw his bike on the floor in the garage. He was sick and tired of the old and rusty contraption. He wanted a mountain bike! He rushed past his mom without saying a word to her and went to his room where he plopped down on his bed. How could he get enough money to buy a bike like Arnold's? Maybe he could sell some of his mom's flowers without her knowing. He was startled by his own thoughts. *What's the matter with me?* he thought. *I let Satan tempt me to steal out of sheer jealousy!*

That night when he was studying his Sunday school lesson, he was surprised to find some answers on questions about the tenth commandment. What a coincidence! For the first time in his life he understood why God had made that law. He had always thought that it was unreasonable. He could readily understand why stealing was wrong. Or killing someone. Or getting divorced. But coveting? How could that be such a serious offence?

But now he realized that envy could open up the door to a lot of other sins. When you covet something, it makes you jealous, and it makes you ungrateful and grumpy. And in the end you might have so much envy in your heart that it could lead to stealing! The Sunday school lesson referred to David, who envied somebody who had a beautiful wife and then, in the end, killed that man so that he could marry his widow.

For homework Jeremy had to make a list of things for which he was grateful. "Gratitude is the best weapon against jealousy!" their Sunday school teacher had said. At the top of his list, Jeremy wrote, "Old Faithful, my ramshackle bicycle!"

**Read the tenth commandment in
Exodus 20:17 and make a list of at least
ten things for which you can thank God.**

"You shall not covet ... anything that belongs to your neighbor. Ex. 20:17

CHILI BEAN, RELAX!

"What are genes, Grandma?" Beth asked. She was sitting at the kitchen table in her grandma's small apartment. Every Monday afternoon after gym she waited there until her parents could come and fetch her. "A gene is a particle in your blood through which the characteristics of your parents are passed on to you," Grandma replied. " Like what?" Beth asked. "You have red hair and green eyes like your father. They were passed on to you through genes." "Is that why I am just as impatient as Daddy?" she asked. "Maybe," grandma said. But Beth had more questions. "Where did Daddy get that gene from?" she asked. "Not from you – you are never impatient!" Grandma laughed. "There was a time when I was very quick-tempered too! My family used to call me Chili-bean! I got frustrated if things didn't happen fast enough. I once got into trouble for kicking the traffic lights. "I would never have guessed," Beth said with surprise. It was hard to believe that her granny, who was always so cool and collected, would do something like that!

"So what made you change?" she asked. "You are never ill-tempered or difficult at all now!" "Well, God taught me a few lessons," she said. "When I hurt my back in an accident, I had to lie flat on my bed for a very long time. While I was there, the Holy Spirit taught me patience. I wasn't able to rush around as I used to."

"Must something like that happen before anyone can change for the better?" Beth asked, worried. "Oh no!" Grandma replied. "You can ask God to teach you to be patient. Every time you think, 'I really cannot wait one second longer,' you should pray. Ask the Holy Spirit to make you more and more like Jesus." Grandma gave her a card with Galatians 5:22 on it. The word patience was underlined with a red pen. Underneath was written: Chili bean, relax!

Read Proverbs 14:29.

HONESTY IS THE BEST POLICY

A terrible thing had happened! Jack's brand new bike had been stolen at school. But he wasn't too upset. "It's no big deal," he said. "Don said that the insurance company will pay us out and I can get a new bicycle again." "Did you lock your bike?" his dad asked. "No," Jack admitted. He was embarrassed because he knew that he had been negligent. "Then the insurance company won't pay a cent!" his dad said. "But Dad, we don't need to tell them!" he argued. "And what will you say when the man from the insurance company asks you if your bicycle was locked?"

Jack went to his room. Tears weren't far away. *Do I have to be so honest?* he wondered. *We pay the insurance company a lot of money each month – surely they can cover the cost of a new bike, and if they want to be fussy, we can just tell a little lie?* But he realized that his parents wouldn't see things this way at all. They were always "honest as daylight" as his grandfather often said.

The next day Jack came up with a very clever solution. "Dad, I can get a mate for Chai. And within a year I can sell their puppies so that I can buy another bicycle!" " And how will you get around in the meantime?" his dad asked. He was thrilled that Jack had thought of such an original plan. "My dad can lend me the money in the meantime!" he suggested with a twinkle in his eyes. Jack's father put his hand into his pocket and took out his checkbook. He also fetched a note pad and drew up a contract.

And that is how Chai got a mate, Lulu, who gave birth to eight gorgeous puppies a few months later. And eight children got a special Christmas surprise that year! A lively little dachshund came to cheer up each of their homes.

Proverbs 12:22 explains how God feels about liars. Also take note of what He says about truthful people.

WORKING WITH CLAY

It was quiet in the family room of the house at Seaside. Mr. Scott had invited his Sunday school class to his beach house for the weekend. He had a few things he wanted them to think about before they started high school. He had given each kid a sheet of paper and a pen and asked them to write down three goals for their high school career. Then he said, "Circle the goal that you think would please the Lord the most." After that he gave each one a piece of clay. They had to make a symbol that would represent that goal.

They got stuck into making clay symbols. Fred was trying to make a shoe. "I want to walk with Jesus," he said. Maude made a heart and said, "I want to show God's love wherever I go." Helen was the artistic one. She sculptured two beautiful hands out of her clay. She said, "I want to do things with my hands that will encourage other people!" Chris made a soccer ball. "I want to make the school team!" he said. "Will that please God?" one of the girls asked. "Of course," he said, "because I'm going to do it for Him!"

Eventually all the masterpieces were displayed on the kitchen table: there was a star, a vase, a candle, a book, and a cross. When everybody had had an opportunity to say something about their clay model, they sang together: "Let the beauty of Jesus be seen in me, All His wondrous compassion and purity! Oh, Thou Spirit Divine, All my nature refine, Till the beauty of Jesus be seen in me!"

Then Mr. Scott prayed, "Lord, You have seen what ambitions these children have for their high school days. Help them to make their dreams come true so that You can be glorified through them! Amen"

Read 2 Corinthians 4:7 and think
what you would have made with the clay
if you had been at Seaside that weekend.

O LORD ... we are the clay, you are the potter. Is. 64:8

THE CRASH HELMET

Freddy was very excited when he got a skateboard for his birthday. But, together with the skateboard, his parents had also given him a crash helmet. "I don't need this," he said. "My friends don't wear them when they go skateboarding!" "Unless you wear it, you will not go skateboarding," his dad insisted. Freddy went to his room, sulking.

But three weeks later something happened that convinced Freddy that wearing his crash helmet was actually a good idea. Eddie, one of their school's best cyclists, had fallen off his bike and was rushed to hospital. He was not wearing a crash helmet when the accident occurred, and was in a coma for three months. His skull had been fractured. One by one, his friends, after visiting him in hospital, began to wear their helmets when they rode their skateboards or went cycling. By the time Eddie came back to school, it had become quite the in thing to wear headgear.

There is a special helmet that God's children should wear. You will find out about it in Ephesians 6:17. You need to wear this helmet to protect your brain because that is where your thoughts come from. The devil, our number one enemy, wants to cause havoc in our minds. That's why the Bible teaches us to wear the helmet of salvation. Through TV shows, music, books, magazines, or the Internet Satan tries to contaminate our minds. When we put on the helmet of salvation, we remind ourselves that we are children of the Living God and we find the strength to say NO to evil thoughts. Then Satan cannot penetrate our minds with his evil ideas.

We must read our Bible regularly and we must choose to think good thoughts. Ask God to help you to make the right choices about what you watch and listen to.

In Ephesians 6:10-17 you will find a
list of weapons you can use against Satan.

PERSEVERANCE WINS THROUGH

Not so very long ago, millions of people around the world suffered from polio. It is a terrible disease that causes paralysis or even death. Many people, even today, have a serious disability because they had polio when they were young. Years ago scientists anxiously sought a cure against this dreaded disease. But nothing seemed to work. It seemed to be a hopeless task.

Dr. Jonas Salk committed his life to finding a cure and a prevention for poliomyelitis. In 1954 he announced that, after 200 experiments, he had developed a vaccine that could be used to prevent polio.

People around the world honored him for his hard work and for not giving up until he had developed a good vaccine. Since then polio has almost been wiped off the face of the earth. When journalists asked him how he felt when 199 of his experiments failed, he told them that he had never failed. "I learned something valuable from each experiment I performed," he said. Instead of seeing his unsuccessful trials as setbacks, he had used each one to learn something.

We should try to develop a similar approach to our work and to the things we pray for. Some people get discouraged much too easily. That's why Jesus said we shouldn't get tired of praying. While you are waiting for an answer to your prayers, you can learn valuable lessons. Read the story in Luke 11:1-13. What does this parable teach us? Ask God to help you not to give up when you have to complete a task or when you don't see your answers to prayer immediately. Imagine what would have happened if Dr. Salk had given up after 199 trials!

**Write down seven prayer requests.
Pray for one of those things on each
day this week and see what happens!**

LIKE JESUS

He took up our infirmities and carried our sorrows. Is. 53:4

Rocky Dennis had elephantiasis. The kids at school often teased him because his face was completely deformed by the disease. One of his classmates once asked him, "Hey, Rocky, why doesn't a freak like you join the circus? You could make a lot of money, you know!" But in spite of all this, Rocky remained friendly and kind. Sometimes he joined in and made fun of himself. Because of his good humor, he was very popular at school. After a while his friends hardly even noticed his distorted facial features.

He loved helping other people. And that is why he offered to help at a camp for blind young people. There he met a lovely blind girl, who appreciated him very much. Because she could not see him, she couldn't judge him by his appearance. He was extremely patient with her and taught her various things, like helping her to understand how colors differ from one other. He did this by putting different objects in her hand that she could associate with each color. Blue was a block of ice, red was a hot stone, and white was a piece of cotton wool.

A beautiful friendship developed between them, but unfortunately, when her parents saw what he looked like, they wouldn't allow her to see him again. Rocky was very disappointed, but he did not get bitter over it. He carried on with his life of service to others and he always forgave people who treated him unfairly.

A film called *Mask* was made of his life and when Christians see this film, they cannot help but think about Jesus. He was also rejected by people, and killed on the cross, yet He loved and forgave people and helped them in any way He could.

Think how you can treat somebody kindly who has been cruel to you.

OCTOBER 29

DO'S AND DON'TS

Nancy sighed when she went into her room. Her mom had once again put a note on her mirror: *Always remember to hang up your wet towel.* Almost every day she found a note somewhere with some do or don't on it. "I'm sure there's no other home in the world that has so many rules!" she said. "Why don't you raise it at our next family meeting?" her sister Alice suggested. They liked the regular family meetings they had, because it gave them a chance to mention their grievances in a positive setting.

Sunday night after supper, the family sat around the table. Dad asked, "Would anyone like to say thank you for anything?" Giles thanked his dad for taking him to school when his bike had a puncture. Alice thanked Giles for helping her with her science project. "And does anyone have anything to complain about?" their dad asked. Nancy saw her chance. "Yes, I want to know why it is necessary to have so many rules and regulations in our home."

Her mom spoke up. "God appointed us as your parents to teach you how to live. If we do not do that, then we disobey Him. The rules we have in this house are to help you to learn good habits." Dad had an idea. He gave each member of the family a sheet of paper. Then he said, "Draw four columns. In the first one, write one of the rules in our home. In the second column, you can write the reason for it. The third column is for you to mention what benefit you get out of it. And in the fourth column, you can suggest what punishment would be appropriate for someone who doesn't keep the rule. In this way we can all have a say in how this home is run." He had even more ideas, " Next week we can make a poster and write the best rules on it and then we'll put it up for all to see!" Even Nancy nodded her head. It did seem like a reasonable plan of action!

Perhaps your family can do something similar.
Write Proverbs 1:8 at the top of your family's poster.

Listen, ... to your father's instruction and ... your mother's teaching. Prov 1:8

THE HERO OF EVEREST

Have you heard of Sir Edmund Hillary? He was the first man to climb to the top of Mount Everest, the highest mountain in the world. Tinseng Norgay, a Sherpa from that region, was his guide during the expedition.

Edmund had been a farmer from New Zealand. But from his earliest childhood, he had loved mountaineering and he had always loved challenges. For almost a hundred years people from the Western world had tried to reach the top of the highest peak in the Himalayan Mountains and at 11:30 on the morning of May 29, 1953, Hillary and Norgay finally reached the top of Everest. Since then more than a thousand people have achieved the same goal, and almost 200 people have died while trying to reach the summit!

Edmund Hillary was knighted by the queen of England and was given the title Sir. He traveled the world talking about his experiences, and became a very rich man. What do you think he did with the millions of dollars that he received? He could have built himself a mansion or he could have retired to live in luxury. But instead, he decided to do something for the poor Sherpas who lived against the slopes of the Himalaya Mountains. He built schools, hospitals, and clinics for them, and made roads and bridges. He ensured that electricity and water were laid on in that area, and he even built an airport.

The Hero of Everest, as he was later known, decided to do something for the people who helped him to become famous. When people asked him why he spent so much time and money on projects to give the Sherpas a better life, he answered, "I was brought up believing that it is our duty to help people who are less fortunate than ourselves."

Isn't that what we as Christians should also believe and do?

Read what the Bible teaches us in Romans 13:8-10.

OCTOBER 31

WHY HALLOWEEN?

The eighth grade Sunday school class wanted to organize a Halloween party. Mr. Green looked at them thoughtfully and said, "I think you should first do some research about Halloween and then we can talk more about your idea."

The next week the kids were eager to discuss what they had learned about Halloween. "It's not just a matter of hollowed pumpkins and strange masks!" Julian said. "It is a celebration involving evil spirits and demons. I don't think I want to be a guest at a party that thinks demons are cool," he added. "Nerd!" Lucille taunted. The class shared what they had discovered about Halloween in the library and on the Internet.

In Ireland summer ends at the end of October. The Irish people believed that spirits were allowed to mingle with people on earth on that day to look for human bodies that they wanted to live in. People were frightened and so lit big fires in their homes and did their best to look unattractive to the wandering spirits.

But when people in that part of the world became Christians they decided to honor family members and other good people who had died on November 1, All Saints Day or, in old English All Hallow's Day. That's why October 31 became known as Halloween - the eve of All Hallow's Day.

"But where do witches, vampires, ghosts, and monsters come into the picture?" Salomé wanted to know. "They are left over from the heathen festival and are a reminder that people believed in evil spirits." Julian explained. "I don't think that we, as Christians, should have anything to do with that!"

"Well, I still think it's OK," Lucille said. "Everyone can meet at our house for a party on Saturday night!" "You're playing with fire!" Julian insisted. "You can come to my house for a barbecue. We'll have some fun that God would approve of!"

**Think about the words in Ephesians 6:12
before you decide to go to a Halloween party.**

November

THE FOUR BLIND MEN

Once upon a time there were four blind men. One day they were taken to a zoo. The zookeeper soon found out that none of them knew what an elephant was, and he couldn't think of a way to describe it to them. "Come here," he said. "You can touch the elephant and then you will know what it is like." Each of the four men reached out and touched the elephant, and each was amazed at what he discovered.

When they went back home they told the other villagers about their trip to the zoo. "Let me tell you what an elephant is like," the first man said. He had touched the huge body of the elephant. "An elephant is like an enormous living wall!" "Not so!" said the man who had touched the elephant's ears. "An elephant is like a big leaf that moves all the time." "That's not true!" said the third man. He had felt the elephant's tusks. "An elephant is a creature with two sharp spears that can kill you!" And then the fourth man gave his view. He had touched the trunk. "You are all mistaken!" he said. "An elephant is like a thick snake!" And no one in the village had any clearer idea of what an elephant is like at all!

The blind men had given such different descriptions because none of them had the whole picture in mind. Each had experienced only an aspect of the animal.

As Christians, we can learn something from these blind men. We should not only read one part of the Bible and then think that we know everything we need to know! Some people only read the Psalms. Others read and reread the four gospels, but never try to understand the rest of the Bible. These people cannot be effective witnesses for the Lord.

As you grow older, you should get to know and love more and more of the Bible so that you can be a reliable witness of the message of God's love.

Read what 2 Timothy 3:16-17 has to say about this.

All scripture is God-breathed and is useful for ... training in righteousness. 2 Tim 3:16

NICKNAMES

Jack put his mouth next to the keyhole of Lisa's bedroom door and called, "Lisa, Goggle-eyes, Chili-bean, Carrot-head, hello!" Then he ran full speed downstairs to the front door. But this time he couldn't get away fast enough. Lisa caught him in the hallway and grabbed hold of the collar of his jersey. She hit him across his back and everywhere she could reach with her ruler. He yelled, "Mom, help!"

His mom was already at the scene of the battle. "What's going on here?" she asked sternly. "Lisa's hitting me," Jack moaned. "That I can see for myself!" his mom answered. "The question is why?"

Lisa was red in the face, and her red hair was disheveled. "He never stops teasing me," she said through her tears. "He's been calling me names again. I can't help having red hair and weak eyesight, can I?" She was just about to hit again, but her mom came in between them.

"Come with me, both of you!" she said. They went and sat round the dining room table. "Lisa," her mom began, "You should try not to be so touchy. Jack's only joking with you, and maybe it's his way of saying that he cares about you." Jack nodded and smiled.

"I don't think he does!" Lisa snorted. "He knows how much I hate it when he calls me by those names!"

"Jack," his mom turned to him, "Go to your room and read Ephesians 4:2-3. And then write it out five times!" Jack obeyed reluctantly. *How does Mother always manage to have a Scripture verse ready when I do something wrong?* he wondered.

You should also read Ephesians 4:1-3 carefully.

HAVE YOU EVER SEEN AN ANGEL?

Have you ever seen an angel? It's not strange if you haven't, because they are usually invisible. But some people have seen angels. It is sometimes an awesome and terrifying experience. Often the first thing the angel says is, "Do not be afraid!"

That's what happened to Mary and to the shepherds. You can refresh your memory about these experiences by reading Luke 1:29 and 2:10.

The Bible says that angels protect us, and we can boldly ask God to send His angels to keep us safe. That is what Corrie ten Boom once did. She was a remarkable woman who was imprisoned in a concentration camp during the Second World War. In one of her books she related an incident that helps us to believe that angels really can protect us in terrible situations.

Before prisoners were put into the concentration camp, they were thoroughly inspected. Corrie really wanted to take her Bible with her, but she knew that if the guards found it on her, they would take it away immediately. So she prayed, "Lord, please send your angels to keep my Bible out of the sight of these soldiers!"

When it was her turn to be searched, something miraculous happened! Not only did the soldiers not see her Bible, but she was also so completely covered by angels that the guards didn't even see her! When it was her turn, the prison guard called out, "Next!" She just passed them without being seen.

God heard her prayer, and He will also "command his angels concerning you to guard you in all your ways" (Ps. 91:11).

**Read Exodus 14:19 and Acts 27:23-24
to get some more info on angels.**

November 4

THE TEST

Adelina Patti was a famous singer. She was married to Baron de Cederstrom. Once she was in Cannes for a concert. She told her friends and family at home, "Please send my mail to the post office at Cannes." They did that, but when she went to fetch her mail the postmaster said, "I cannot give this to you. How do I know that you are the Baroness de Cederstrom?" She took all the letters and cards that she had with her out of her handbag and showed them to the postmaster. But he was not satisfied.

Then Madam Patti had a bright idea! She stood in the middle of the room and started to sing one of the songs that had made her famous throughout the world. She sang it with the same passion and skill that she showed on the stages of big theaters. Soon the post office was full of admirers. "It's Patti!" "It must be the Baroness de Cederstrom!" they whispered as they listened in awe.

The official behind the counter walked meekly to a drawer and fetched all the mail that had been sent to the baroness. "I must ask your forgiveness, Madame!" he said while everybody applauded. "Here is your mail."

If we are children of the living God then our lives should show the evidence of it. The world will never believe in the saving power of Jesus if they do not see it in our lives. There is a saying, "Actions speaks louder than words." Let our actions convince people that Christ makes a real difference in our lives. Jesus had said that we can know a tree by its fruit (Mt. 7:20). When people look at your life, do they see that you are a genuine Christian? The postmaster was convinced by Patti's behavior, not her words!

Ask the Holy Spirit to help you to display all the fruit of the Spirit that Galatians 6:22-23 tells us about.

NOVEMBER 5

DISCOURAGED?

Robin Graham was the youngest person ever to sail solo around the world in a yacht. He was only sixteen-years-old when he started on this journey. He faced wild wind and waves for three years before he once again sailed into the harbor from which he had set out on his journey. He had had a multitude of experiences and learned many lessons. People who hear his story always gasp when they hear how his boat was struck by a tornado. The mast broke off and it was a miracle that his boat did not capsize in that storm.

But Robin said that the biggest trial came when he found himself in the doldrums. That is the part of the ocean near the equator where the wind seldom blows and the currents do not help the boat to move forward. For many days, *The Dove* lay dead still. He felt terribly frustrated and discouraged. He decided that he would give up on the whole adventure. He took some gasoline and poured it all over the deck. Then he set it alight. But, when he saw the flames he came to his senses again and immediately extinguished the blaze before everything on board was burned to ashes.

Eventually Robert sailed into the harbor at Los Angeles again. A crowd of people waited for him with posters and balloons and cheerful music. He was a hero. His perseverance and commitment had paid off!

Have you ever been down in the dumps about something? Did you pray about it? Don't despair! The Bible tells many stories about people who thought that everything was hopeless ... and then God intervened! Think about Hagar, Hannah, Jonah, and David. Ask God to get you out of the doldrums of discouragement, as He did for these Bible characters.

Read how God took Elijah out of the cave of despondency in 1 Kings 19:1-19.

The LORD is my strength and my shield; my heart trusts in him. Ps. 28:7

NOVEMBER 6

KEEPING A PROMISE

Anthony was sitting on the sidewalk after baseball practice, waiting. His dad had promised to fetch him at five and it was now almost six. One by one all the other kids had left, but there was no sign of his dad. Coach Hill saw him and asked, "Can I take you home?" "Thank you, Sir!" he said. "But my dad will come and fetch me." Coach Hill got into his car and drove off. It was a hot day and as Anthony wiped the sweat from his brow, he thought about the math homework that he still had to do when he got home. *What could have happened to dad?* he wondered. A bright red car stopped next to him. "Can I give you a lift?" the driver asked. But Anthony's parents had warned him not to get into a car with strangers. "No thanks!" he said. "My dad is coming to fetch me!" The smart red car pulled off.

Anthony waited and waited. He knew that his dad would keep his promise. At last he saw his dad's blue car turn the corner. "Sorry, Son!" his dad said. "I had a flat tire! You probably thought I had forgotten about you." "I knew that you would come," said Anthony. "But you will have to help me with math tonight," he added.

Anthony was convinced that his dad would keep his word. He never broke a promise. And we can be even more sure that Jesus will also never break a promise. Although two thousand years have passed since He promised that He would come again to fetch us, we can still be sure that He will do so. You can read His promise in any of the following Scripture passages: John 14: 1-3; Matthew 26:64; Acts 1:11 and Hebrews 9:28.

Nobody knows exactly when Jesus is coming back, but we should always be ready for His coming. We must not think that because He hasn't yet come that He won't. He will not break His promise.

**Learn one of these Bible verses
and repeat it to yourself often.**

NOVEMBER 7

A SPECIAL OPPORTUNITY

Richie was struggling with his reading. His sister was playing outside because she had finished all her homework. But his mom wanted him to read his lesson out loud one more time. This time was a bit better than the fist try. "We can read it again tomorrow morning before school," his mom said as he threw his book onto the table and ran outside. *Why does Hazel get things right so easily while I must always struggle*, he thought angrily.

A few days later Miss Spock gave him a letter to give to his mom. He stood and watched as she opened the letter and read it. "What does she say?" he asked nervously. His mom did not answer immediately. "She says you are dyslexic!" "Is that a disease?" he asked. "No!" his mom said. "It only means that the words in your book look different to you than to other people." "Am I stupid?" he asked, worried. His mom gave him a big hug. "Of course not," she said. "To tell you the truth, I think that people who are dyslexic need to be cleverer than others because they have to unravel everything before they can read it."

Richie wanted to hear more about this thing that he had that his classmates and sister didn't have. His mom said, "Did you know that the apostle Paul also had a condition that bothered him at first?" "Really?" he asked with interest. "Yes, some people say that he had a stutter when he spoke. Others say he had trouble with his back, or maybe bad eyesight. But whatever it was, later in his life he said that he was glad he had it!" "But why?" Richie asked with surprise. "He said that he was glad about his weakness because it gave God an opportunity to show what He could do with a struggler." "That's interesting!" Richie exclaimed as he walked to his room. His mom had really given him something to think about!

Read 2 Corinthians 12:7-10 to see
what Paul had to say about his disability.

My grace is sufficient for you ... my power is made perfect in weakness. 2 Cor. 12:9

UNWELCOME VISITORS

Napoleon was a great French General. One night he allowed his soldiers to sleep in a beautiful cathedral. People were horrified the next morning when they saw soldiers lying asleep on the pews. "How dare Napoleon allow those rude, uncouth men into the holy House of God! It's a disgrace!" But one of the priests said, "What a fuss you make about something that is really not that serious. It would be far better if you were as angry about wrong thoughts that rest in your minds. It is much worse being hospitable to evil thoughts than kindly allowing a group of tired soldiers to sleep in a church building. Our bodies are the temple of God and if we harbor evil thoughts, we contaminate the dwelling place of the Most High."

How can we get rid of bad thoughts? When a man once confessed to a priest that he often had impure thoughts, the priest answered, "Remember that you can never think two thoughts at the same time. Whenever you make room for a good thought, the bad thoughts will have to go. Keep chasing away evil thoughts in this way, and you will soon find that your thought life has become much purer!"

In Acts 19:17-20 we read how the Christians in Ephesus made a huge pile of all their books with wrong messages and burnt them. The Bible tells us that these books were valued at fifty thousand silver coins. Yet while the flames licked at the pages of these books, the people praised God. What a bonfire! They destroyed every book that might draw them away from God by polluting their minds with impure thoughts. And what was the result? Acts 19:20 says, *"In this way the word of the Lord spread widely and grew in power."* This would not have been possible if they had held onto improper thoughts.

Maybe it's time for you to clean up God's temple. Do something about the books, CDs, videos, and posters that keep Jesus out of your thought life.

NOVEMBER 9

TOO PROUD?

Theodore's dad was the school principal. All the children and the teachers greatly respected his father, but Theodore wished that his dad was more dignified. His dad drove an old jalopy, and was often seen in conversation with the insignificant kids at school. Theodore would have loved his dad to be more discreet and stylish.

One Saturday morning the school held a fun day on the school playground. The children loved it! They battled each other with chunks of watermelon. They joked and jested with glee! Afterwards the grounds looked like a real battlefield. Theodore was just about to clean himself off with the hosepipe when he saw something totally embarrassing: his dad was busy picking up the litter! He wanted to run and hide. Couldn't his dad simply have instructed some of the kids to clear up? Theodore thought he wasn't acting at all like a principal should! He was humiliating himself in front of the whole school by acting like a cleaner. Theodore couldn't face it any longer. He ran to the locker room, vanished into a cubicle, and closed the door behind him. Soon he heard footsteps, and a voice said, "Softy is a grand chief, don't you think? Fancy helping us clean up the place!" "Yes, he is one of a kind," another voice replied. "Let's hurry so we can go and help him."

Suddenly Theodore saw his dad in a new light. He realized that he had been too proud to be a servant like his dad and he remembered that the Bible teaches God's children to be humble. He had been concerned about his own image, while his father had been carrying out Jesus' instructions. After all, He said that those who want to lead must be like servants. Theodore hurried outside so that he too could help with Operation Cleanup.

Read Matthew 23:11 and remember these words whenever you have to do menial work.

SAFE IN THE STORM

Amy Carmichael was a missionary to India. She wrote quite a few books about her experiences in that country. She also wrote many essays about the value lessons she learned from things in nature. Once she described how she had seen a sunbird building its nest. These birds usually build small homes with a little roof and a canopy. They hang from the branches to which the birds attach them.

A child or a wild animal can break that nest so easily, she thought. *And the rainy season will soon be here! How will that fragile little nest ever survive when the wind and stormy weather break loose in all its fury?*

But when the rainy season came, she was amazed to see what happened to the nest. Through her window she watched as the nest moved up and down with the branches of the tree in which it had been built. And the little bird was safe and sound inside, resting its head on the canopy. When the rain poured down, she noticed that the bird had placed the nest under the leaves in such a way that they acted like gutters that drained the water away from the nest. Every now and then a huge drop of water landed on the beak of the bird and she would drink it as if it were nectar from heaven. The storm raged fiercely but the sunbird sat peacefully on her eggs, swinging to and fro in the wind.

Amy often faced serious crises in her work as a missionary. When she saw how peaceful the little bird was in the midst of the storm, she realized that she also had reason to be calm and collected. God's promises were even more secure than that nest!

Do you sometimes feel as if you are caught in the middle of a storm? Does that make you feel scared and panicky? Try to picture the sunbird calmly carrying out her duty even though things around her were pretty scary.

Read Isaiah 26:4. It is one of God's promises that can help you to stay calm during a storm.

NOVEMBER 11

LISTENING INSTEAD OF TALKING

Other kids often called Gordon a nerd. He was a quiet boy who didn't like parties and who was too shy to speak up in class. He was probably so self-conscious because his family moved around so much. He sometimes felt as if he belonged to a circus that constantly moved from one town to the next. As soon as he had made friends in one place, his dad got a job somewhere else. "Gordon will be very adaptable one day," his aunt used to say. But it didn't work out that way. Each time they moved, he found it more difficult to adapt. It was extremely difficult to make friends at schools where kids had already formed close-knit groups. He was even too scared to go outside at recess. He preferred to stay in his classroom and do his homework. He became more and more shy and lonely.

But then something happened that helped Gordon to leave all his shyness behind him. Peter Norman stayed behind with him in class one lunchtime. "May I ask you something?" he said. When Gordon nodded, Peter said, "My mom said I could invite a friend to go to our beach house this weekend. Would you like to join us? I'm too embarrassed to invite kids to our home because my dad has a drinking problem. But you know what it is like to be different." Gordon couldn't believe his ears! The class captain had asked him to spend a weekend with his family! "I'll ask my parents," he said and tried not to look too eager.

That Saturday on the rocks at Arniston Gordon asked, "Why did you choose me to come with you?" Peter picked up an oyster shell and threw it deep into the sea. Then he said, "Because you listen more than you talk." *It seems that there is room for a nerd like me on the face of the earth, after all,* Gordon thought with a grateful heart.

What is more important: Talking or listening?
See if you can find the answer in James 1:19.

HE MADE A DIFFERENCE

Long, long ago there were no movies or football matches. In those days people went to huge amphitheaters to watch animals and humans fight bloody battles. The spectators enjoyed these fights to the death. The Coliseum in Rome could seat 80,000 people who loved being entertained by the gladiators.

Telemachus was a Christian who was convinced that this violent entertainment had to be stopped. One day he went with the crowds to the amphitheater. Two sword-fighters entered the arena and cried, "Hail Caesar! Those about to die, salute you!" Then they started to fight fiercely. The brave priest made his way through the crowd of spectators and ran into the arena. The people on the stands thought he must be crazy. But he walked up to the fighting men and shouted, "In the name of Christ, stop this madness!"

The people on the stands screamed for the guards to remove Telemachus so that the fight could go on. One of the gladiators pushed him over. But Telemachus got onto his feet again and shouted, "In the name of Christ, stop!"

Then the spectators started to chant, "Kill him! Kill him!" And one of the swordfighters did just that. He stuck his sword right through the body of the courageous man of God. Before he died, Telemachus managed to say one more time, "In the name of Christ, stop this madness!"

The large crowd fell silent. It was as if people realized for the first time what a despicable thing took place in that arena week after week. They all went home with remorse in their hearts. It was the last time that that amphitheater was used for such violent and bloody recreation.

Are you also prepared to stand up against things that are wrong in your community?

Read the story about Stephen in Acts 7:54-60.

NOVEMBER 13

A FAIRY-TALE

You probably don't believe in fairies and you know that a legend isn't a true story. But this legend about a wise fairy really makes one think:

Once upon a time there was an orphan who was very unhappy. Her foster parents did not treat her well and she felt as if nobody cared about her. Then, one day, she found a butterfly that had been caught in a rose bush. It was struggling to get free, but its delicate wings kept getting caught on the twigs and thorns. The little girl walked closer and cautiously tried to disentangle the tiny wings.

She worked patiently until the butterfly could use its spoilt wings again. Then suddenly the butterfly changed into a fairy. "Thank you for helping me!" she said. "Because you have been so kind to me, you can wish for anything and I will see to it that it comes true!" The little girl thought for a while and then said, "I want to be happy!" The fairy whispered something in her ear and flew away.

From that day on, the little girl changed miraculously. She was radiantly happy and wherever she went she made people smile. Many people wondered what the secret of her happiness was. When she grew old and lay on her deathbed, her friends gathered around her. "Tell us the secret of your happiness!" they begged. "What did the fairy whisper in your ear on that day?"

"She said that I must remember that all the people that I met, needed me. Even if they were confident or rude, young or old, healthy or sick, they all needed me!"

Are you looking for happiness? If you know Jesus personally, you will know true happiness. You will then look at people with loving eyes and you will realize that they all need you! In that way, God will fill your life with gladness.

Read Ephesians 5:1-2.

Live a life of love, just as Christ loved us. Eph 5:2

THE THIRD COMMANDMENT

The Melville family was watching a film on television. A vicious dog attacked a woman. "Oh my God!" she said as she tried to break loose. Mr. Melville turned off the sound. "Was it wrong of that woman to say that?" "Of course!" Hannah replied. "She used the Lord's name in vain." Patty didn't agree. "She cried out to God because she was desperate. It was, in a way, a kind of prayer!" "I wonder," their dad said as he turned the sound back on. The same woman was looking at an expensive piece of jewelry. "Jesus!" she said, probably because it was very pretty. "That wasn't a prayer!" Hannah said with conviction. "She did not use Jesus' name with respect and reverence." Her dad turned off the TV.

At first Patty and David, her younger brother, were upset because their dad wouldn't let them watch the end of the movie. But then they saw that he was serious about the issue. He looked sad. "Jesus paid an enormous price on the cross because He loves us. We should never use His Name as a meaningless expression. And God is holy. His Name shouldn't be used unthinkingly."

Now Mrs. Melville spoke up, "If we use God's name without thinking about the living, holy God whom we serve, we are guilty of disobeying the third commandment." "What's that again?" David asked. Their mom fetched her Bible and read Exodus 20:7: *"You should not misuse the name of the Lord your God, for the Lord will not hold anyone guiltless who misuses his name."*

"Let's rather play the new board game that Aunt Martha gave us for Christmas!" Patty suggested. David ran to fetch it. He wasn't going to infuriate God just because of a stupid TV program!

**Ask God to help you not to
misuse His wonderful Name.**

NOVEMBER 15

FLOWER POWER

The sixth grade class was working on a project on flowers. Each could choose any flower as the focus of the project. Jane had chosen tulips. When her cousin got married, her bouquet consisted of orange tulips, and they had become Jane's favorite flower.

As she worked on the project, she discovered that at first tulips were only found in Turkey. The name Tulip comes from the word turban, the headgear that's worn in Turkey. A professor from Western Europe, who visited Turkey, took some of the bulbs home with him because he wanted to use them for medicinal purposes.

His neighbors were amazed at the beautiful flowers they saw in his garden, and asked him to give them some of the bulbs. But he refused pointblank. So one night they stole some of his bulbs and started to grow and distribute the magnificent tulips themselves. People all over Europe loved this special flower. They were dreadfully expensive, but some people even went into debt just to be able to buy the plants.

Tulip mania spread like a disease across the world. Poor people dreamed about getting rich quickly and rich people dreamed about getting richer. A shoemaker announced that he had cultivated a black tulip. Two merchants from Harlem bought the black tulip from him at an exorbitant price, and then crushed the expensive bulb under their feet. Why? Because they themselves had cultivated a black tulip and they wanted no competition!

Eventually the price of tulip bulbs fell drastically and people lost enormous amounts of money because they had ordered bulbs at sky-high prices. They are not as expensive any more, but they are still beautiful flowers and the Netherlands exports 1,2 billion tulip bulbs each year!

**Read what Jesus had to say about
beautiful flowers in Matthew 6:28-30.
What can we learn from these Bible verses?**

THE CONVERSION

The film *The Cross and the Switchblade* shows the true story about the conversion of the cruel gang leader, Nicky Cruz. He was once the most dangerous criminal who roamed the streets of New York City. But then David Wilkerson arrived on the scene. He believed that God had called him to work among the gangsters of this big city.

Nicky wanted nothing to do with the young preacher. One day, when David tried to convince him that God loved Him and to accept Jesus Christ as his Savior, Nicky threatened him with a knife. But David said, "You can cut me up into tiny bits, Nicky! But every piece of me will still say, 'I love you!'" These words started Nicky thinking about many things and when David invited Nicky's gang to attend one of his services, Nicky agreed.

To everybody's astonishment, David asked Nicky's gang to take up the offering. The gang of juvenile delinquents grinned broadly. Did the stupid preacher really think that they would give him the money? But when they were getting ready to escape with all the money, something made Nicky stop in his tracks. He just couldn't bring himself to leave. The Jesus of whom David had preached suddenly became a reality to him. He ordered his gang members to do what David had asked, and they walked onto the platform and gave the money to him. At the end of the service, Nicky told David, "I've committed my life to Jesus!"

Nicky joined David in his work. In the back streets and alleys of New York, they worked together to help young people turn their backs on drugs and crime. What happened to Nicky on that night that made him change so drastically? The Holy Spirit convicted him of the fact that he desperately needed Jesus in his life. And He also shows *us* that we are lost sinners who need Christ.

You can read what John 16:5-11
has to say about the Holy Spirit.

OUR HEAVENLY BROTHER

Aeschylus lived in Athens a very long time ago. He wrote such beautiful poetry that people still read and appreciate it today. But one day he committed a serious crime. The people of Athens were furious! They wanted to ban him from their city and send him off to a far-away island.

But Aeschylus had a brother who loved him dearly. When he heard how severely his brother was going to be punished, he went to Athens to see if he could do something for him. He was heartbroken when he saw his brother in chains. What could he do to help him? Then he thought of a plan. He had been a courageous soldier who had fought for Greece in many wars. And during those wars, he had received many serious wounds. His body was covered with the marks and scars of spears and swords with which he had been pierced in combat.

The old soldier stood in front of the judge who was appointed to sentence Aeschylus. He loosened his cloak and showed his back and breast to the judge. "These are the wounds and scars that I received in battle to defend my country!" he said. Then the people who attended the court case started to shout, "Let Aeschylus go free because of the wounds of his brother!" The judge softened when he witnessed all this and he told the guards to let the prisoner go free. Aeschylus could go home as a free man!

Like Aeschylus, we are guilty before God, our Judge. We have so much sin and guilt that God has the right to punish us forever. But Jesus, our heavenly Brother, stands between God and us with the wounds that He received on the cross. If we confess that we are guilty and call on Jesus as our Savior, God will also declare us innocent and let us go free.

Read Psalm 103:8-13 to find out how far God removes our transgressions from us.

So far has he removed our transgressions from us. Ps. 103:12

NOVEMBER 18

GAMBLING

"Is it wrong to gamble?" Paul asked his dad one night. His uncle had won a lot of money at a casino and Paul thought it would be a good idea for his dad also to try his luck at the gambling machines. He had often thought it must be great to be able to buy lottery tickets. He thought: *Maybe Lady Luck will smile on me one day!* His dad seemed to read his thoughts. "Remember, Christians don't believe in luck," he said. "We trust in the Lord to provide for all our needs!"

"Yes, but perhaps the Lord wants to do it via the Lotto," Paul teased. "That's what all Christians who gamble always say. But it goes against everything that the Bible teaches. God does not want us to get rich by making others poor. We are called to love our neighbors as ourselves. That means that we are not entitled to a lot of money that poor people have lost through gambling." "But it's not only poor people who gamble," Paul protested. "Unfortunately, it often is the poorest people who gamble, hoping that they could become rich in an instant. Some of them get hooked on gambling and gamble away their very last cent. Just this week there was an article in the newspaper about a man who committed suicide because he had so much debt through gambling."

Paul's dad had more to say, "We who are children of God are not permitted to do as we like with our money. We must make sure that we spend it on things that please the Lord." "But the Lottery gives a lot of money to good causes!" Paul said. "A very small percentage, yes!" his dad agreed. "But that does not justify all the evil that goes with it!"

That Sunday, their pastor preached on 1 Timothy 6:10. Paul knew that God had something to teach him through those words.

Look up what the preacher's topic was on that Sunday.

MY MASTER TRUSTS ME

There was once a shepherd who looked after his master's sheep in a distant field. One morning a hunter came by. "How far is the nearest village?" the hunter asked. "Eight miles," said Steve, "but the road to it is very bad." The hunter looked at the winding dirt road and said, "Will you please take me there?"

"I am sorry, Sir, but I cannot leave my master's flock unattended. The sheep could get lost or wolves could attack them." "What does it matter?" the hunter asked. "It's not your flock and your master won't miss one or two sheep. I will pay you well: I'll give you the same amount of money that you usually earn in a year!"

"I cannot do that," Steve said. "My master trusts me with his sheep. If I use the time that I should have spent tending the sheep to help you, it would be like stealing."

When the hunter saw that the shepherd could not be bribed, he suggested something else, "All right, can you do me another favor? Please go to the village and buy me some food. I will look after the sheep while you are gone, and pay you handsomely."

"I cannot do that either, Sir," Steve replied. "The sheep do not know you and besides, how can I trust you? A minute ago you tried to get me to do something dishonest!"

The hunter realized that he would never convince the shepherd to leave the sheep. He set out to look for the village himself. A month later, the farmer visited Steve. "A high-ranking government official told me how honest and reliable you are. I would like to appoint you as the manager of my farm!" he said.

See what 1 Corinthians 4:1-2 says about reliability.

It is required that those who have been given a trust must prove faithful. 1 Cor 4:2

LEARN FROM THE WORD

Some scientists once built a massive cage in which they kept 120 mice. They gave them food and water, and kept the cage clean. After three years there were 2,200 mice in the cage. Now because there were too many mice in the cage, things became chaotic. The older mice were still quite well behaved, but the young mice did nothing but eat and sleep all day. The females were upset by this behavior and they maltreated the younger ones. After a while no more new mice were born and there was so much fighting amongst the rest of the mouse population that they eventually all died. And this was in spite of the fact that they had plenty of food and water and a large, clean cage.

The researchers who had conducted this experiment said that the same could happen to human beings if the population grew too dense. "People will crowd each other's space and they will lose their moral strength. There will be no values and everything will end in chaos!" That's what the scientists predicted.

We cannot rule out the possibility that something like that could happen. But if people started to live by the teachings of the Bible, there will always be hope for peaceful co-existence. As long as we do as the Word of God says, there will be goals to achieve and solutions to be found. The Bible gives us moral guidelines for living together in love. If we all aim to glorify God, there will be peace on earth even if there are countless multitudes living around us.

A pastor once used this story to illustrate a point in one of his sermons. His congregation was motivated to study the Bible with new eyes, and many new Bible study groups were started in that city. Remember, the Bible is our handbook for living and we should consult it regularly if we want to live happy, fruitful lives.

**Read Proverbs 3:5-7. It has something
to say about our need for guidance.**

JONI

Have you ever thought what it would be like to be a quadriplegic? Joni Earickson had to adjust to living as a quadriplegic when she was only seventeen-years old. As a young girl, she loved swimming and she was a good diver. She even dreamed of competing in the Olympic Games one day. But on an outing to Chesapeake Bay, she dived into the water from a boat, and suddenly realized that she could feel absolutely nothing! She had hit her head against the bottom of the bay and broken her neck! She was paralyzed from her neck down and would not be able to use her arms and legs ever again.

Doctors did what they could and people all over the country prayed for her, but to no avail! Her arms and legs hung limp. Joni became very depressed. It was an awful thought to realize that she would have to rely on other people's help for the rest of her life. She was angry with God for letting something like this happen to her.

She was not healed as the man at the pool of Bethesda was healed by Jesus. But He did heal her broken spirit. She is one of the most motivating and inspiring people in the world today. Many churches and other organizations started to invite her to share her experiences with them. She has also written several books, and a film has been made of her life.

She learned to paint with her mouth and she sings the most beautiful songs of praise to God. Once, in front of a packed stadium she said, "I'd rather be in this wheel-chair with God than walk on my own two feet without Him!"

Joni even married later in her life. If you ever come across a book by Joni Earickson Tada, do yourself a favor and read it!

Read Psalm 31. It is one of Joni's favorite psalms.

I say, "You are my God." My times are in your hands. Ps. 31:14-15

FIVE IMPORTANT MINUTES

Every morning Julian met his friend Dan at the front gate of his house. Then they cycled to school together. Julian often wondered what took place on the verandah at Dan's house every morning. The Sterlings gathered outside the front door, formed a loose circle, stood there for a few minutes, and then scattered in different directions. "What do you guys do every morning?" he asked Dan one Monday. "Come a little earlier tomorrow, then you can see for yourself!" Dan said with a laugh.

At 7:45 on Tuesday morning, Julian walked up the garden path. One by one, the Sterlings came outside until all the family members were there. They invited Julian to join them. "Let's pray!" Mr. Sterling said. "Lord, we cannot start this day without You. Help us to do our very best at school and at work. Send your angels to protect us from evil. Help us not to give in to the temptations of Satan to do wrong. Let your Holy Spirit be our guide. Help Julian who is joining us in prayer this morning. Let him meet You at every turn during the day. We pray this in the Name of Jesus, Amen."

"Do you do that every morning?" Julian asked when they rode off a little later. "Yes, and each one gets a turn to pray," Dan said. "Does it work?" Julian wanted to know. "Find out for yourself!" his friend said with a smile. That night when Julian got into bed, he thought, *Well, it certainly worked for me today! I encountered the Lord at every turn. When I was writing the history test, when William asked me to smoke a cigarette with him, and when that taxi almost ran into me at the traffic lights!* He fell asleep with the firm intention of setting aside five minutes every morning to keep an appointment with God.

Look up what Jesus did before He started on His daily schedule (Mark 1:35)

STRANGERS AMONG US

Pastor Goosen and his wife Magda love God faithfully. They love telling people who do not know Jesus all about Him. Many people from different countries come to study in South Africa. Some of these students are from countries where Bibles are banned. When they arrive in South Africa to study they meet Christians and they can hear about Jesus. The Goosens go out of their way to make friends with these students and make them feel at home.

One afternoon the Children's League at a church in Stellenbosch asked the Goosens to come and tell them about their mission. Pastor Goosen said, "In Matthew 25:43 Jesus told us to be kind to strangers." Then he told the kids about the many foreign students who feel lonely and sad while they are far away from their own homes. "Some of them have children who go to school here but have no friends," he said. "We invite them to our home and help them to adjust to all the new things around here. And then we also tell them about the wonderful God that we serve. One day, when they go back to their own country, they can tell their friends about the Lord."

When the pastor and his wife had left, the children talked about what they had heard. "Let's decide what we can do for strangers who are living among us!" their leader said.

When the Children's League had their Christmas party that year, there were quite a few unfamiliar faces around the tree. The kids had invited their schoolmates who came from foreign countries to join in the celebrations. They had also invited Pastor Goosen to come and tell the Christmas story to all of them.

"Sometimes we needn't go to foreign countries to teach foreigners about Jesus. The Lord brings them right to our doorstep," one of the boys remarked as they were cleaning up afterwards.

**Think what you can do for an
immigrant in your community.**

THANKS!

"It won't be possible!" Harriet's mother said. "We simply haven't got the money." Harriet understood why her mom said that, but she was still terribly disappointed. The school choir was going to a choir festival overseas, and she would have to stay behind. Although people in the community had sponsored the trip, each member of the choir still had to contribute a large amount to cover their personal expenses. Harriet's mom was a single parent and she really couldn't afford any luxuries.

Harriet prayed fervently, "Lord, nothing is impossible for You! If You think it's a good idea, please supply the money that I need to be able to go with the choir?"

Three days later Mrs. Woodrow from their congregation phoned, "I was wondering whether you could come and help me in the kitchen on Saturday. I am catering for a big wedding!" Harriet went to help her, and when they had cleared everything away afterwards, Mrs. Woodrow handed her an envelope. Inside were 6 crisp new bank notes. Harriet was delighted and put the money into her Piggy bank straight away. Very quickly, the news of Harriet's need spread throughout the community and more and more people gave her small tasks to do, and then added some money to her fund. She looked after kids, washed windows, did some shopping, and polished furniture.

That summer she went to Europe with the school choir. But when she returned, she did not forget how the members of their church had helped her. She decided to do something in return. She started helping at Sunday school and when the pastor asked for volunteers to work in the kitchen after church functions, she was the first person to write down her name. "It's the least I can do to show the people at church how much I had appreciated their help!" she said.

**Read Luke 17:11-19 and remember to
thank God and people who are kind to you.**

THE BATH TOWEL

The Herberts won a weekend at a luxury holiday resort. Julius couldn't remember when last he had had so much fun. They went out to sea in a boat, played ten-pin bowling, and swam in a heated swimming pool. Everything was "on the house", as his dad repeated every now and then with a big smile. Apart from all the entertainment, they also enjoyed fabulous meals.

On Sunday night, they arrived home, exhausted, but happy. They began to unpack and get ready for school the next day. But when Julius's mom took the stuff out of his bag, she groaned. "Oh no!" "What's wrong?" he asked. "You packed one of the hotel's bath towels in with your things." she said. "Hey, that's great!" Julius exclaimed. "It's such a super soft towel!" But his mom shook her head. "We will have to return it! You can put it in a parcel tonight and mail it tomorrow. I will write a letter and pay the postage."

"The people at the hotel won't know that we took it," he complained. He hated wrapping parcels. Somehow it was never a neat job after he'd finished. "They might not know," his mom replied, "but we know that it's not ours, and the Lord knows about it, too. He wants His children to be honest."

Three weeks later a letter came from the hotel manager.

Dear Herbert family, Thank you for sending back the bath towel. This was the first time that anybody took the trouble to send back goods that belong to us. I have posted your letter on our notice board. It will be an inspiration for me and my staff to follow your example and be honest at all times. With kind regards, Jack Stanes, Manager.

This letter soon found its way onto the Herberts' fridge door. Julius knew exactly why.

**For whom should we always take pains
to do what is right? See 2 Corinthians 8:21.**

THE BUSH FIRE

Hector was spending the school vacation on his uncle's farm. But on the very first night of his stay, disaster hit that area. A bush fire broke out along the Massive Mountain range and soon reached Uncle Jack's farm. Everybody on the farm ran around to do what they could to protect the tree plantations. Hector went with the farm workers on a truck. The firefighters lined up on alongside the dam with buckets of water and branches from the surrounding trees to try to keep the flames at bay. But the wind was a nuisance. It caused sparks to fly far and wide so that new areas caught on fire. It seemed as if they would never be able to stop the relentless flames.

Hector got a fright when a big cobra sailed past him. A buck fled through the plum orchard. Nobody took much notice of these animals, though. Their eyes were fixed on the crackling fire that was devouring the pine plantation. Late that night the workers made their way back to the farmhouse. The wind had finally turned direction and the fire was under control. Aunt Karin gave them all some refreshing, cool lime juice with lots of ice in it. That night they all slept like babies. Only Uncle Jack lay awake. He couldn't stop thinking about all the damage that the fire had caused. The pine trees had been growing so well.

At dawn the next morning the farm truck took the workers back to the scene of the fire. They looked at the smoldering tree trunks. "In the spring the ground will be covered by beautiful undergrowth!" Aunt Karin said. "The ash that's lying around now will be food for various new plants that will flourish in these open spaces next year!" she said.

When Hector went home after the holidays, he often remembered that fire and he marveled at the thought that good things could come out of the biggest catastrophe.

Read in John 12:32 about the good results that came out of the disastrous event of Jesus' crucifixion.

LOTS OF SPACE

"How are you, Granny McKay?" the pastor asked. "Not too bad, Pastor! But I will never be happy in this little apartment. There just isn't enough room to move about!" The pastor had no words of comfort for Granny McKay who felt that she needed more space in order to be happy. On his way home the pastor had a great idea! He would make a few arrangements, and, if all went according to plan, Granny McKay would soon be quite satisfied with her accommodation.

That weekend Granny's children and grandchildren arrived unexpectedly. "We have come to visit for a while!" they said. "The more, the merrier!" Granny said. On Monday morning, a neighbor brought two cats to her. "Will you look after them for a week or two? I have to go to hospital!" "Of course I will," Granny McKay said. "One day you'll do me a favor in return!" All week long visitors streamed in and out of Granny's house. "We've just come to say 'hello'!" they said. "That's wonderful," Granny would say, but her apartment seemed to get smaller and smaller. After a while she had no room to put a thing down.

Then one morning the children started packing. Her neighbor came to fetch her cats and the visitors stayed away. Suddenly it was quiet in Granny's apartment. She looked around her and uttered a sigh of relief. "My word, but I have a lot of space again!" she said, contentedly. When the pastor saw her the next Sunday, he asked, "How are things in your little apartment?" She looked puzzled. "Well, to tell you the truth, my little home has suddenly become quite big enough for me!"

Are you discontented with things in your life? Not enough money? Not enough opportunities? Not enough space? Imagine what it would be like if it were even worse (as it really is for millions of people around the world) and count your blessings!

Read what Paul said in Philippians 4:11.

I have learned to be content whatever the circumstances. Phil. 4:11

THE CHOICE

Harry grabbed his satchel and left the classroom in a hurry. He wanted to catch up with his friends before they all left on their bikes. He was keen to find out what they had decided about a get-together for that evening. They were planning to play football in the park and have a barbecue afterwards. It was Friday, and they had nothing scheduled for the next day so their parents didn't insist on an early night!

As he turned the corner, he bumped into Sam who was moving in the opposite direction in his wheelchair. "Sorry!" he said as he picked up Sam's books that had gone flying all over the place in the collision. "I was actually looking for you!" Sam said, laughing. "Don't you feel like coming over to my place tonight? It's my birthday and my mom said I could take out a great action video for us to watch!" "Oh! Happy birthday!" Harry said, taken aback. "Who else is coming?" Sam dropped his head. "The other guys can't come. Football in the park or something," he mumbled, embarrassed. He looked at Harry with pleading eyes.

Harry glanced out of the window. His friends were already on their way home. If he still wanted to catch up with them, he would have to run. He realized that he would have to make a quick decision. Sam obviously needed a friend to make his birthday special, but he would much rather have gone with the rest of the guys. He thought for a while and then said, "What time should I be at your place?"

How do you think Sam felt when Harry said these words? How did Jesus feel? We often have to make equally difficult choices. But it is not so difficult to know what Jesus would have done in Harry's place. Philippians 2:3-7 will confirm your thoughts about this.

Who is the most unpopular kid in your class?
Why not plan something special for him or her?

YOU ARE JUST AS SPECIAL!

You have probably heard of Mother Teresa. She was a nun who worked in the streets of Calcutta among the poorest of the poor people. She once told this story.

I had permission from the Indian government to collect medicine that people did not use. I could store these medicines and use them for the thousands of people who could not afford it. I had volunteers who went from home to home to gather old medicines in baskets. One day a man came to me in great desperation. "Mother," he said, "my only child is very, very ill. We took her to the doctor and he prescribed certain medication. But this remedy is only available in England. What can we do?"

At that very moment a man entered the clinic with a basket full of surplus medicine. On top of the packages and bottles Mother Theresa found the specific tablets that the little dying girl needed. If the medicine had been underneath all the others she would never have seen it. If it had arrived a few minutes later, the child would not have got it. But the medicine could be given to the child and she recovered!

Psalm 113:4 -6 says, *"The Lord is exalted over all the nations, his glory above the heavens. Who is like the Lord our God, the one who sits enthroned on high, who stoops down to look on the heavens and the earth?"*

There are millions of children in the world and God provided for one little girl in the back streets of Calcutta. He saw to it that the right remedy among hundreds of different kinds of medication arrived at the right time and the right place for her sake. He loves you just as much and He is just as concerned about you. Always remember that!

**Thank the Lord for His
personal love and concern for you.**

AMAZING GRACE

Amazing Grace is probably the best-known hymn in the whole Christian world. It was originally written by John Newton. "I once was lost, but now I'm found" is a summary of the life of the writer. He had once been a reckless slave trader, but he gave his heart to Jesus and later became a preacher.

John Newton's mother was a Christian who taught him from the Bible since early childhood. Although she suffered from bad health, she did all she could to teach him about the Lord. She made him memorize portions of Scripture and taught him hymns and prayers.

She died before he was seven years old. But by that time he could read the Bible and all through his life he remembered how she had prayed for him. She had taken in the laundry of rich people, and while she bent over the tub washing their clothes, she prayed for her son. Her tears mingled with the soapsuds in the bath. She prayed that he would be a useful child of God one day.

But John lived a godless life, first as a rough sailor on one of his father's ships and then as a slave dealer on his own ship. And then, one stormy night, he came to the end of his tether. When it seemed as if the ship was about to sink, he called upon the Lord to help him and his life was saved.

After that, his life underwent a dramatic change. He became a preacher who led many people to the Lord. He also wrote the beautiful words of the hymn *Amazing Grace.*

The Lord used the enduring faith and prayers of a simple washerwoman to eventually bring a prodigal son back to his Father's home.

Read Proverbs 22:6. Was it true of John Newton's life?

December

DECEMBER 1

TOGETHER

There are many interesting stories about things that have taken place at various Olympic Games. One of the most touching stories is probably that of Derek Redmond. He was Britain's champion runner in the 400-meter event, and his ambition was to bring home the gold medal from Seoul in 1988. But he was injured 2 minutes before the finals and had to drop out of the race. He was deeply disappointed. He had to undergo five operations before he was able to run again. But he began to practice again as soon as he could. And he was ready to join the British team that went to the Games in Barcelona four years later.

He made it to the semifinals, and did very well for the first two hundred meters. But suddenly he felt an excruciating pain in his leg. He had torn a muscle in his thigh!

When he collapsed, the medical attendants ran on the field with a stretcher. But he waved them away. Then a man in a white cap and T-shirt ran past the security guards and officials and onto the field. It was Derek's father, Jim. He spoke to his limping son, "Derek, you needn't carry on!" he said. But Derek struggled forward. "Well, then we'll do it together!" Jim said.

Shoulder-to-shoulder the two of them hobbled along in the fifth lane. All the other runners passed them and Derek was openly weeping. But he did not stop until he stumbled over the finishing line. By this time the 65,000 spectators were on their feet, cheering and applauding. Derek did not win the gold medal, but he won the admiration of thousands of people on the stands and in front of television sets around the world because he finished the race in spite of a serious setback.

The Bible says that life is like a race. And our Father, God, encourages us and helps us every step of the way, especially when we are having a hard time.

Read Hebrews 13:5-6.

DECEMBER 2

GOD'S ZOO

Bill loved animals and he was very excited when a friend invited him to join his family for an outing to the zoo. Although he was thrilled to see the animals close-up, he was also sad. Back home he told his mom, "Animals must have had a wonderful time before God created human beings! You should have seen those poor animals today! The elephant was so frustrated. He was bored stiff, scrubbing himself against a wall. The lion was lying in the sun, chasing flies away with his tail. And a big bear had worn a deep furrow, treading up and down along the fence. If it weren't for us humans, all these animals would have been wild and free and happy in God's world of nature."

"I know what you mean," his mom said. "People do a lot of injustice to animals by taking them from their natural habitat. And some animal species are being wiped off the face of the earth. I've heard that the elephant population has been cut in half during the last decade. There are fewer and fewer animals like rhinos because hunters shoot them or set traps for them. And apart from that, forests are chopped down and the natural habitats of animals are destroyed."

"I'm not only sorry for the animals," Bill's father added. "I'm also sad that future generations of the world's children might never see wild animals in their natural surroundings. When I see wild animals in their natural habitats, I am filled with awe. I find myself praising the Creator for them. When animals' homes are destroyed and they are removed from where they were created to live, we rob people of the opportunity of being thrilled by the glorious beauty of God's creation!"

That night Bill's family read Job 38 and 39 together and they counted how many wild animals are mentioned in those chapters. Then they read Job's response to God's words in Job 42:1-5.

You can fill a scrapbook with pictures of animals and donate it to the children's ward at your local hospital.

THE LITTLE TORTOISE

Trust in the LORD and do good; dwell in the land and enjoy safe pasture. Ps. 37:3

A family of tortoises decided to organize a picnic. Painstakingly they planned all the details for this event. The preparations took them a full seven years! Then they started looking for a suitable spot for their picnic. After two years, they found a site that was just right for the party. They began to unpack their baskets. But oh dear! They soon discovered that no one had packed any salt. What a disaster! How could they possibly have a picnic without salt?

After a long discussion they finally decided to send Little Tortoise home to fetch some as he was the fastest in the family. He wasn't very keen, but he agreed to do it on one condition, "Nobody must eat anything until I get back!" One by one each member of the tortoise family nodded their heads in agreement. They promised that they would touch nothing until the day he returned. Little Tortoise shambled off into the bushes.

The rest of the tortoises settled down to wait. A whole year passed by. Then another. And a third. "That's it!" said the oldest tortoise. "I'm not going to wait any longer!" and he reached for a tasty looking sandwich.

Suddenly the bushes behind the old tortoise rustled, and out came Little Tortoise! "Aha! Caught red-handed!" he shouted. "I knew that you wouldn't wait for me. And now I'm not going to fetch the salt either!"

What do you think was wrong with Little Tortoise? Was he lazy, or scared, or simply naughty? No, his mistake was that he trusted nobody and only expected the worst. Some people are just like that. They make life extremely difficult for everyone around them. We should rather expect good things from life and learn not to distrust every single person we meet.

Read Psalm 37:1-3

DECEMBER 4

THE SMALL WOODEN CROSS

Be very careful, then, how you live – not as unwise, but as wise. Eph 5:15

On the side of a highway outside Cape Town, there is a small wooden cross. On the sixteenth of each month, a little green car stops there and a woman gets out. She puts fresh flowers next to it and stands there for a while with her eyes closed, her head bowed as if she is praying. When she leaves a little later her eyes are red and swollen from crying. If the little wooden cross could talk, it would tell a sad tale of what occurred on that spot a few years ago.

A group of teenagers were on their way home from a party. They were cheerful and noisy. They had been drinking – but they thought not too much. And the guy driving didn't have a license, but he was, he thought, an experienced driver. He drove a little too fast, but still within the speed limit. The car radio was on and they were all singing loudly, but not distracting the driver too much. The atmosphere was great and they were all looking forward to the weekend that lay ahead. Nobody thought that all these ingredients were the ideal recipe for disaster.

Suddenly a blinding light appeared in front of them. "Can't the stupid fool dim his headlights?" one of the boys shouted. Suddenly they heard a crash and they were all shaken as everything went topsy-turvy. Glass and steel flew in all directions into the darkness of the night. One of the girls screamed at the top of her voice.

Hercu Knipe was killed in that accident. Jo-Ann May will be confined to a wheelchair for the rest of her life. Neil Ferreira, the self-confident driver of his dad's smart car, received a heavy fine. And each of them has to live with the nightmare for the rest of their lives: A woman in a small green car who regularly parks along the highway to lay a wreath of flowers on the small cross where her son died.

Carelessness can have serious consequences.
Read what the Bible has to say in Ephesians 5:15-20.

HEALTHY ADVICE

Fran's parents were divorced. She lived with her mom, but stayed with her dad on some weekends and during school holidays. It puzzled her to think that the two of them could ever have been married. They were as different as night and day! Her dad was a health-fanatic, while her mom put a high priority on things like going to church, reading the Bible, and praying regularly. Her mom believed that she should do all she could to keep her spiritual life healthy, but her dad was more concerned with being physically fit.

Many evenings, Fran's mom was too tired to prepare a meal, and they would just have a take-out hamburger for supper. But her mom never missed family devotions, even when they were exhausted. Her dad would never ever eat junk food! He went to the gym early every morning, and he often asked Fran to jog with him on Sunday mornings.

They're both freaky, she often thought. Her dad had a healthy, fit body, but no relationship with the Lord. Her mom obviously loved God passionately, but she didn't sleep enough, didn't get enough exercise, and didn't eat properly.

Fran realized that there had to be a more balanced way of life. You need to look after your health: it is a gift from God. But you also need to work at becoming spiritually mature.

She was glad when the youth pastor talked about this issue one Friday night. "Open your Bibles to 1 Corinthians 6:19-20 and tell me whether it is important for Christians to have a healthy lifestyle." And after they had reached an agreement on this, he said, "Now turn to 1 Timothy 4:8 and see how important it is that we stay spiritually fit as well!"

Look at both of these portions of Scripture and ask yourself whether you are caring enough for your body, which is the temple of the Lord. Do you spend enough time becoming spiritually fit?

DECEMBER 6

A LESSON IN GRATITUDE

Early one morning the doorbell rang. "What do you want?" Vera asked the child who was standing there. "My mother is ill. She needs some medicine," he said. "Who's your mom?" Vera asked. "Charity," he answered. Charity was the charwoman who cleaned their house each week.

Vera's mom came to talk to Washington, Charity's son. "I will take you home and we can take some medicine to her." "But Mom," Vera objected, "you promised to take me to the mall today!" "I know," her mom replied. "But Charity seems to be seriously ill. We can go shopping later on." Vera sulked. Newtown was far from where they lived. *There won't be time to go to the mall after this,* she realized. "Come with me!" her mom invited.

After a while they turned off onto a dirt road. Children in old clothes and no shoes were playing in the dust. Washington asked Mrs. Mitchell to stop outside a dilapidated house made of sheets of corrugated iron. The house was neat and clean. Faded red linoleum covered the floor and pictures cut from magazines were pasted against the walls. A small Dover stove stood in the front room, and in front of it was a table and three rickety chairs.

Charity was in the bedroom. She coughed when she greeted them. Vera's mom gave her some medicine and put a carrier bag filled with groceries onto the table. Vera went outside and looked over the top of the rundown houses in the squatter camp to the blue mountains in the distance. "Lord, forgive me for being so ungrateful," she said.

Back home she took out a suitcase and packed it full of clothes and other things that she didn't need any more. She put her favorite blue T-shirt on top of everything. That's for Washington, she thought. She felt a lot of respect for the young boy who had walked for more than two hours without complaining to fetch some medicine for his mother.

Read Proverbs 21:13.

HEROES AND ROLE MODELS

Hank, the church youth leader asked the Teenage Club to bring pictures of their heroes to the next meeting. He handed out some tape and they put their pictures on the walls. Then he gave each of them a chance to say something about their heroes. Most kids had brought posters of pop stars. "Do you realize that your so-called hero had been caught selling drugs?" Susan asked Felix. "I didn't choose him as my hero because of his lifestyle. He's my hero, because I like his music!" Felix replied.

There were also some sport stars in the new gallery of heroes that had been put up. "My football hero is my inspiration!" said Warren. "When I look at pictures of him, I get new stamina for practicing." Two of the girls had put up pictures of the same movie star. "He is gorgeous and famous!" they agreed.

Then Hank spoke up, "There is a difference between a celebrity and a hero," he said. "Heroes do heroic things, even though they are not well-known. Sarah's English teacher is not famous, but she admires him because of his lifestyle. Other people become famous because the media gives them a lot of publicity. But there is often very little about their lives or characters that Christians should want to copy."

"We should choose our role models very carefully," Hank said just before they went into the kitchen for hot chocolate. He asked one of the guys to read Philippians 3:17. Paul said that he followed Jesus' example and that he was, in turn, a role model to other Christians.

Then Hank prayed, "Lord, far above all these heroes, You are our greatest Hero. Let us follow Your example so that we can become good role models to others!"

Think carefully about a suitable role model, and then put a picture of that person in your room to remind you about following and setting a good example.

DECEMBER 8

HOW TO MEDITATE

Carrie's mom heard strange noises coming from her daughter's room. She opened the door and saw Carrie sitting on the floor, cross-legged and with her eyes closed. She was mumbling the same strange sounds over and over. "What's going on here?" her mom asked. Carrie explained, "Miss Struben taught us a new way of praying! You sit in this position and try to think of nothing at all. It is the most wonderful way to relax!"

"It definitely isn't prayer!" her mom said. "Your teacher has shown you the basics of Transcendental Meditation. Many Eastern religions practice it as part of their religion. You get into a yoga position and repeat a mantra until your mind becomes blank and you get in touch with the Universe. So they say! But that is not what prayer is all about." Her mom was very serious. "But Miss Struben said that the Bible also teaches us to meditate!" Corrie said. "Yes, but when people in the Bible spoke of meditation they meant that we should concentrate on thinking about God."

While her mom was talking, she opened Carrie's Bible that was lying next to her bed. She pointed to Psalm 77, "You can read here how Asaph meditated right through the night," she said. Carrie read the psalm slowly and noticed that the words 'meditate', 'remember', 'mused' and 'thought about' were used frequently. Suddenly she could clearly see the difference between T. M. and prayer. A Christian who prays and meditates centers his thoughts on God, not on nothing! Christians meditate because they love God and because they want to know Him better. While we meditate, we pray. We listen, we think, or sing our songs of praise, not mantras!

You can kneel or sit cross-legged with closed eyes and sing a song of praise while you think about the words of the psalm. That is one way in which a Christian can meditate!

December 9

Saved!

Uncle Sam spoke about the Lord whenever he had an opportunity. If anybody said, "I'm so worried!" He'd say, "Tell God about it!" Or if someone said, "That person will never change!" he would comment, "God can change his life!"

Uncle Paul was Uncle Sam's friend, but he got irritated when his friend spoke about the Lord all the time. "Who are you trying to impress?" he once asked when Uncle Sam was elaborating on all the good things that God had done in his life. "If you don't slow down a bit, you're going to become a fanatic," he warned.

Uncle Sam didn't say a word in response. But then he saw a worm creeping along one of the plants on Uncle Paul's porch, and he had a marvelous idea! He walked into the garden and gathered a few dry sticks and leaves. He made a circle of them on the paving stones. Then he put the worm in the middle of the circle, took out a box of matches, and set the sticks and leaves on fire.

When the flames began to rise, the worm started to panic. It was looking for a way out. It swayed back and forth desperately, and lifted its head as high as it could to try to escape the heat. It was trapped! Then Uncle Sam knelt next to the fire and put his finger next to the little worm. It climbed onto his finger and Uncle Sam carefully put it on the green leaf of a plant nearby. Uncle Paul watched his friend with interest wondering what point he was wanting to make with this demonstration. Uncle Sam said, "This is what Jesus has done for me. I was trapped by sin and He came and miraculously saved me. How can I keep quiet about it?"

If we really realized how lost we were in our sin before Jesus came to save us, we would also use every opportunity that we have to tell people about His saving grace.

Read what Peter and John had to say in Acts 4:20.

JUST ONE SWIG

Rowena had had a bottle of beer at a party. And then one of the boys offered her a glass of brandy. "Just have a swig!" he said. It tasted vile and she gasped for air as it went down her throat. But afterwards she felt fantastic and had a great time at the party. *Now I know what to do if I want to feel good about myself!* she thought. Soon she started to drink every weekend.

One Sunday morning her mom found her in the bathroom, red in the face and kneeling in front of the toilet. "I have a terrible headache," she complained. "You have a hangover!" her mom said. "How long has this been going on?" certain things about her daughter had been worrying her recently but she hadn't really followed up. Now a lot of things came to her mind: How Rowena often sneaked into her room after a party, the bad odors on her clothes, the empty bottles in the trashcan …

Rowena was feeling too sick to argue. She cried and talked incoherently. "I think I'm an alcoholic!" she told her mom. "Do you think there's any hope for me?" "Well, if you admit that you have a problem, half of the battle is won." Her mom tried to hide how shocked she was. An hour later she and Rowena sat together on the patio in front of their house. Rowena told her mom everything. Her mom said, "You have a big problem. We will have to send you to someone who can help you. I don't have enough knowledge about this condition. But this I know, Jesus helped prostitutes and criminals and sick people to live a normal life again. He will also help you, if you ask Him to. It's not going to be easy, but I will stand by you." "Thanks, Mom!" Rowena said shyly.

Then her mom passed her Bible to Rowena. "Read Psalm 38," she said as she walked away. Rowena took the Bible and read David's words with compassion, as if it were her own prayer.

**You can also read Psalm 38,
as well as Ephesians 5:18.**

Do not get drunk on wine … Instead, be filled with the Spirit. Eph 5:18

A TRUE STORY

Anne Thomas was on her way home after church. Halfway there she suddenly thought about her friend, Mrs. Burger. Often on a Sunday morning Anne would drop in at her friend's place after the service, just to say "hi". She had no plans to go there on that day though, because she was expecting guests for lunch.

But the thought of the elderly lady didn't leave her. She felt such a strong urge to go to her that she made a U-turn and found herself on her way to the apartment building where Mrs. Burger lived. "This is crazy!" she told herself. "You know that you have no time for a visit today!" But she carried on nonetheless. She ran up the stairs and rang the doorbell of number 15. No reply. She tried again. Dead silence. "Now see!" she told herself. "You have wasted a lot of precious time and the casserole won't be ready when your guests arrive!"

As she turned to leave, she heard a faint sound. Or was it her imagination? No, there it was again. "Help me!" a voice called softly. Anne put her ear to the keyhole and listened intently. It was Mrs. Burger's voice! But how could she get into the apartment? Anne found the caretaker to unlock the door. The two rushed inside and found the old lady on the floor of the bathroom! Half-frozen, bewildered. She had slipped and fallen, and lay there on the floor praying that somebody would hear her call of distress. The Lord had heard her plea and He had urged her young friend to go and help her!

God listens to the cries of His children, and His Spirit leads us to people who are in despair. We should not ignore that still small voice!

Psalm 34:18-21 suits this story.
Don't you think so, too?

DECEMBER 12

THE LIFESAVER

A young boy was walking home from school one Friday afternoon. He noticed one of his friends carrying all his schoolbooks, and struggling not to drop them. *Why is Kyle taking all his books home over a weekend?* John wondered. The next moment he saw a group of kids swarm toward Kyle and push him over. They laughed and scoffed at him while he fumbled in the dust for his spectacles. "Nerd!" they shouted.

John walked up to Kyle. "Can I help you?" he asked in a friendly way, and helped Kyle to pick up his books. "Thanks!" Kyle said, trying to blink away the tears in his eyes. They walked home together. "Would you like to play basketball with me tomorrow?" he asked when they reached Kyle's home. "Sure!" Kyle said gratefully. That Saturday they played together and on Monday morning, when John saw Kyle struggling with his pile of books, he helped him carry them back to school. It was the beginning of a long friendship.

Four years later, on graduation day, Kyle received a prize for academic excellence. He had to deliver a speech. "Honored guests and friends," he said, "when you receive an award like this, it is necessary to thank all the people who made it possible for you to be successful," he said. "I want to thank my teachers, my parents, and my friends who encouraged me to do my very best. I want especially to thank John. During my first year of high school, I went through a time of terrible depression and I decided to take my own life. I took home all my schoolbooks to save my parents the trouble of having to fetch them afterwards. And that Friday afternoon John was so kind to me that I decided that life was worth living after all." The audience sat absolutely still. John was especially amazed. Everybody realized once again how precious a little bit of kindness can be.

In Philippians 1:3-11 you can read
how much Paul's friends meant to him.

DECEMBER 13

THE BEE

Mandy was terrified of bees. When she was a toddler, she nearly died after a bee had stung her. The doctor had said that she was allergic to bee stings.

One afternoon Mandy and her sister sat in the sun next to their swimming pool. Suddenly she heard the humming of a bee and jumped up. She shouted and ran away, but the bee followed her. Her mom, who was watering the flowers nearby, dropped the hose and tried to catch the bee. When it settled on the fence she was able to grab it in her hand. The bee then stung her! She let the bee fly away again, but Mandy was still shivering and crying out of fear.

"The bee cannot harm you any more," her mom said and tried to comfort her. "Look, here is the sting. Come closer and feel here! The angry bee has lost its sting forever!" Mandy looked at her mom's hand. It was red and swollen and in the middle she saw the tiny black sting!

Which Bible story does this remind you of? Do you remember what Thomas said after Jesus' crucifixion and resurrection? *"Unless I see the nail marks in his hands and put my finger where the nails were, and put my hand into his side, I will not believe it."* A week later Jesus said to him, *"Put your finger here, see my hands … Stop doubting and believe."* Then Thomas said, *"My Lord and my God!"*

Today, when we think about the hands of Jesus scarred with the marks of the nails, we remember how He died for us on the cross. He bore the sting of pain and death so that we could be set free. Because He paid for our sin with His blood, God will not punish us and if we accept Him as our Savior, we have the promise that we will one day live with Him forever. Aren't you glad about that!

**Read John 20:20-29 and praise Jesus
for enduring so much pain on your behalf.**

DECEMBER 14

BEN AT HOME AGAIN

There was a hustle and bustle at the Gordon's house! The bathroom had to be changed, the furniture was being rearranged, ramps had been built, all because Ben was coming home! He had been in hospital for more than a year after a dreadful accident. Now he was a paraplegic and confined to a wheelchair. The whole house had to be adjusted to suit his needs and to make it easier for the family to care for him.

At first Elaine had been very glad that her brother was home again. But as time went on she couldn't help feeling a bit jealous of all the fuss that was made over him. Her parents spent hours doing things for him and there was hardly any time for her.

Of course, she felt lousy about being jealous! At least she could climb the stairs and run about and reach for the cookies in the kitchen, and her brother could do none of those things. But when people kept on bringing books and games and candy for Ben, she couldn't help feeling neglected!

One afternoon Aunt Bertha came to visit. She talked to Ben for a while and then she came to sit with Elaine in the garden. She had a big bag with her. "And how are you?" she asked. Elaine dropped her head and said nothing. "I think that you are a very brave girl!" her aunt said. "First you had to look after your dad while your mom was in hospital and now you are doing the chores of two children in this house. I'm sure it's not always easy to see how Ben gets all the attention. But, remember, Jesus is pleased when He sees that we are unselfish." Elaine was very glad that there was someone who understood what she was feeling. "I brought you something," Aunt Bertha said. She put her hand in the bag and pulled out a little black kitten. Elaine pressed it to her heart. "Thanks so much," she said with tears in her eyes. "Meow!" said her new playmate.

David took care of someone who was crippled. Read about it in 2 Samuel 9:1-13.

DECEMBER 15

THE LEGEND OF THE BELLS

There is a legend of a church in Europe that has a special tower. The bells in this tower produced the most beautiful sounds imaginable. But, the legend says that no bell ringers ever went into that tower to ring the bells. The people of the village believed that angels sometimes came down from heaven to make the bells chime.

Every Christmas eve all the inhabitants of the town came together to worship in the church. They would bring presents for the Christ-child, which would be put on the altar to be used for God's work in the area. The villagers believed that the bells chimed when Jesus was especially glad about a gift that someone had brought to the church.

One Christmas Eve two young boys wanted to attend the service. It was already getting dark when they reached the outskirts of the village. Suddenly they came across an old woman who had fallen. Try as they would, they could not help her to get up. Finally the older boy said, "You go to church, brother! And afterwards, bring someone here to come and help us. We cannot leave this lady lying here unattended. I'll give her some of the food we brought for the journey home." When the younger boy looked doubtful, his brother said, "Go along! It's not necessary for both of us to miss the Christmas service." Then he gave him a coin to put on the altar for Jesus.

Some precious gifts were laid on the altar that night: jewelry and expensive silks and lots of money. But no sound came from the top of the bell tower. Then the little boy walked up to the altar and put his brother's coin next to all the fancy gifts, and the bells in the tower started to chime softly. Sounds sweeter than those heard for a long, long time drifted from the tower and filled the valley so that all, far and wide, were enchanted by the beauty of the music.

Read a similar story in Mark 12:41-44.

DECEMBER 16

THE TABLECLOTH

A young minister and his wife were asked to take over a failing church in Brooklyn. When they arrived in October, they were shocked to find that the church building was dilapidated.

They worked hard to get the church ready for the Christmas service. But on December 19, a vicious storm raged over that area. The roof above the pulpit had been leaking and had caused an inner wall behind the pulpit to collapse. *Now we won't be able to have our Christmas service here*, the pastor thought.

But on his way home he passed a rummage sale in aid of charity. He stopped and saw a beautiful embroidered tablecloth among the old clothes and secondhand goods that were being sold. It was just the right size for covering the wall behind the pulpit! He bought the tablecloth and hurried back to the church. The rain had started pouring down again, and he noticed an elderly woman standing on the sidewalk outside the church. She had just missed her bus. "Come and take shelter in the church while you wait," he said to her.

The woman sat in one of the pews while he put up the cloth. It fitted perfectly and it looked exquisite! In the middle of the wonderful embroidery pattern was a cross. The woman who had been sitting at the back of the church came forward, her face pale and her eyes large with surprise. "Pastor," she asked, "where did you get that tablecloth?" And then she told him how she had fled from Austria during the Second World War. Many of her things had been left behind – including that tablecloth, which she had embroidered herself.

What a wonderful story that preacher could tell his congregation on that Christmas Eve! When Jesus was born miraculously on that first Christmas, it was the beginning of many wonderful things that would happen for those who believe in Him.

Read John 10:10.

THE CHRISTMAS GIFT

Ann knew that Santa Claus wasn't really real, but she pretended that she still believed in him. *If I let my parents know that I know he's not real, will I still get gifts in my stocking on Christmas morning?* she wondered. So she continued the habit of writing a letter to Father Christmas every year. In it she told him of all the nice things that she hoped to get from him. Then she would give the letter to her mom and ask her to post it.

One Christmas morning she was up early. She made coffee for her mom and dad and took it to their room. "Merry Christmas!" she sang out joyfully. "May I go and see what Santa has brought me?" she asked. "Of course!" her mom said. "See if there's something under the Christmas tree!"

Her parents followed her to the lounge. "Oh!" she cried out, excited. She found a lovely book, a painting set, a brand new tennis racquet, and a pair of sunglasses. "Santa has brought me almost everything I asked for!"

Then she found something more in the toe of her stocking. She reached deep down and pulled out a pack of brightly colored gel pens! She wanted to open it straightaway, but suddenly she looked at all the wonderful gifts around her and thought about her friend Janet, who loved writing and drawing. Janet came from a very poor family and Ann wondered whether she received even one Christmas present.

"I'm going to give these pens to Janet!" she said. Her parents looked at each other and smiled. "Jesus will be glad!" her mom said. "Yes," her dad agreed, "especially since it is His birthday today!"

**In Matthew 10:42 Jesus tells us
how we can make His heart glad.**

"Your prayers and gifts to the poor have come up as a memorial offering." Acts 10:4

DECEMBER 18

THE CHRISTMAS PARTY

Lawrence and his sister Mary were really looking forward to the company Christmas party. But two days before the party, Mary got flu and the doctor said that she had to stay in bed for a whole week. When Lawrence and their dad left for the party that night, she was still feverish and coughing badly. Lawrence felt really sorry for her, but all the fun and games at the party made him forget his sister very quickly. He had his eyes fixed on a shiny red fire truck that was hanging from the tree. He was wondering which lucky child would get that present!

Then the chairman of the company stood up. "I am going to read out your names and when I do, you can come and choose a toy from the tree. Remember that we give each other presents because God gave us the gift of His Son at Christmas. He sent Jesus, His most precious possession, to us on that very first Christmas." And then he challenged them, "Perhaps you could also give away a valuable possession of yours this Christmas!"

"Lawrence Foster" his name sounded over the microphone. The fire engine still hung from its branch on the tree, gleaming and beautiful, but Lawrence had made an important decision. He walked up to the tree and pointed to a beautifully dressed doll. The company chairman smiled at him as he took it off the tree and gave it to Lawrence. As he walked back the other kids were laughing and teasing him.

But Lawrence walked straight to his dad. "Dad, I chose this doll for Mary!" he said. His dad gave him a warm hug. He knew what this unselfish deed had cost Lawrence. He also knew that Jesus was delighted that he had been so unselfish.

All the good characteristics of a Christian's life are found in Galatians 5:22-23. Which one did Lawrence show that night at the Christmas party?

Precious Gifts

The Youth Club was planning their last get-together for the year. The kids usually brought along small gifts that they exchanged at their end of year party. But this year Robbie, the youth leader, had another suggestion. "Let's give the money that we would have spent on gifts for our missions project. We can then give each other another kind of gift." "Like what?" the kids wanted to know. "Well, in 1 Thessalonians 5:11, the Bible says that we should encourage one another. We can tell each other the things we like and appreciate in each other."

Each kid drew two names from a hat. "You have two weeks to think about something encouraging to say about your friends," Robbie said. "And remember – this is a gift to your friends, so let's not spoil it with silliness."

That meeting was unforgettable. Robbie played gentle music in the background, and they all sat in a circle on the floor. One by one the children had a turn to sit on a pile of cushions in the middle of the room. A candle was lit and given to the kid whose turn it was, and then they listened to what the others had to say about them.

"You made me feel at home at the youth group." "You came to fetch me every night, even when it rained." "Your smile was an inspiration to us all." "Your knowledge of the Bible motivated me to study the Bible more regularly." "You showed us that we can still be kind to others, even when you're having a bad time." These and many other things were said that night.

Each of the thirty kids who attended received a gift that would stay in their hearts for the rest of their lives. As one girl put it, "I'll try to be the person that my friends believe I am!"

Why don't you suggest the same type of meeting for your youth group?

DECEMBER 20

HAPPY BIRTHDAY, DEAR JESUS!

A few days before Christmas Mrs. Wiley said at dinner, "Let's organize a birthday party for Jesus this year!" Susan and Freddie were immediately excited about the idea. After all, everyone loves a party!

But Gertrude wanted to know a few things first. "Who will be invited?" she asked. "All the kids in our neighborhood," her mom said. "It will take a lot of work!" Gertrude objected.

But her mom replied, "It will be worth every minute's preparation and every crumb on the floor. We will give all the kids in our street who are not Christians a chance to hear about Jesus! And those who are Christians will have a wonderful reason to celebrate. We can spur one another on toward love and good deeds." The Wiley's knew that these words came from Hebrews 10:24, because their mom had written it on a poster which hung behind the bathroom door.

Slowly Gertrude also became enthusiastic about her mom's idea. They started discussing the things that had to be done: sending out invitations, putting up decorations, planning games, making snacks, and getting the music organized.

"And who's going to pay for all this?" their dad asked. "We will use our savings!" the two girls volunteered. "It will be our birthday gift for Jesus." "I'll make ginger beer," Freddie offered. The family sat for a long time, making plans. Then their mom said, "It's bedtime! Let's ask God to bless our plans, and then we can talk about it again tomorrow."

Freddie prayed, "Dear Lord, You know everything, so this won't be a surprise party for You. But You can help us to make a success of it, so that everyone can once again marvel at your lovingkindness.'"

You could also have such a party for Jesus!

DECEMBER 21

A FREE GIFT

"Santa Clause won't bring you any Christmas presents this year!" Justin taunted his sister Greta. "You've been nothing but trouble lately!" Greta knew that Father Christmas wasn't real, but she also knew that she did not really deserve any Christmas gifts. Over the previous few weeks she had disobeyed her parents quite a lot, and caused them all kinds of heartache.

When Greta went to bed that night, her heart was filled with remorse. *Why had she been so bad?* She was certain that her behavior had also displeased the Lord and she felt that she couldn't even ask Him to help her sort out the mess she was in.

On Christmas morning she woke to the sound of church bells ringing joyfully. A choir on the radio was singing *Oh, Come All Ye Faithful*. She walked slowly into the family room, really not expecting to see any presents for her under the tree. But as she glanced at the pile of brightly wrapped gifts, she saw a huge parcel with her name written on it! She opened it and gasped! It was the scooter that she had wanted so badly!

"I didn't think that I deserved a Christmas gift this year," she said as she hugged her mom. Her dad replied, "We don't give each other gifts because we deserve them. At Christmas time we remember God's gift to humanity. He gave His Son, Jesus, to us, even though not one of us deserved such a gift. Jesus came because God loves us. And we bought you this present because we love you!"

"Thank you so much," she said, while giving her dad a warm hug. And then she looked up and said, "Thank You, Lord!" Before she ran outside to try out her new scooter, she said, "I'm turning over a new leaf right now, just you wait and see!"

See what Romans 5:8 has to say about this.

HEAVEN ON EARTH

"Is there really such a place as heaven on earth?" Keith asked. "My life seems rather to be like hell on earth." His mom just carried on scouring the pot in the kitchen sink. She understood what he meant, but she didn't say a word. Her life had been difficult right from the start, and each day was a struggle to make ends meet for her four children and herself.

But Abigail was a Christian and she took her children to church and Sunday school every Sunday. A Christmas party for the children of the church had been planned for that evening, and she was going to take all four of her children there. "Will you please help me to get the little ones ready for tonight?" she asked Keith. "And when they hand out the presents, don't let them open theirs! We must keep them for Christmas day." Keith was ready to protest, but his mom remained firm. "Otherwise there won't be anything to look forward to on Christmas day!"

There were lots of refreshments at the community hall that night. When Santa Claus handed out the gifts, Keith's mom put theirs in a basket. Back home she put them under a pot plant that they had decorated with tinsel. Often, during the next few days, the children stood in front of their little Christmas tree and gazed at the parcels with curious eyes. They had felt them carefully and even tried to smell what was inside! Keith was sure that there was a baseball bat in his parcel. At night he dreamed of being a famous baseball player, and he could almost hear how the crowds cheered as he hit home runs! *Maybe that's what is meant by heaven on earth,* he thought. *Dreaming about what lies ahead. Looking forward to the joy that still awaits you!*

On Christmas morning he hugged his bat tight against his chest. "Thank You, God, for giving me a taste of heaven on earth!" he said and ran outside to find some friends.

Read 1 Corinthians 2:9. It sure seems as if all our dreams will one day come true!

"No mind has conceived what God has prepared for those who love him." 1 Cor. 2:9

THE GIFT

Long, long ago a good, wise king lived in Persia. He loved his people and wanted to find out more about how they lived. He wanted to know what made them glad and what made them sad. So he dressed in peasant's clothes and wandered through the streets of the different cities in his country. Often he would go into houses, but nobody knew who this stranger really was.

One day he started up a conversation with a poor man he met on the sidewalk and later he went with him to his home. The man lived in the basement of an old mansion. They had a good time in each other's company. The king was kind and friendly to the man and spoke many encouraging words to him. Before the king left, the poor man offered him a meal. Together they ate stale bread and drank black coffee.

Some time later the king visited his poor friend once again, but this time the king revealed who he actually was. The king expected the man to ask him for a gift or for a favor, but instead, the man said, "You left your grand palace to visit me in my dark, little room. You shared my simple meal with me. You gladdened my heart with your friendly words. You have given expensive gifts to many people, but to me you gave something of yourself. I am most grateful for that!"

Jesus also left the grandeur of heaven to live on earth with us. He experienced for Himself what it is like for us to live on earth. The Bible says that He came to earth to become an ordinary person. Most people did not think that He was important at all. They treated Him badly and eventually killed Him. Yes, Jesus gave Himself to us. And because of His resurrection from the dead and ascension to heaven, we can go to Him with all our troubles. He completely understands everything that we are going through.

Read the words of Hebrews 4:15.

A HOME FOR JESUS

David was very excited indeed! He had traveled to Jerusalem from Bethlehem for the feast of Pentecost. There had been so many rumors and strange stories in the last few weeks that he wanted to see for himself what was going on. People were saying that Jesus, the Teacher, had been crucified in Jerusalem but that he had been raised from the dead. Others said that He had then ascended into heaven. David wondered what to make of all these stories.

He had a secret interest in this man, Jesus. He suspected that 33 years earlier, this man might have been born on his premises. One night he and his wife had given lodging in their stable to a man and his pregnant wife because there wasn't any room for them in the inn. Some shepherds later told them that the baby that had been born there that night was the promised Messiah. Many years later, when he heard how Jesus traveled throughout Palestine teaching people about God, he felt quite guilty: *Shouldn't he have made another plan that night?*

Just then he saw hundreds of people gathering in one of the side streets of Jerusalem. A man was talking to them. "It's Peter!" they said. David listened intently to what Peter had to say. He explained that God had poured His Holy Spirit on the disciples that day, and had come to live in the hearts of those who believed that Jesus had died to save them from their sins. David was amazed. *Could he have a chance now to give the Messiah a proper place to stay?*

"Those who accepted his message were baptized, and about three thousand were added to their number that day." That's what Acts 2: 41 says. Among them was David, the innkeeper.

This is only a made-up story, but it reminds us that Jesus, who had no place to lay His head when He was born, can today live in our hearts through His Spirit.

Read 1 Corinthians 3:16.

DECEMBER 25

NO ROOM

The Moores were on their way to spend the Christmas holidays in the mountains when their car started to give them trouble. After several stops they realized that they would never reach their destination before dark. "I think we'll have to stay over somewhere," Mr. Moore said. "And in the morning we'll have to have the car fixed before we travel further." So they started looking for a sign that would show them where they could spend the night. But at all the guest lodges and hotels they saw a similar message: NO ROOMS AVAILABLE.

They stopped for something to eat at a brightly lit all-night diner. *O Little Town of Bethlehem* was playing over the sound system. While they were feasting on hamburgers and fries, Myrtle said, " Now I know how Joseph and Mary felt when they couldn't find a room for the night." "I think it was much worse for them," her mom said. "Remember, Mary was expecting a baby and she didn't travel in a luxury car like ours!"

Eventually they found room in a motel along the road. The bar was full of people who had had too much to drink. "To good ol' Christmas," one of them shouted as the family passed by. When they started to unpack for the night, Mr. Moore said, "Many people have Christmas parties, but they have no room for Jesus in their lives. They have written SORRY, NO ROOM! on the doors of their hearts.

Before they climbed into bed in the big motel room, Mr. Moore read from Luke 2, "*She gave birth to her firstborn, a son. She placed him in a manger, because there was no room for them in the inn.*" Then he prayed, "Lord, thank You that we can afford to sleep in this motel tonight. You had to stay in a stable when you came to earth. Please help us always to have room for You in our hearts."

**Is there something special that you want
to say to Jesus on this Christmas day?**

FRANCOIS LEARNS TO LOVE JESUS

Pastor Johan Bloemhoff tells children on the streets in Paris Bible stories and teaches them Christian songs. Many children in France come from homes where their parents don't believe in Jesus and a lot of them don't know the Bible at all. When the children he evangelizes show an interest in the stories about Jesus, Pastor Bloemhoff invites them to join the Kids' Club that regularly gets together at his home. Francois Cyrot was one of these children.

At first he just came to the meetings because he liked the songs. He didn't seem to pay any attention at all when the minister was telling the stories. He was restless and at times he was a real nuisance. Pastor Bloemhoff nearly sent him home one day because he was so naughty.

Then one day Pastor Bloemhoff went to South Africa to visit his family. While he was there, he visited many churches and spoke about the work he was doing in Paris. Everywhere he went, he asked people to pray that Francois would also learn to love Jesus. Meanwhile, back in Paris, Francois missed the Kids' Club meetings a lot and he longed for his friend to return.

When Johan returned to Paris and the Kids' Club started meeting again, Francois turned up as usual. But this time he listened attentively when the minister was speaking. One day he asked what he should do if he wanted to become a child of God. Johan read John 1:12 to him, and he accepted the Lord as his Savior.

Not long after that, his mother also became a Christian. Why? Because she had seen what a difference becoming a Christian had made in her son's life. Johan let the people in South Africa know: *Your prayers made a difference! Francois and his mother have learned to love Jesus!*

Pray for the children of France.

DOES GOD EVER GET ANGRY?

Let's pretend you're in Mr. Shear's Sunday school class. He asks you, "Do you think that God ever gets angry?" You listen to what some of the children say, "Never! He is a merciful God. The Bible says that He takes our sin as far away from us as the east is from the west." "God is love. I don't think He gets angry." "He is not like people who get angry. He is God and He doesn't get upset about the little things that irritate us." "I agree, and I don't think that He will ever get so angry that He would cast people into hell!"

And then you hear your teacher say, "You are all right when you say that God is loving and merciful. But the Bible also teaches us that He can get very angry about sin. Joshua 7:1 says, *"The Lord's anger burned against Israel because Achan had been disobedient."* And Romans 2:8 says that there will be wrath and anger against people who reject the truth and follow evil. Ephesians 5:6 tells us, *"Let no one deceive you with empty words, because of such things God's wrath comes on those who are disobedient."*

What would you have said? Do you agree with the children or with Mr. Shear? Remember that God punished Jesus for the sins of people and that everybody who believes that will be forgiven. But, even though we will not spend eternity in hell if we have accepted Jesus as our Savior, we still have to face the consequences of our sins.

That is why we should fight sin in our life and try to do everything we can to warn people who do not want to have anything to do with God. They will have to bear the consequences of their sinful deeds and will one day have to come face to face with a really angry God.

You can read more about the anger of God in Psalm 2, but note what it says about His mercy in verse 12.

His wrath can flare up in a moment. Blessed are all who take refuge in him. Ps. 2:12

December 28

Beware of Witchcraft

A big notice had been put up at the community center inviting people to attend a seminar on Wicca. "What's that?" Colin asked. "Let's look it up," his mom said. They learned that people who practice Wicca believe that they can tap into the powers of nature and use strange rituals to cast spells. "Is it like magic?" Colin asked. "Yes," his mom said. "People who practice Wicca believe that they can manipulate nature in order to bring them prosperity and success."

"Are they Satanists?" Colin asked with growing interest. "No," his mom said. "Many of them don't even believe in Satan. They say that they only do good things, and that they would never harm anybody with their witchcraft."

Colin thought about how he could impress all the Harry Potter fans at school with all these new facts. "Why don't you go to that meeting and then come and tell me all about it!" She smiled, but said emphatically, "No, never! These people believe that they should make use of powers in nature and in themselves to succeed in life. We believe that God's power is available to us and that we should rely on Him and trust Him with every aspect of our lives. And these people are playing with fire. Supernatural power comes either from God or from Satan. When people deny God, and worship pagan gods in the hope of finding supernatural power, they are playing right into the hands of Satan – even if they don't think he exists. That's why God said that we should have nothing to do with sorcery."

"Where does the Bible say that?" Colin asked. His mom paged through her Bible and said, "In Leviticus 19:26." "Well, then I'll probably have to go and pack my broom away in the attic!" Colin said teasingly.

Make sure that you don't keep things because you believe that they can bring you some good luck. Jesus alone should be our source of joy and power!

USE ALL YOUR POWER

Simon huffed and puffed. He was building new roads for his toy cars in the backyard. But now he had uncovered a huge rock that was blocking the way and he couldn't move it. He was being very careful not to ruin his mom's flowerbeds. He dug with his little spade all around the rock and tried again. But to no avail! The rock didn't move. *I wish that I was just a little bit stronger*, he sighed.

His dad had been watching the sweat and toil through the kitchen window. Eventually he opened the kitchen door and walked over to Simon. "Why don't you use all your strength?" his dad asked. The little boy looked at his dad questioningly. "But I have!" he said. "I tried with all my might but this rock won't move!"

His dad bent down and wriggled the rock from side to side for a while. Then he shifted it onto its side on the grass. "Is this where you want it?" he asked. Simon looked at his dad with admiration. He hoped he would one day be just as big and strong as his dad! "See, Son?" his dad said. "You hadn't used all the strength available to you. My strength was here for you to call on all along. All that you had to do was to ask me to help you!" Simon thought for a while. Then he looked at his dad with a broad grin. "Thanks, Dad!" he said. "I'll try to remember that in future!"

Are their things in your life that you find too difficult to handle? Maybe some kids at school give you a hard time, or you struggle with difficult schoolwork, or your parents seem to expect too much? Use all your power! Remember that the power of the Almighty God is available to His children. All we have to do is ask!

Read Psalm 50:15 and see what God expects of us when we face difficulties.

AT THE FOOT OF THE RAINBOW

A group of Christian students held a great outreach for kids who were on holiday near Stony Bay. One meaningful activity that they encouraged the children to do was to paint one wall of the clubhouse. A paint dealer in the town donated a whole lot of paint to them, and the kids painted a beautiful rainbow across the wall. It was great fun!

On New Year's Eve, one of the students talked to them about God's promises. "Did you know that there are more than 1,500 promises of God in the Bible?" he asked. "And remember," he added, "a rainbow is the symbol of God's faithfulness." He told them the story of Noah and the ark as a reminder of God's promises, and he read Genesis 10:13, *"I have set my rainbow in the clouds and it will be the sign of the covenant between me and the earth."*

The students then asked the kids to write down one wish that they had for the New Year. They gave each one an envelope, and asked them to address it to themselves. Then the notes were put into a postbox at the foot of the rainbow.

"You've probably heard about the legend that there's a pot of gold at the foot of every rainbow. Although that's just a story, you can place your wish into this red box as a prayer to God," the speaker concluded. Then they all sang together, "I to the hills will lift mine eyes, from whence that come my aid!" That song is based on a promise of God in Psalm 121:1.

Just before Easter that year, Juan received a letter. The note was in his own handwriting and said, **"I pray that You would help me to do better in my schoolwork this year."** He remembered when and where that letter had been written. "Thank You, Lord, for being true to Your promises!" he prayed.

Draw a rainbow and write Psalm 89:34 on it.
Keep it as a bookmark in your Bible and try to
notice the many promises of God in His Word.

SCRUNCH UP THE OLD YEAR

It was the last day of the year. It hadn't been a good year for Hannah. She had had to spend three months in hospital, and had consequently not done very well at school. She hadn't really felt up to the work and didn't really try very hard. When she looked back on the old year, she felt a total failure. She had been a fussy patient and was forever grumbling at home. No wonder her friends had stopped visiting her regularly!

Hannah's mother brought her some ice tea. She had also placed a magazine on the tray. "Read the article on page 20," her mom said. Hannah paged through the magazine. *"Scrunch up the old year!"* read the caption on that page. *"Don't live in the past. Don't dwell on things that cannot be changed. Live for the future!"* the writer advised. And then she told the readers how she had gotten into the habit of making a list every New Year's Eve. The list consisted of all the things she was leaving behind her – all the things that she was not going to allow to spoil her future. She wrote that, on December 31, she said good-bye to the things that she had done wrong and to all the disappointments of the past. And then, when the sun rose the next morning, she would scrunch up the page on which she had written her list and shove it in the trashcan.

Hannah started writing. When she went to bed that night, she set her alarm clock so that she could be up before the sun rose the next morning. As the first reddish glow slipped over the mountaintops, she walked out onto the balcony and burned the scrunched papers of dark memories and disappointments of the past year. She also recommitted herself to God, the Father of lights, who could help her to build a new list of triumphs for the New Year.

Why don't you also scrunch up the bad memories of the past year and start the New Year together with Jesus? See what Paul had to say in Philippians 3:13.

Forgetting what is behind and straining toward what is ahead. Phil. 3:13

INDEX

Peace	20 Oct
Peer pressure	13 Jan; 30 Mar; 19 Apr; 25 May; 30 Aug
Perseverance	5 Jan; 16 Jan; 31 Jan; 17 Feb; 4 Sept; 20 Sept; 27 Oct
Pornography	30 Sept
Prayer	30 Jan; 28 Aug; 13 Sept; 22 Nov; 30 Nov
Prejudice	17 Jan; 16 Mar; 3 Sept
Property	10 May; 23 June
Purity	8 Nov
Relationships	21 Aug
Reliability	9 Apr; 20 Apr; 20 Aug; 6 Nov; 19 Nov; 4 Dec
Role-modeling	29 Jan; 13 Mar; 7 Dec
Salvation	14 Mar; 5 Aug; 26 Aug; 23 Sept; 17 Nov; 9 Dec; 13 Dec
Satan	4 May; 15 July; 26 Oct
Schoolwork	14 Aug; 17 Aug
Self-esteem	4 Jan; 25 Mar; 5 Apr; 10 Apr; 21 May; 9 June; 22 June; 14 Aug; 29 Nov
Serving others	27 Feb; 23 July; 3 Oct; 4 Oct; 12 Oct; 16 Oct; 13 Nov
Sin	5 Mar; 24 Apr
Spiritual Growth	27 Apr; 16 Sept
Stress	3 Aug
Success	5 Jan; 16 May; 22 June; 3 July; 4 Aug; 12 Sep
Sunday	13 Aug
Television	16 Aug
Temper	4 Mar; 20 May; 15 June; 7 Aug
Temptations	2 Mar; 21 Apr; 22 May; 11 July; 6 Aug; 8 Nov
The Aged	9 Mar; 24 Aug
The Bible	15 Feb; 14 Jul; 17 Jul; 1 Nov; 20 Nov
Trusting God	30 Apr; 9 Sept; 25 Sept; 31 Dec
Unselfishness	3 Jan; 8 Apr; 16 Apr; 2 May; 3 Oct